2006 Poetry Competition for 7-11 year olds

YoungWriters

a pocketful of

RHYME

Imagination for a new generation

The Midlands

Edited by Young Writers

Editorial Team:
Lynsey Hawkins
Allison Dowse
Claire Tupholme
Donna Samworth
Annabel Cook
Aimée Vanstone
Gemma Hearn
Joseph Devine
Angela Fairbrace
Laura Martin

 Young**Writers**

First published in Great Britain in 2006 by:
Young Writers
Remus House
Coltsfoot Drive
Peterborough
PE2 9JX
Telephone: 01733 890066
Email: youngwriters@forwardpress.co.uk
Website: www.youngwriters.co.uk

HB ISBN 1 84602 415 3

Cover design by Tim Christian
Design by Mark Rainey

FOREWORD

Young Writers was established in 1991 and has been passionately devoted to the promotion of reading and writing in children and young adults ever since. The quest continues today. *Young Writers* remains as committed to the nurturing of poetic and literary talent as ever.

This year's *Young Writers* competition has proven as vibrant and dynamic as ever and we are delighted to present a showcase of the best poetry from across the UK and in some cases overseas. Each poem has been selected from a wealth of *A Pocketful of Rhyme* entries before ultimately being published in this, our fourteenth primary school poetry series.

Once again, we have been supremely impressed by the overall quality of the entries we have received. The imagination, energy and creativity which has gone into each young writer's entry made choosing the poems a challenging and often difficult but ultimately hugely rewarding task - the general high standard of the work submitted ensured this opportunity to bring their poetry to a larger appreciative audience.

We sincerely hope you are pleased with this final collection and that you will enjoy *A Pocketful of Rhyme - The Midlands* for many years to come.

A-Z OF SCHOOLS

Albrighton County Junior School,
  Albrighton   23
Apley Wood Primary School, Telford   33
Ashfield Park CP School, Ross-on-Wye   53
Bishop Rawle CE Primary School,
  Cheadle   61
Braunston CE Primary School,
  Braunston   68
Brookside Primary School, Brookside   83
Captain Webb Primary School, Dawley   94
Clifford Primary School, Clifford   97
Cradley CE (VA) Primary School,
  Cradley   101
Crudgington Primary School,
  Crudgington   115
Dorrington CE (A) Primary School,
  Dorrington   125
Eastfield Primary School, Thurmaston   129
Exeter Junior School, Corby   148
Fulford Primary School, Fulford   163
Glenfield Primary School, Glenfield   168
Gnosall St Lawrence CE Primary
  School, Gnosall   181
Great Bowden CE Primary School,
  Great Bowden   204
Greenfield Primary School,
  Countesthorpe   210
Gretton CP School, Gretton   246
Hanley Swan Primary School,
  Hanley Swan   250
Hathern CE Primary School, Hathern   257
Hinstock Primary School, Hinstock   263
Higham Ferrers Junior School,
  Higham Ferrers   270
Holy Redeemer Primary School,
  Pershore   295

Lindridge CE Primary School,
  Tenbury Wells   306
Manor House School,
  Ashby de la Zouch   312
Mordiford CE Primary School,
  Nr Hereford   316
Our Lady & St Werburgh's RC School,
  Newcastle   332
Rowlett Community Primary School,
  Corby   357
St Bartholomew's CE Primary School,
  Quorn   359
St Joseph's Catholic Primary School,
  Malvern   400
SS Mary & John CE (VA) Primary
  School, North Luffenham   427
SS Peter & Paul's Catholic Primary
  School, Newport   434
St Mary's CE Primary School, Colton   440
Shevington Community Primary
  School, Shevington   447
Shobdon Primary School, Leominster   462
The Grove Primary School,
  Melton Mowbray   466
The Richard Crosse CE Primary
  School, Kings Bromley   468
The Willows Primary School, Penkhull   478
Thorpe Acre Junior School,
  Loughborough   479
Whittington CE Primary School,
  Whittington   482
Witton Middle School, Droitwich   483
Woodcote Primary School,
  Ashby de la Zouch   519

A-Z OF AUTHORS

Aaron Burdett (9)	275	Amal Abufares (11)	458
Aaron Houseman (9)	441	Aman Kaur (8)	443
Aaron Lund (8)	29	Amanda Stanton-Nelson (9)	388
Aaron Pritchard (11)	268	Amber Cox (9)	501
Abbey Ford (10)	226	Amberley Vessey (9)	233
Abbie Holliday (10)	493	Amelia Colver (10)	171
Abbie McCormack (10)	381	Amelia Thomas (10)	245
Abbie Saunders (8)	141	Amy Barratt (9)	115
Abbi-Jayne Rickson (8)	326	Amy Binley (10)	432
Abby Thompson (9)	86	Amy Brough (10)	67
Abi Beddard (10)	54	Amy Carter (10)	492
Abigail Collins (8)	402	Amy Davies (10)	126
Abigail Edwards (9)	442	Amy Gage (9)	25
Abigail Hughes (10)	343	Amy Gilson (10)	293
Abigail Norman (11)	170	Amy Harris (10)	36
Abigail Thompson (9)	496	Amy Huckbody (10)	289
Abigail Upton (9)	468	Amy Newman (11)	234
Adam Cato	177	Amy Pyper (10)	149
Adam Turner (9)	316	Amy Ridge (11)	58
Afifa Oamar (9)	342	Amy Stubbings (8)	93
Aidan Petrie (9)	490	Amy Whittaker (8)	252
Aiden Bray (11)	168	Amy Williams (9)	257
Aileen Baker (9)	487	Andrew Barrass (9)	384
Ajay Mohan (9)	478	Andrew Martin (10)	33
Akil Allen (9)	43	Andrew Pover (10)	338
Alasdair Berry (8)	287	Andrew Russell (9)	383
Aleesha Choda (9)	71	Andrew Ward (11)	290
Alex Bedford (9)	477	Andy Sentance (11)	385
Alex Cunningham (10)	389	Angel Aspinwall (8)	70
Alex Mayer (10)	435	Angelmae Long (9)	168
Alex Slater (8)	395	Annabel Shotter (11)	469
Alex Snart (10)	141	Annabelle Banner (10)	489
Alexander Cobbin (10)	258	Annabelle Judge (7)	370
Alexander Stallard (10)	508	Anthony Connolly (11)	453
Alexandra Elliott (10)	524	Anthony West (9)	32
Alexia Mann (8)	281	Anya Smith (9)	272
Alfie Moxon (8)	384	Aron Payne (8)	200
Alice Bourner (10)	177	Aron Williams (8)	327
Alice Brankin (10)	406	Arron Howard (9)	178
Alice Bright (7)	414	Arron Matharu (10)	135
Alice Cassie (11)	211	Arthur Kelly (10)	284
Alice Cox (7)	373	Asha Patel (7)	370
Alice Crawshaw (10)	460	Ashleigh Fletcher (9)	51
Alice Henson (10)	257	Ashleigh Jade Hinton (9)	496
Alice Mercer (9)	205	Ashley Chan (9)	505
Alice Read (9)	472	Ashley Fisher (7)	74
Alice Venables (9)	98	Ashley Holmes (9)	269
Alice Winters (11)	297	Ashley Lincoln-Hollis (11)	390
Alicia Biffen (9)	378	Ashley Ross (11)	173
Alicia Doonan-Jones (9)	25	Ashley Stanton (11)	318
Alim Khan (9)	42	Ashley Thorneycroft (9)	290
Allister Fenton-Jones (10)	221	Ashley Tomlinson (10)	32

Name		Name	
Ashton Wood (8)	23	Brittany Moss (10)	499
Austin Sullivan (9)	474	Brogan Burley (9)	230
Aysha Sainsbury (9)	237	Brogan Fedden (10)	419
Barbara Silva (9)	148	Bronwyn Piggins (9)	138
Beatrice Shotter (9)	471	Bronya Creary (9)	272
Becca Hill (9)	439	Brooke Tranter (9)	46
Becki McHugo (9)	206	Bryn Stubbings (9)	423
Bella Ferros (9)	97	Bryn Tallett (8)	81
Ben Brown (8)	145	Caitlin Begley (9)	198
Ben Burgin (9)	386	Caitlin Haq (10)	34
Ben Collins (10)	425	Caitlin Holmes (9)	160
Ben Fillery (7)	311	Caitlin Oates (11)	59
Ben Hadfield (9)	143	Callum Brodie (9)	157
Ben Holter (8)	199	Callum Dickinson (10)	432
Ben Juckes (8)	319	Callum Haskew (10)	434
Ben Lane (9)	506	Callum Langley (10)	274
Ben Moir (9)	280	Callum Nelson (9)	161
Ben Page (10)	358	Callum Shropshire (10)	96
Ben Szehofner (7)	90	Callum Warrilow (9)	144
Ben Taylor (10)	439	Cameron Betteridge (10)	243
Ben Thomas (9)	278	Cameron Dunnett (8)	108
Benjamin Dean (10)	58	Cameron Godfrey (8)	202
Benjamin Fullagar (8)	104	Cara Logue (9)	153
Benjamin Hall (10)	373	Carolina Sansom (10)	244
Benjamin Reeve (10)	394	Caroline Andrew (9)	373
Bernadette Bates (10)	180	Casey Cook (10)	359
Beth Abbott (10)	162	Catherine Kelleher (11)	517
Beth Martin (9)	26	Catrina Yang (9)	45
Beth O'Flynn (10)	377	Ceri Jones (10)	510
Bethan Grant (10)	236	Cerys Furlong (7)	28
Bethan Knapper (10)	63	Cerys Lloyd (8)	266
Bethan Smeeton (10)	205	Chantal Ormesher (10)	455
Bethaney Wright (10)	480	Charles Boffey-Rawlings (9)	119
Bethany Haynes (9)	518	Charley Fuller (11)	285
Bethany Johnson (9)	93	Charley Wainwright (9)	124
Bethany Rollett (9)	227	Charlie Binley (10)	431
Bethany Simpson (10)	376	Charlie Brookes (11)	109
Bethany Williams (8)	309	Charlie Griffiths (11)	85
Bethany Wood (9)	283	Charlie Hammond (10)	51
Bethany-Jane Morgan (10)	158	Charlie Lockhart (11)	381
Billie Burnett (10)	66	Charlie Rankin (9)	111
Billie Westwood (10)	259	Charlie Statham (8)	172
Billy Addison (8)	388	Charlie Wyles (7)	154
Billy Bodenham (10)	357	Charlote Perry (11)	514
Billy Carnall (8)	146	Charlotte Barnacle (11)	174
Billy Freame (11)	286	Charlotte Burridge (10)	518
Blaize Kerr (10)	136	Charlotte Chapman (8)	267
Bodhran Brito (10)	324	Charlotte Cooper (10)	340
Bradley McGinlay (8)	148	Charlotte Cumley (10)	289
Bradley McGuire (9)	448	Charlotte Fenton (9)	195
Brandon Elkington (8)	138	Charlotte Freeman (9)	279
Brandon Rock (7)	29	Charlotte Godwin (9)	451
Bridie Hall (10)	56	Charlotte Hanna (11)	241
Brittany Chandler (7)	156	Charlotte Hart (10)	323

Charlotte Lyon (9)	70	Daisy Glover (10)	480
Charlotte Oakley (8)	332	Daisy Ruse (9)	97
Charlotte Rooney (8)	406	Daisy Snelson (7)	82
Charlotte Schofield (10)	392	Dale Needham (10)	521
Charlotte Stone (10)	45	Dan Fitch (8)	136
Charlotte Thomas (9)	25	Dan Greenhill (10)	227
Chelsea Machin (8)	24	Dan Rawlings (7)	253
Chelsea Marston (8)	201	Daniel Bahia (9)	37
Chelsea Scott (10)	160	Daniel Burton (8)	71
Cherie Harris (9)	91	Daniel Cattle (9)	436
Chloe Barrow (9)	428	Daniel Ginger (9)	119
Chloe Bolsover (9)	221	Daniel Glover (9)	215
Chloe Coltman (9)	138	Daniel Griffiths (11)	463
Chloe Fletcher (8)	198	Daniel Kelly (10)	456
Chloe Griffiths (9)	307	Daniel Merriman (10)	516
Chloe Hancox (7)	90	Daniel Mooney (10)	414
Chloe Jackson (9)	424	Daniel Moorhouse (10)	466
Chloe Mitten (7)	252	Daniel Moss (10)	175
Chloe Morgan (11)	59	Daniel Munn (9)	213
Chloé Morson (9)	225	Daniel Patterson (10)	468
Chloe Oram (10)	216	Daniel Pettingale (9)	477
Chloe Palmer (6)	88	Daniel Pink (11)	523
Chloe Raynor (11)	423	Daniel Pritchard (9)	470
Chloe Woolley (8)	28	Daniel Rees (8)	156
Chris Gamble (9)	210	Daniel Revell (8)	410
Chris Rouse (11)	513	Daniel Rich (9)	473
Chris Thomas (9)	49	Daniel Thompson (8)	151
Christian Dandy (9)	110	Daniel Whitehouse (10)	29
Christian Graham (10)	42	Daniel Wiggins (9)	291
Christian Hine (9)	125	Danielle Allford (10)	367
Christopher Pearson (10)	192	Danielle Burney (11)	296
Christopher Pearson (9)	69	Danielle Coley (8)	277
Christopher Salt (10)	468	Danielle Davies (9)	446
Christopher Stanley (9)	495	Danielle Fenner (10)	364
Christopher Westwood (8)	27	Danielle Olivant (11)	133
Claire Cottingham (7)	159	Danielle Pinney (9)	180
Claire Eaton (9)	292	Danielle Slattery (10)	524
Claire Walker (9)	261	Danielle Tildesley (9)	243
Class 6LL	154	Danielle Whitehouse (9)	354
Claudia Langley-Mills (9)	315	Danni McCormack (9)	66
Clodagh Lodge (10)	495	Darcie Farnsworth (9)	121
Cody Parker (11)	286	David Cawthorne (10)	56
Connah Farley (10)	457	David Lennon (9)	243
Connor Heathcote (10)	180	David McTague (9)	500
Connor Mason (10)	219	David Naylor (10)	89
Connor Mitchell (8)	144	David Pollard (8)	301
Connor Pezzaioli (9)	192	David Walton (8)	408
Connor Thompson (10)	302	Deanna Miles (11)	394
Conor Price (9)	465	Deborah Allen (10)	428
Courtney Meakins (10)	155	Decklan Yates (10)	458
Craig Lawrence (11)	464	Dexter Davidson (8)	132
Craig Smith (9)	347	Dexter Williamson (10)	485
Daisy Collins (9)	255	Dilon Norris-Story-Day (8)	253
Daisy Davies (10)	115	Dominic Applewhite (10)	392

Dominic Forte (11)	516	Emily Wright (9)	453
Douglas Osbourn (10)	122	Emma Bradley (11)	467
Duncan Morgan (9)	316	Emma Burgess (8)	123
Dylan Harrison (7)	26	Emma Cooke (11)	213
Eamon Maarabouni (9)	356	Emma Cumley (9)	294
Edward Burt (10)	500	Emma Dawson (7)	82
Edward Halliday (10)	38	Emma Furlong (8)	371
Edward Latham (9)	380	Emma Garley (8)	281
Edward Lines (8)	407	Emma Kendall (9)	40
Edward Terry (8)	254	Emma Large (11)	131
Elaine Lee (10)	34	Emma Lovett (9)	387
Eleanor Barnes (9)	482	Emma Nolan (8)	282
Eleanor Bonser (9)	316	Emma Pingstone (11)	493
Eleanor Campbell (9)	450	Emma Price (11)	183
Eleanor Clements (9)	421	Emma Pritchard (11)	261
Eleanor Cooper (8)	395	Emma Rogers (8)	287
Eleanor Courtman (8)	251	Emma Shepherd (10)	121
Eleanor Mason (7)	371	Emma Stafford (11)	382
Eleanor White (10)	360	Emma Wilson (11)	206
Eleri Normington (9)	424	Emma Witt (10)	150
Eliot Broadbridge (8)	319	Emma Witty (9)	43
Elisa Glover (10)	396	Erica Bayliss (7)	445
Elizabeth Clementson (12)	459	Erica Ferris (10)	218
Elizabeth Norris (10)	369	Esme Bamber (10)	207
Elizabeth Wells (9)	389	Esme Dyson (10)	483
Elizabeth Wood (10)	372	Esmé Hill (10)	217
Ella Averill (11)	292	Esme Troughton (10)	246
Ella Houghton (10)	512	Euan Hill (9)	191
Ella Sutherland (10)	99	Euan Rae (8)	390
Ellë Osborne (8)	77	Evan Cooper (7)	331
Ellie Gosling (10)	235	Evie Doherty (10)	433
Ellie Macleod	154	Evie Moxon (10)	379
Ellie Pitchford (9)	261	Evie Smith (11)	433
Ellie Smith (10)	359	Faraaz Moosavi (9)	284
Ellie Wilford (10)	466	Faye Turnbull (11)	232
Elliot McDonald (8)	404	Fayola Knebel (9)	352
Elliot Pulver (10)	514	Fern Hill (9)	118
Elliott Richards (8)	176	Fern Moore (11)	265
Ellis Chan (10)	41	Ffion Trent (10)	472
Elloise Cooper (10)	53	Fiona Noble (10)	420
Emily Arnold (11)	250	Florence Ward (10)	292
Emily Cheung (10)	52	Frances Pegg (9)	282
Emily Cooksey (10)	77	Francesca Marston (10)	185
Emily Fenney (7)	445	Francesca Moreland (9)	478
Emily Goodwin (10)	164	Francesca Purser (7)	128
Emily Greenow (9)	324	Frazer Jones (9)	239
Emily Hill (9)	50	Fred Devereaux (11)	290
Emily Mason (10)	176	Fred Van Vuren (9)	111
Emily May (9)	490	Freddie Hall (7)	309
Emily Paine (9)	400	Freddy Charters (8)	110
Emily Shuttlewood (9)	420	Freya Newton (10)	31
Emily Simpkin (11)	186	Gabby Mundin (11)	180
Emily Stanier (8)	328	Gabriella Neal (9)	313
Emily Taylor (10)	298	Gabrielle Warrilow (10)	85

Gemima Hull (11)	425	Hannah Prestwich (10)	322
Gemma Mansell (11)	95	Hannah Watson (8)	476
Genevieve Tyrrell (10)	422	Hannah Wilkinson (10)	455
George Allan (11)	391	Harriet Bradbury (10)	353
George Crozier (7)	76	Harriet Lloyd (9)	252
George Mills (11)	510	Harriet Lowe (9)	346
George Nichols (10)	427	Harriet Oliver (10)	377
George Shattock (10)	314	Harriet Pascoe (8)	403
George Smailes (9)	27	Harrison Heath (9)	351
George Thomas (10)	60	Harry Baum (10)	369
George Vellam (9)	242	Harry Bee (10)	324
Georgia Burns (9)	202	Harry Bowers (9)	200
Georgia Deakin (10)	376	Harry Collett (9)	271
Georgia Smith (9)	267	Harry Dowling-Bingel (11)	302
Georgia Whitehouse (9)	519	Harry Lake (11)	508
Georgia Williams (10)	48	Harry Osbourn (11)	117
Georgie Douglas (10)	219	Harry Rogers (11)	94
Georgie Fender (7)	447	Harry Sawyers (10)	523
Georgie White (8)	23	Harry Spence (10)	49
Georgina Bayliss (10)	486	Harry Underwood (9)	277
Georgina Biggin (11)	503	Harvey Anderson (7)	253
Georgina Carter (10)	48	Harvey Wakefield (8)	264
Georgina Hockenhull (8)	124	Hattie Lewington (8)	82
Gerald Ashie (10)	46	Hayden Sutherland (9)	151
Glen Speight (11)	179	Hayley Dobson (11)	262
Glenn Charles (10)	315	Hayley Jarvis (10)	140
Grace Bennett (9)	142	Heath Stretton (9)	207
Grace Clark (9)	249	Heather Onions (10)	482
Grace Crocker (9)	419	Henry Henderson (8)	103
Grace Glover (10)	134	Henry Kelly (9)	279
Grace Oldfield (9)	301	Henry Potter (7)	399
Grace Pearson (10)	444	Hollie Brown (9)	293
Grace Robins (8)	28	Holly Bradley (10)	358
Grace Varney (9)	221	Holly Findley (9)	385
Grace Walker (6)	89	Holly Guy (9)	268
Gracie Johnson (11)	116	Holly Madden (10)	231
Grant Homer (10)	150	Holly Millward (7)	398
Gregory Blundell (10)	79	Holly Newton (10)	508
Halle McCarthy (10)	365	Holly Rounds (9)	190
Hamish Reid (10)	429	Holly Singleton (8)	203
Hanane Belaroussi (10)	135	Holly Surr (10)	274
Hannah Allured (11)	220	Holly Whatsize (11)	217
Hannah Bishop (11)	440	Imogen Tooms (11)	204
Hannah Bown (7)	253	Indya Ramsay (11)	291
Hannah Condliffe (8)	165	Insiyah Bharmal (9)	480
Hannah Coyle (8)	475	Isaac George (8)	106
Hannah Dobbs (10)	57	Isabelle Dix (7)	310
Hannah Evans (10)	295	Isobel Fallon (10)	298
Hannah Foster (10)	314	Isobel Farr (8)	309
Hannah Grubb (10)	299	Issy Heath (7)	403
Hannah Hadebe (10)	438	J A Batty (9)	174
Hannah King (10)	497	Jack Bilby (7)	109
Hannah Osborne (7)	83	Jack Brine (10)	442
Hannah Poole (10)	351	Jack Crooks (10)	30

Jack Eggerton (9)	116	James Kent (9)	386
Jack Fellows (10)	488	James Moruzzi (9)	321
Jack Ford (11)	474	James Spearing-Brown (9)	487
Jack Haworth (9)	248	James Swingler (11)	513
Jack Hoban (10)	515	James Taylor (10)	116
Jack Hollins (10)	466	James Till (11)	186
Jack Insley (10)	260	James Ward (7)	308
Jack Nadin (7)	90	James Warner (8)	123
Jack Sixsmith (9)	450	James Wood (11)	56
Jack Skitt (11)	83	Jamie Cook (9)	498
Jack Solloway (11)	504	Jamie Dewing (11)	132
Jack Trafford (11)	459	Jamie Hardy (10)	520
Jack Watson (10)	471	Jamie McEwan (10)	248
Jack Woods (10)	456	Jamie Wright (9)	160
Jackson Davis (9)	242	Jasmin Piercy (10)	208
Jacob Broadbridge (8)	318	Jasmine Broadbent (9)	401
Jacob Goddard (10)	368	Jasmine Leftley (9)	145
Jacob Layfield (9)	379	Jasmine Ravenhill (8)	251
Jacob Matthews (7)	251	Jay Akred (9)	485
Jacob McGarrity (9)	501	Jay Edwards-Murphy (9)	48
Jacob Scott (10)	110	Jayde Stafford (9)	223
Jacob Wright (8)	72	Jeevan Johal (11)	35
Jacque Wootton (9)	349	Jeffrey Lamb (10)	431
Jade Allard (10)	114	Jennifer Bayliss (9)	443
Jade Ann Hewlett (10)	484	Jennifer Collier (10)	130
Jade Callis-Capell (8)	365	Jennifer Lewis (10)	115
Jade Carter (8)	26	Jennifer Merrell (8)	171
Jade Harasymiw (9)	522	Jenny Ansell (8)	68
Jade Marshall (8)	207	Jess Goodall (11)	511
Jade McKillup (11)	299	Jessica Bailey (9)	503
Jade Sheldon (9)	256	Jessica Ball (8)	92
Jade Vazquez (10)	522	Jessica Barber (10)	344
Jade Walker (10)	149	Jessica Bird (11)	188
Jade Wells-Larter (9)	143	Jessica Cavanagh (10)	120
Jade Wright (9)	161	Jessica Cole (11)	209
Jake Gutteridge (11)	34	Jessica Goddard (7)	399
Jake Insley (9)	519	Jessica Hill (10)	325
Jake Jones (10)	191	Jessica Land (9)	190
Jake McCarthy (7)	395	Jessica Mathars (10)	95
Jake Pullen (9)	147	Jessica Mead (11)	426
Jake Samardzija (9)	382	Jessica Rawlings (9)	252
Jake Scott (9)	228	Jessica Roberts (10)	24
Jake Shorrocks (10)	451	Jessica Rymill (10)	285
Jake Wardle (10)	454	Jessica Scott (8)	202
Jakob Garner (10)	165	Jessica Sleeman (10)	54
James Arrowsmith (9)	41	Jessica Smith (7)	78
James Brown (10)	152	Jessica Syred (10)	64
James Clough (10)	319	Jessica Tarran (10)	296
James Cooke (8)	250	Jessica Trower (9)	24
James Eaton (10)	294	Jessica Widdowson (11)	216
James Fisher (8)	27	Jodi Garner (8)	166
James Fletcher (9)	483	Jodie Anderson (9)	280
James Geary (10)	368	Jodie Williams (10)	38
James Hancock (9)	452	Joe Gwyther (7)	411

Joe Holmes (8)	158	Kasia Beacher (10)	206
Joe Rhodes (9)	184	Kate Coventry (9)	117
Joe Rose (9)	50	Kate Greenow (8)	327
Joe Senior (8)	254	Kate Martin (11)	169
Joe Tunnicliffe (11)	187	Kate Williams (11)	57
Joe Watts (10)	113	Katherine Danckert (10)	297
Joe Webb (10)	211	Katherine Kirkham (9)	489
Joe Winstone (8)	389	Katherine Thorpe (11)	258
Joel Hughes (8)	277	Kathryn Bailey (7)	417
Joel Webster (11)	457	Kathryn Hallt (10)	184
John Dipple (9)	507	Kathryn Wood (10)	482
John Walvin (8)	71	Katie Aletras (10)	134
John-Henry Cooper (11)	117	Katie Ann Mythen (11)	437
Jonah Stead (8)	380	Katie Berwick (8)	179
Jonathan Adams (10)	197	Katie Dunwell (9)	256
Jonathan Rose (9)	314	Katie Edwards (9)	117
Jonathon Pickering (9)	156	Katie Farmer (7)	481
Jordan Addison Phillips (9)	250	Katie Ford (9)	224
Jordan Brookes (8)	101	Katie Frearson (9)	430
Jordan Davies (7)	29	Katie Furber (8)	269
Jordan Davis (11)	53	Katie Holgate (10)	451
Jordan Halliday (10)	479	Katie Lloyd (10)	304
Jordan Jamieson (9)	358	Katie Nagington (8)	264
Jordan Kenney (9)	449	Katie Ratcliffe (9)	341
Jordan Shaw (9)	469	Katie Ronch (11)	81
Jordan Small (9)	149	Katie Small (9)	33
Jordan Turrell (7)	310	Katie Smith (11)	131
Jorja Dawson (10)	153	Katie Stanley (10)	472
Joseph Andrews (9)	315	Katie Stanworth (9)	50
Joseph Brennan (10)	457	Katrina Palin (10)	35
Joseph Osborn-Grummett (11)	259	Katy Warner (10)	117
Joseph Porton (8)	91	Kayleigh Wallace (11)	447
Josephine Mooney (7)	410	Keily Munden (10)	142
Josh Andrews (10)	379	Kelly Brown (10)	263
Josh Banner (9)	111	Kelly Staunton (10)	448
Josh Johnson (9)	188	Kelsi Varney (10)	214
Josh Kelly (11)	40	Kendra Taylor (11)	262
Josh Robinson (8)	138	Kerri-Jane Greenhalgh (11)	465
Josh Salvin (9)	242	Kerry Gallagher (10)	131
Joshua Bowker (7)	91	Kevin Jo Sung Tse (10)	297
Joshua Cooper (8)	82	Kia Barnett (9)	282
Joshua Cox (11)	291	Kia Gwyther (8)	408
Joshua Davies (7)	107	Kiedis Clay (9)	227
Joshua Gladman (10)	31	Kiera Nicholson (9)	275
Joshua Horam (9)	271	Kieran Ball (9)	31
Joshua Philpott (10)	412	Kieran Dean (8)	108
Joshua Potterton-Orton (9)	241	Kieran Gilson (10)	275
Joshua Scoins (10)	440	Kieran McArdle (10)	511
Joshua Utting (7)	147	Kieran Meredith (9)	177
Josie Chapman (10)	303	Kieran Prescod (9)	288
Jovan Gordon (9)	177	Kieren Bennett (9)	73
Justin Allerton (11)	476	Kieron Tregidga (9)	438
Justin Chapman (10)	162	Kim Victor-Trott (10)	57
Karine Price (11)	494	Kimberley Blueman (10)	506

Name	Number	Name	Number
Kimberly Frost (9)	167	Leigh-Anne Bell (10)	247
Kimrun Basra (9)	473	Lemeece Sargent (9)	363
Kirk Howells (9)	374	Leo Bristow (10)	323
Kirsten Doig (11)	137	Levan Peart (10)	44
Kirsty Allan (8)	383	Lewis Batchelor (9)	139
Kirsty Mackley (10)	142	Lewis Dykes (9)	463
Kirsty Maguire (9)	67	Lewis Mazzone (8)	75
Kirsty Naismith (9)	178	Lewis Pywell (9)	378
Kirsty Pridding (11)	430	Lewis Sandbrook (9)	51
Kirsty Rea (9)	100	Leyla Al-Ashaab (9)	92
Kodi Andrews (10)	394	Leyla Sezer (10)	169
Kulraj Kaur (11)	51	Liam Baker (9)	143
Kurt Ledger (11)	172	Liam Cowzer (10)	431
Kurt Poppleton (7)	103	Liam Davies (9)	452
Kyle Barker (10)	505	Liam Haycock (10)	181
Kyra Leneveu (7)	91	Liam Johnson (10)	89
Larissa Chamberlain (10)	218	Liam Munt (9)	278
Laura Andrews (10)	381	Liam Southwell (11)	209
Laura Baggaley (9)	461	Liandda Burnett (11)	65
Laura Carey (9)	278	Libby Bowler (9)	227
Laura Compton (10)	509	Lillie Collins (11)	55
Laura Fitch (10)	133	Lily North (9)	222
Laura Fleming (9)	199	Lily Ramsden (9)	437
Laura Flude (9)	222	Lisa Hales (9)	153
Laura Hazlewood (8)	102	Lisa Hampson (11)	170
Laura Hearn (10)	262	Lisa Ruddy (10)	129
Laura Price (10)	125	Lisa Sheppard (9)	125
Laura Roberts (9)	499	Lizzie Francis (10)	374
Laura Smith (7)	397	Lois Pritchard (9)	263
Laura Wilde (11)	127	Loren Bradshaw (11)	521
Laura Wykes (9)	442	Lorna Winnington (9)	201
Lauren Allcock (10)	187	Lorrie Sole (8)	147
Lauren Banks (10)	447	Louis Boffy (8)	102
Lauren Birch (9)	123	Louise Cosby (10)	223
Lauren Bond (10)	84	Louise Cowcill (8)	445
Lauren Burt (10)	258	Louise Cummings (7)	92
Lauren Corbett (10)	32	Louise Pye (10)	169
Lauren Dipple (10)	512	Lucas Porter (8)	79
Lauren Dykes (11)	464	Lucia Lemos (8)	152
Lauren Dyson (11)	515	Lucy Cramp (7)	397
Lauren Guestford (10)	39	Lucy Cupit (10)	189
Lauren Hamper (10)	270	Lucy Fewtrell (10)	88
Lauren Hart (8)	325	Lucy Gilkes (9)	361
Lauren Hilton (10)	245	Lucy Harrison (10)	247
Lauren Kirkpatrick (11)	293	Lucy Harrison (8)	304
Lauren O'Hanlon (10)	436	Lucy Hickenbotham (10)	172
Lauren Purser (10)	486	Lucy Holland	475
Lauren Smith (10)	246	Lucy Martin (11)	80
Layla Allebone (11)	288	Lucy Murray (11)	240
Leah Baines (8)	151	Lucy Nealon (11)	238
Leah Heath (9)	400	Lucy Rushton (10)	63
Leah Shackman (8)	163	Lucy Solloway (9)	498
Leanne Potter (10)	306	Lucy Wickett (9)	418
Leigha Taylor (10)	243	Lucy Wilde (9)	126

Lui McMahon (8)	189	Megan Clephane (10)	428
Luke Andrew Salmon (10)	232	Megan Fairbrother (11)	230
Luke Butler (10)	454	Megan Glenholmes (11)	120
Luke Doherty (9)	441	Megan Hunter (8)	390
Luke Girling (9)	502	Megan Jenkyn (7)	398
Luke Hamps (10)	44	Megan Lamb (10)	427
Luke Mathewson (10)	266	Megan Lewis (10)	118
Luke Middleton (9)	368	Megan Marshall (9)	128
Luke Parr (10)	226	Megan Morrison (7)	362
Luke Pontin (9)	265	Megan Thomas (9)	484
Luke Sykes (8)	396	Melissa Carroll (10)	303
Lydia George (10)	62	Melissa Dawkins (11)	236
Lydia Parkhill (10)	113	Melissa Stedman (7)	159
Lydia Stephens (8)	300	Melissa Williams (8)	158
Lynton Fleming (8)	151	Melodie Bowering (10)	436
Maddie Gough (7)	75	Mia Mellor (11)	237
Maddie Sutton (9)	387	Michael Byard (10)	375
Maddie Wheway (9)	222	Michael Cunningham (9)	329
Madison Regan (10)	335	Michael Drummond (10)	96
Maia Harrison Bond (9)	387	Michael Evans (11)	33
Maisie Scoins (7)	446	Michael Flatman (8)	397
Maisy Cooksey (7)	80	Michael Foley	154
Mankeert Kaur (10)	444	Michael Howard (11)	168
Marcus Smith (9)	337	Michael Lyons (10)	265
Margaret Martinelli (9)	320	Michael Watson (10)	229
Marie-Claire Alfonso (8)	415	Michelle Tozer (10)	166
Marilyn Coles (10)	288	Michelle Tozer (10)	120
Mark Cappellina (9)	401	Mickey Manship (10)	520
Mark Fell (9)	500	Mikey Hollis (10)	321
Martha Buckle (7)	416	Milica Novakovic (8)	152
Martin Herbert (10)	136	Millie Hicks (8)	124
Mary Carroll (10)	153	Millie Hicks (9)	466
Mary Thornber (10)	427	Mir Spreckley (9)	100
Mary Whitting (8)	320	Mohamed Ismail (9)	449
Matt Ross (9)	240	Mollie-Rose Dooley (11)	470
Matthew Astley (7)	399	Molly Baxter (11)	239
Matthew Beaumont-Pike (9)	464	Molly Benfold (9)	452
Matthew Brown (11)	467	Molly McCormick (7)	155
Matthew Chambers (10)	273	Morwenna Vaughan (9)	308
Matthew Dale (10)	229	Munpreet Chatha (10)	127
Matthew Dooley (8)	409	Myles Brown (11)	130
Matthew Hurley (11)	78	Nancy O'Brien (11)	435
Matthew Lawson (9)	228	Naomi Davis (11)	260
Matthew Pearce (11)	474	Natalie Jeakings (10)	465
Matthew Scott (11)	492	Natalie Johnson (10)	131
Matthew Shirley (9)	336	Natalie Rhodes (11)	510
Matthew Stuart (11)	86	Natalie Sharp (9)	43
Matthew Walton (9)	37	Natasha Davies (9)	61
Max Overton (8)	145	Natasha Keane (11)	358
McCaulley (9)	210	Natasha Marsh (10)	462
Megan Barnes (10)	242	Nathan Brand (10)	357
Megan Bradley (8)	193	Nathan Cooke (9)	44
Megan Burke (10)	355	Nathan Kirkbright (10)	292
Megan Chanin (9)	386	Niamh O'Mara (10)	366

Nicholas Gibbon (10)	62	Rachel Barnwell (7)	83
Nick Hollis (11)	233	Rachel Bromley (9)	269
Nicola Pringle (10)	163	Rachel Flatman (10)	393
Nicole Atter (9)	280	Rachel Hackett (9)	504
Nicole Broomhall (11)	94	Rachel Hancock (11)	460
Nicole Hunt (9)	222	Rachel Harrison (10)	65
Nicole Keeling (9)	150	Rachel Heggs (10)	214
Nicole Theakston (11)	426	Rachel Peacock (10)	519
Nicole Woolley (10)	36	Rachel Sullivan (8)	83
Nikki Craven (10)	187	Raphael Garland (9)	99
Nikki Hutcheon	148	Rashpal Bhakar (10)	43
Nikki Payne (11)	138	Reanne Hulet (11)	55
Nur Syafiqah Nor Azman (8)	481	Rebecca Britton (10)	39
Nyle Tomlinson (8)	300	Rebecca Burton (10)	87
Oliver Blount (9)	378	Rebecca Crowe (10)	203
Oliver Bullock (7)	396	Rebecca Maxwell (7)	416
Oliver Jeffs (9)	270	Rebecca Medlin (9)	273
Oliver Perry (9)	193	Rebecca Oughton (10)	224
Oliver Powell (8)	328	Rebecca Price (8)	194
Oliver Wakefield (10)	263	Rebecca Purcell (10)	48
Olivia King (8)	73	Rebecca Read (10)	220
Omar Qasim (11)	509	Rebecca Roe (10)	166
Orlaith Owen (8)	251	Rebecca Stokes (11)	30
Oscar Robinson (10)	313	Rebecca Warren (10)	234
Owen Rogers (9)	323	Rebecca Waterman (10)	88
Paige Baines (8)	146	Rebekah Norton (10)	462
Paige Gartlan (10)	276	Reece Reynolds (11)	507
Paige Jones (8)	204	Reegan Campion-Westwood (10)	197
Paige Moore (10)	268	Rhiann Colman (9)	160
Paige Sharman (9)	116	Rhianna Hubbard (9)	238
Paris Emmerson (9)	522	Rhianna Longstaff (10)	411
Parissa Bagheri (11)	507	Rhiannon Harris (11)	47
Pascal Risi (11)	429	Rhiannon Jones (8)	283
Patrice Attias (9)	312	Rhiannon Pailing (10)	317
Patrick Boyle (8)	27	Rhys Ayres (10)	396
Patrick Harrison (11)	305	Rhys Cooper (9)	329
Patrick Morgan (8)	101	Rhys Green (10)	64
Paul Williams (11)	204	Ria Merifield (11)	291
Perry Clayton (10)	520	Richard Craven (10)	196
Peter Baggley (10)	333	Richard Hart-Mould (10)	332
Peter Bennett (9)	112	Ricky Evans (8)	306
Peter Goodwin (10)	167	Riordan Knott (9)	313
Philippa Bricklebank (9)	72	Robbie Andrews (7)	398
Phoebe Dunbar (8)	382	Robbie Crooks (10)	30
Phoebe Smart (11)	181	Robbie Smith (7)	155
Poppy Brown (9)	376	Robbie Watts (8)	104
Poppy Gentleman (10)	375	Robbie Wilkins (11)	284
Poppy O'Rourke (9)	350	Robert Ansell (10)	68
Poppy Owsin (10)	215	Robert Brewer (10)	486
Priyesh Mistry (8)	146	Robert Jefferies (9)	360
Rachael Bradford (10)	85	Robert Lee (8)	270
Rachael Hackett (9)	185	Robert Simpson (8)	388
Rachael Jones (9)	195	Robina Neupane (8)	412
Rachel Baker (8)	282	Robyn Collins (10)	99

Robyn Dewing (8)	129	Sarah Culley (11)	467
Rosa Sulley (10)	208	Sarah Dakin (9)	166
Rosie Cox (8)	330	Sarah Innes (11)	257
Rosie Hall (8)	307	Sarah Moore (10)	231
Rosie Haynes (7)	81	Sarah Scatcherd (9)	463
Rosie Lewis (10)	134	Sarah Scotford (10)	317
Rosie Lewis (10)	139	Sarah Walker (11)	112
Rosie Mead (9)	417	Sarah Warner (10)	175
Rosie Thomas (9)	42	Sarah-Louise Fogell	148
Ross Mather (10)	50	Scarlet Roberts (9)	491
Rowan Davis (9)	260	Scott Driscoll (10)	89
Roxane Kirkham (9)	502	Scott Lynes (9)	279
Ruth Gilliand Simon (10)	264	Sean Cato (10)	391
Ruth Pollard (10)	302	Sean Kerr (11)	300
Ryan Allen (10)	45	Sean Lowe (10)	364
Ryan Johnson (7)	93	Sean Somers (9)	374
Ryan Kirk (10)	393	Sebastian Applewhite (8)	384
Ryan O'Connor (9)	348	Sebastian Lee (10)	119
Ryan Phillips (11)	52	Shane Curtis (11)	467
Ryan Raper (11)	86	Shane Davies (11)	59
Ryan Stewart (9)	161	Shannon Barker (10)	479
Ryan Veasey	163	Shannon Bowyer (9)	285
Sadie Bromley (9)	205	Shannon Burrows (9)	179
Saffron Blissett (10)	287	Shannon Clewes (10)	121
Sahith Nama (10)	523	Shannon Edwards (10)	45
Sally Clive (8)	255	Shannon Evans (10)	173
Sam Begley (9)	352	Shannon McLelland (10)	358
Sam Benjamin (11)	320	Shannon Onions (9)	49
Sam Cain (10)	367	Shannon Taylor (10)	393
Sam Coupland (11)	429	Shannon Upton (10)	84
Sam French (8)	366	Shantelle Pearce (10)	35
Sam Fury (10)	359	Shaun Fairbrother (11)	174
Sam Jones (10)	228	Shaun Pearcy (9)	407
Sam Jordan (9)	267	Shelley Mills (10)	163
Sam Marshall (10)	295	Siân Barron (11)	182
Sam Mould (11)	212	Sian Cobham (9)	26
Sam Pollard (7)	371	Siân Dimblebee (10)	208
Sam Prestwich (8)	330	Sian Sliwinska (8)	303
Sam Richardson (10)	385	Simon Howells (10)	61
Sam Stevens (7)	326	Sinead Cross (7)	157
Sam Tebbutt (9)	276	Siobhan English (9)	119
Sam Tetlow (9)	372	Siobhan Gardner (10)	461
Sam Thorley (9)	334	Siôn Thomas (9)	339
Sam Wilde (10)	453	Sophia Pelusi (10)	425
Samantha Griffiths (11)	74	Sophie Beckett (9)	231
Samantha Harrison (9)	363	Sophie Bujdoso (7)	370
Samantha Matravers (11)	311	Sophie Coles (8)	283
Samantha Thompson (10)	459	Sophie Ellerton (10)	176
Sammy Bryan (10)	194	Sophie Ferguson (9)	249
Samuel Baines (9)	345	Sophie Fortey (10)	322
Samuel Garner (7)	129	Sophie Foston (9)	137
Samuel Watts (10)	182	Sophie Haigh (8)	280
Sandro Moreira	162	Sophie Hancock (9)	226
Sarah Berriman (11)	475	Sophie Hassell (10)	225

Sophie Hill (11)	287	Tim Stokes (9)	221
Sophie Hollis (8)	331	Todd Smallwood (7)	105
Sophie Leach (9)	178	Tom Boldry (11)	112
Sophie O'Flynn (10)	372	Tom Cannon (9)	164
Sophie Purcell (10)	87	Tom Grisley (11)	249
Sophie Robinson (9)	266	Tom Higgs (11)	60
Sophie Vallance (9)	481	Tom Hurren (8)	28
Sophie Vick (10)	491	Tom Morris	228
Sophie Wain (9)	226	Tom Shepherd (10)	49
Sophy Sherwood (7)	409	Tommy Farr (9)	312
Srdan Stjepanovic (7)	157	Toni Fletcher (9)	306
Stacey Beach (11)	58	Tori-May Owen (8)	413
Stefan Wells (11)	168	Trudie Ward (9)	196
Stephanie Hopkins (10)	132	Tyler Butler (9)	150
Stephanie Norman (8)	171	Tyler James (9)	281
Stephanie Young (8)	69	Tyler Wright (10)	135
Stephen Allen (9)	375	Tyra-Jade Newman (8)	289
Steve Singh (10)	235	Vanessa Hsieh (11)	47
Steven Rawlings (10)	494	Vanessa Willetts (10)	458
Steven Trotter (9)	210	Veeran Govan (9)	361
Stuart Lewis (8)	311	Vicky Black (11)	162
Suet Lee (10)	44	Victor Ingham (9)	23
Summer Hill (8)	295	Victoria Bennett (10)	76
Suzanna Sabin (8)	404	Victoria Densley (10)	441
Tabitha Lewis (8)	402	Victoria Harris (11)	312
Tamara Vukosavljevic (9)	152	Victoria Lake (9)	488
Tara Gregory (11)	517	Victoria Pilgrim (11)	434
Tee-jay McCulloch (9)	161	Victoria Price (7)	480
Tempany Wynn (10)	87	Victoria Roskams (10)	413
Terry Folwell (11)	357	William Brown (10)	113
Tessa Boyd (9)	367	William Cooper (10)	114
Tessa Dunbar (10)	398	William Doherty (9)	186
Thomas Bridges (9)	115	William Fender (10)	443
Thomas Brown (10)	159	William Gray (7)	415
Thomas Dance (10)	149	William Hallt (8)	201
Thomas Devey (9)	474	William Owen (9)	122
Thomas Fearns (10)	357	William Parker (9)	244
Thomas Fidler (9)	286	Xander Colombo (8)	305
Thomas Gray (10)	418	Yvonne Ma (10)	179
Thomas Hewitt (10)	362	Zachary Brant (10)	304
Thomas Longley (9)	271	Zack Foster (10)	173
Thomas Morris (10)	89	Zak Anderson (9)	212
Thomas Mullaney (7)	82	Zak Lawrence (9)	105
Thomas Pennack (8)	183	Zak White (10)	312
Thomas Powell (9)	462	Zara Purvis (9)	42
Thomas Williams (11)	98	Zoe Holmes (8)	317
Thomas Wright (9)	70	Zoe Pearson (7)	90
Tiffany-Jayne Bull (9)	276	Zoe-Mae Dalby (10)	362

THE POEMS

Lullaby

Slumber, slumber little one
Let your tired eyes drift away from the day
Slumber little one!

Slumber, slumber the night has come
The hour arrives
Tomorrow it will be sunlight.

You are tepid,
Let your quick legs slide to the end of your bed,
Slumber little one!

Slumber,
Let your weary mind drift aimlessly away.

Slumber,
Today it is you
But it is Mother always.

Slumber,
Tomorrow you will take the bow and the knife.

Victor Ingham (9)
Albrighton County Junior School, Albrighton

Summer

Summer with bright colours like yellow.
It tastes like creamy ice cream.
It sounds like people sprinting in the sun.
It looks like a lovely hot summer's day.
It smells like red roses in the hot air.
It makes me jump free into the scented air.

Georgie White (8)
Albrighton County Junior School, Albrighton

Colours Of The World

Black is like a piece of black, messy coal.
Orange is like a busy bee.
Brown is like a tree rustling in the wind.
White is like the snow in Canada.
Red is like an exploding firework.
Green is like the spring grass.

Ashton Wood (8)
Albrighton County Junior School, Albrighton

Colour Senses

Yellow is like something shiny and hot like the sun.
Purple is like the quiet library.
Blue is like a hot bath for me.
Pink is like my mum's fragrance.
Brown is like chocolate dripping.
Green is like a mermaid's tail.
White is like yummy ice cream.
Grey is like a shark swimming up.
Black is like a baby cat born.
Red is like a glowing sun.
Orange is like fruit juice.

Chelsea Machin (8)
Albrighton County Junior School, Albrighton

My Dog

I see a spotty dog
Burying his bone like a tractor.
Wagging his tail like a piece of grass blowing in the wind.
Brown as a table, white as snow.
Oval as a shape.
Fur like a shock.
Calls like a howling fox.
Barks like people shouting.
Suddenly it strikes like lightning.

Jessica Trower (9)
Albrighton County Junior School, Albrighton

My Dog

I spy a sneaky dog
Jumping and creeping like a cheeky spy.
Happy and soft like a silk bed.
As white as a sheep.
Healthy, shaped like an egg.
Soft as silky music.
Calls like a singer.
Runs as fast as a cheetah.
Soft as a silky music.

Jessica Roberts (10)
Albrighton County Junior School, Albrighton

Colours

Red is like a trumpet sound because red is strong
And a trumpet has a strong sound.
Yellow is like something soft and warm.
Pink is like the smell of roses.
Orange is like the feeling from a lovely bright sun.
Purple is like a thunderstorm.
Blue is like running water.
Black is like hearing bumps in a dark room.
Brown is like dry grass in winter.
Cream is like an ice lolly.
Gold is like the bright sun.
White is like the snow on your face.

Amy Gage (9)
Albrighton County Junior School, Albrighton

The Autumn Moon

Autumn is crisp brown, dark red and amber.
It tastes like hot chocolate and marshmallows.
It sounds like a downpour of rain.
It smells of dazzling bonfires on a dark night.
It looks like a whirl of crispy leaves.
It makes me feel like the autumn moon high in the sky.

Charlotte Thomas (9)
Albrighton County Junior School, Albrighton

Wordly Thoughts

As red as a sweet rose.
As bumpy as a beautiful beaver.
As quiet as a silky snake.
As slow as a swimming swan.
As bright as a beaming sun.
As busy as a black bat.
As good as a galloping goat.
As fat as a frightened fox.

Alicia Doonan-Jones (9)
Albrighton County Junior School, Albrighton

Colours Of The Rainbow

Orange is like a burning fire,
Black is like a piece of bright brown toast,
Pearl is like the feeling of sand on a warm day.
Peach is like a cold, bitter day.
Sky blue is like a lovely holiday in Spain.
Brown is like a large tree with masses of thin twigs,
Bending, bowing, hanging.

Sian Cobham (9)
Albrighton County Junior School, Albrighton

Spring

Spring is wasp yellow and snow white.
It tastes like juicy apples and runny honey.
It sounds like lambs bleating in the grassy fields.
It looks like the amber sun and sky moving round and round.
It smells like scones and fruit cake that are all mine.
It makes me feel happy and safe.

Beth Martin (9)
Albrighton County Junior School, Albrighton

Winter

Winter is dark grey, long nights.
It sounds like trees rustling and rattling in the wind.
It tastes like milk on my cornflakes.
It looks like a white blanket on the ground.
It smells like bacon sizzling under the grill.

Jade Carter (8)
Albrighton County Junior School, Albrighton

Winter

The snow is like sugar white cold.
It tastes tasty when I have tomato soup at Christmas.
It sounds like snow when it falls from the sky.
It looks like crystals.
It smells like Christmas dinner.
I feel like a snowman.

Dylan Harrison (7)
Albrighton County Junior School, Albrighton

Summer

The summer is when you play out and people get hot.
The sun is bright, orangey yellow.
It tastes like toast and water.
It smells like ice cream.
It sounds like buzzing bees.
I feel hot when I go out, into the garden.

Patrick Boyle (8)
Albrighton County Junior School, Albrighton

Spring

Spring is light brown and grass green.
It tastes like lovely pancakes and hot chocolate.
It sounds like small birds singing.
It looks like the shining sun.
It smells like an approaching summer's breeze.
It makes me feel happy.

Christopher Westwood (8)
Albrighton County Junior School, Albrighton

Spring

Spring is as bright as grass green.
It tastes like sweet pancakes and crunchy chocolate.
It sounds like fresh air is coming in.
It looks like the colours of the rainbow.
It smells like sweet blossom on the flowers.
It makes me feel cosy and warm.

James Fisher (8)
Albrighton County Junior School, Albrighton

As Loud As A Rock Band

As bright white as a brand new limo
As gradual as a slimy slug.
As slim as a piece of paper.
As dark as a haunted house.
As lazy as a litter lout.
As strong as a grizzly bear.
As violent as a murderer.
As loud as a rock band.

George Smailes (9)
Albrighton County Junior School, Albrighton

Spring

Spring is pearl pink, rosy red, grass green, shimmering silver.
It tastes like cold lemonade and shocking strawberry ice cream.
I hear the rattling, rocking and rustling of new life.
Blossoming trees are all around.
It smells like new grass growing.
I feel like running around in the hot, yellow sun.

Cerys Furlong (7)
Albrighton County Junior School, Albrighton

Summer

Summer is a lovely time of year!
The sun's colour is wasp yellow.
I hear the butterflies gliding to the flowers.
It makes me feel happy and free!
I see it's beautiful because of the birds hopping in the garden
As fit as a boy or girl!

Grace Robins (8)
Albrighton County Junior School, Albrighton

Rainbow

As bright as a booming moon.
As flat as a sunray.
As busy as a running badger.
As quiet as a rat.
As good as pink.
As fit as a fox.
As slow as a bumpy tortoise.

Chloe Woolley (8)
Albrighton County Junior School, Albrighton

Colour Senses

As quiet as a slithering snake,
As busy as a giant crowd.
As squashed as a mouldy apple.
As fit as a sprinting gym teacher.
As slimy as a wiggly worm.
As slow as a wrinkled turtle.
As red as a new postbox.
As bright as a reflecting emerald.

Tom Hurren (8)
Albrighton County Junior School, Albrighton

I Asked The Little Boy Who Cannot See

Brown is like the feel of a strong piece of wood.
Orange is like the hot bright sun.
Black is like the smell of a dark cave.
White is like my soft pillow.
Green is like the smell of dark grass.
Grey is like the pitter-patter of rain.
Silver is like the cold handlebars on a bike.

Brandon Rock (7)
Albrighton County Junior School, Albrighton

I Asked The Little Boy Who Cannot See

Black is like the quiet, still night.
Orange is like the taste of my orange juice.
Brown is like the taste of my chocolate milkshake.
Gold is like the hot, scorching sun.

Jordan Davies (7)
Albrighton County Junior School, Albrighton

My Snake

I spotted a snake in the grass
Hunting its prey like a hound,
Slithering like a worm or a snail.
Its colour was browny and orange like a cheetah.
It was as long as a ruler.
It had a fish's skin.
It was silent like a mouse.
It climbed trees and hid under rocks.
It shed its skin.

Daniel Whitehouse (10)
Albrighton County Junior School, Albrighton

Winter

Winter brings white snow into the year.
It tastes like flavoured ice.
It sounds like crunchy snow.
It looks like white clouds.
It smells like hot chicken.
It makes me feel happy.

Aaron Lund (8)
Albrighton County Junior School, Albrighton

My Snake

I see a slithering snake
Slithering in some broken bark like a twisty river.
Going round corners like it's stuck in a maze.
Dark brown like some bark off a tree.
Smooth and delicate like a sheet of glass.
Long and crooked like a twig off a tree.
Hisses like some wind on a mountain.
Squeezes its prey like some air squeezed in a balloon.
Suddenly it sprays poison at its prey.

Robbie Crooks (10)
Albrighton County Junior School, Albrighton

My Dog

I spot a dog like a tin of food.
Watching me like a mouse.
Moving like a tortoise.
Bright like sunshine.
Fat like an ogre.
Furry like a sheep.
Barks, slobbers, howls like a sick motorbike.
Runs at you like you're food.
Suddenly it licks you like a puppy.

Rebecca Stokes (11)
Albrighton County Junior School, Albrighton

My Dog

I notice a dog
Running like a cheetah.
Zooming like a sports car.
As gold as the sun.
Shaped like a wolf.
Fur like wool.
Barking like a fox.
Eating like a pig.
Suddenly it sleeps like a baby.

Jack Crooks (10)
Albrighton County Junior School, Albrighton

My Rattlesnake

Staring at its prey as still as a rock.
Slithering along the ground like a ball on a ramp.
It can be yellow, brown or black.
Its body is as thin as a hosepipe.
It feels like a scaly eel.
It hisses like static and rattles like a maraca.
It can swallow things ten times its size.

Kieran Ball (9)
Albrighton County Junior School, Albrighton

My Dog

I notice a dumb dog
Running like an odd donkey.
Fast as a slim cheetah.
White as the new snow.
As thin as a rough snakeskin,
And hairy like a bear in the morning.
Barks like a French horn.
Eats like a fat pig.
Looks at a cat, then it strikes!

Joshua Gladman (10)
Albrighton County Junior School, Albrighton

My Snake

I spy a sleeping snake in the sun.
Slithers like a lion hunting.
Hunting like a cheetah.
Green and yellow like leaves in the summer.
Long as a worm.
Slippery scales like a fish.
Hisses like the wind.
Sleeping like a baby.
Suddenly it strikes at a mouse.

Freya Newton (10)
Albrighton County Junior School, Albrighton

My Dog

I spot a bad dog.
Watching the world go by like an old man.
Slow like a snail.
Brown like a chocolate bar.
Plump like an orange.
As fluffy as a bear.
Barking like a trumpet.
Chomping his food like a lion.
Suddenly he strikes at a cat!

Lauren Corbett (10)
Albrighton County Junior School, Albrighton

My Dog

I spot a dog hiding under a table.
Sleeping like a bear in the winter.
Sprinting like a cheetah.
Black, white and light brown like a photo.
Fat like an enormous pig.
Fluffy like a frizzy pillow.
Barking like a werewolf.
Splashing in water like a fish.
Wet dog.

Ashley Tomlinson (10)
Albrighton County Junior School, Albrighton

My Dog

I spy a barking dog.
Staring like a lion at its prey.
Staring like foxes.
Black-brown like a tree trunk.
Long, quite fat, like a boar.
Smooth as a Porsche.
It barks like a loud car.
It eats like a cow.
It wins like a cheetah.

Anthony West (9)
Albrighton County Junior School, Albrighton

Pleasant Poetry

Summer is yellow like a wasp.
Its taste is like a mouthful of ice cream.
A soft sound is a sunny sun shining.
It looks like bright green grass.
It smells like some flowers in the farmer's field.
It makes my friends play.

Katie Small (9)
Albrighton County Junior School, Albrighton

The Day The Zoo Escaped . . .

The lion marched out proudly,
The crocodile snapped out fiercely,

The panda strolled out quickly,
The flamingo walked out quietly.

The giraffe galloped out quickly,
The monkey swung out excitedly.

But the hippo,
Stubbornly,
Just stayed where it was.

Andrew Martin (10)
Apley Wood Primary School, Telford

The Day The Zoo Escaped . . .

The tiger trotted out quickly,
The crocodile snapped out fiercely.

The monkey swung out proudly,
The elephant stomped out slowly.

The giraffe galloped out brightly,
The alligator snapped out lightly,

But the hippopotamus,
Stubbornly
Just stayed where it was.

Michael Evans (11)
Apley Wood Primary School, Telford

The Day The Zoo Escaped . . .

The monkeys swing out swiftly,
The gorilla gripped stiffly.

The elephant stomped slowly,
The flamingo did a roly-poly.

The penguin paddled out slickly,
The jaguar leapt out quickly,

But the hippopotamus
Stubbornly,
Just stayed where it was.

Jake Gutteridge (11)
Apley Wood Primary School, Telford

The Day The Zoo Escaped . . .

The day the animals escaped . . .

The flamingo waddled out funnily,
The monkey swung out swiftly.

The crocodile snapped out fiercely,
The jaguar pounded out slowly.

The penguin slid out brightly,
The antelope ran out quickly,

But the elephant
Stubbornly,
Just stayed where it was.

Caitlin Haq (10)
Apley Wood Primary School, Telford

The Day The Zoo Escaped . . .

The tiger dashed out quickly,
The jaguar marched out slowly.

The panda walked out heavily,
The monkey swung out swiftly.

The flamingos flew out brightly,
The antelopes ran out quietly,

But the hippopotamus,
Stubbornly,
Just stayed where it was.

Elaine Lee (10)
Apley Wood Primary School, Telford

The Day The Zoo Escaped . . .

The monkey swung out swiftly,
The crocodile crept out fiercely.

The elephant stomped out slowly,
The tarantula crawled out quietly.

The panda strolled out leisurely,
The penguin plodded out quickly,

But the rhinoceros,
Stubbornly,
Just stayed where it was.

Shantelle Pearce (10)
Apley Wood Primary School, Telford

The Day The Zoo Escaped . . .

The panther sneaked out silently,
The crocodile crawled out violently,

The penguin waddled out solitarily,
The turtle crept out slowly,

The meerkat hopped out jumpily,
The camel trotted out lumpily,

But the elephant,
Stubbornly
Just stayed where it was.

Katrina Palin (10)
Apley Wood Primary School, Telford

The Day The Zoo Escaped . . .

The crocodile snapped out fiercely,
The tigers marched out seriously.

The cheetahs propelled themselves out quickly,
The tarantulas strolled out slickly,

The giraffe galloped out proudly,
The gorilla swung out loudly,

But the elephant,
Stubbornly,
Just stayed where it was.

Jeevan Johal (11)
Apley Wood Primary School, Telford

The Noise Collector
(Based on 'The Sound Collector' by Roger McGough)

A man came this morning
Didn't say a word,
Took every sound out of . . .
The house.

The flipping of the paper,
The banging of the letter box,
The sizzling of the bacon,
The crunching of the cereal.

The snoring of my dad,
The ringing of the alarm clock,
The moaning of my brother,
The shouting of my mum.

The noise of the engine,
The roar of the exhaust,
The squeaking of the brakes,
The shouting of the drivers.

The screaming of the baby,
The speaking from the television,
The zipping of the bag,
The speaking from our mouths.

The banging of the car door,
The banging of the front door,
The trotting of the noise of the shoes.

Now we have no sounds,
We can't speak,
All we can do is listen and play,
As now the man who didn't say a word,
Took all our sounds in a bag.

Nicole Woolley (10)
Apley Wood Primary School, Telford

My Dog

Seven o'clock in the morning you will hear her snore,
That's right she snores.
The windows shake a little . . . oh well.
I go downstairs to let her out
And I find her with her nose on the stairs
Waiting for my dad to take her for a walk.
Seven-thirty she has just come back from her walk,
She's panting like a spitting cobra,
The house is a horror!

Amy Harris (10)
Apley Wood Primary School, Telford

Inside The Horrible House

Inside
    The
        Horrible
            House
                There is
An action aquamarine ant alerting,
A brilliant beige bear bouncing,
A cursing crimson caterpillar crunching,
A dangerous damson dragon drawing,
An eccentric emerald elephant echoing,
A fresh flame fish flapping,
A great green griffin gazing,
A humming hazel horse handwriting,
An insulting indigo insect interrupting,
A jaunty jade jellyfish jumping,
A kicking khaki kitten knitting,
A lurking lime lion lying,
A moody maroon monkey moving,
A nutty navy newt nailing,
An obsessed orange ox obsessing,
A party purple pig prancing,
A quality quicksilver quail quacking,
A really red rabbit running,
A strong scarlet snake slithering,
A tricky turquoise troll talking,
An ugly umber unicorn unicycling,
A valuable violet vampire vanishing,
A warring white whale whipping,
An excitable xanthia exoskeleton exploding,
A yanking yellow yak yawning,
A zapping zinc zombie zipping
Inside
    The
        Horrible
            House.

Daniel Bahia (9)
Apley Wood Primary School, Telford

Frustration

Frustration is red, black and brown mixed with grey,
It smells like burning rubber melting,
Frustration tastes like a sickly, minty medicine,
It sounds like an angry throbbing,
It feels hot and squelchy, cold and hard,
Frustration lives in the Earth's core.

Matthew Walton (9)
Apley Wood Primary School, Telford

Strange Day

Hello! My name is Michael Way,
And today I had a very strange day.

Our teacher at school, started drinking people's blood,
And zombies have taken over the neighbourhood.

My dinner was cooked by a fire-breathing lizard,
Which was being controlled by a spell-casting wizard.

There's a mummy in my wardrobe, the bogeyman in my bed,
And Frankenstein's monster has taken residence in my shed.

The manager of the shoe store is the monster, Bigfoot!
His advisor is a werewolf, its fur as black as soot!

Well I've got to go now, there's an alien in my way,
But I'll finish by saying, I've had a very strange day!

Edward Halliday (10)
Apley Wood Primary School, Telford

Days Of The Week

Monday is homework day
Get all of it done.

Tuesday is science day
Something to look forward to.

Wednesday is pancake day
It's a big treat.

Thursday is running day
I get worn out.

Friday is cleaning day
What a joy!

Saturday is rush day
But it's still exciting.

Sunday is fun day
Lots of time to play.

Jodie Williams (10)
Apley Wood Primary School, Telford

Kim

My sister's name is Kim,
She is really thin,
Like her friend Tim,
I think she fancies him,
She makes my mind spin.

She is loving,
After she has been for a jog,
She's puffing like mad,
She has a thing,
In the morning,
No one is to touch her,
She is like a hedgehog,
She thinks it's ming.

She's really funny,
She loves money.

So that's my sister Kim.

Lauren Guestford (10)
Apley Wood Primary School, Telford

A New Day

Wake up in the morning,
See the sun shining,
Hear the alarm clock ringing,
While the birds are singing.

But what I always say,
I wish it was Saturday,
But then again it's a new day,
So I get to go with my friends and play.

When it's night,
I always get a fright,
I am scared of the dark,
While I can hear the clock, *tick tock*.

Rebecca Britton (10)
Apley Wood Primary School, Telford

Inside The Horrible House

An active aquamarine anteater doing archery,
A bouncy beige budgie playing basketball,
A crowing crimson crab doing cricket,
A distressed damson dog playing dodgeball,
An echoing emerald elephant elephanting around,
A frantic flame flamingo fooling,
A grumpy green giraffe growling,
A harassed hazel horse hanging,
An immature indigo iguana inventing,
A jogging jade jaguar juggling,
A kinking khaki kangaroo knitting,
A limping lime leopard looping,
A mean maroon monkey marrying,
A nutty navy nim nipping,
An opulent orange orang-utan oozing,
A precious purple pig plunging,
A quick quicksilver quail quivering,
A rough red rabbit racing,
A sly scarlet snake slithering,
A tangled turquoise tiger tiptoeing,
An ugly umber uncle umpiring,
A vicious violet vole vibrating,
A wicked white witch whipping,
An x-rayed xanthic exoskeleton exploding
A yucky yellow yak yelling,
A zitty zinc zebra zapping,
Inside the horrible house.

Emma Kendall (9)
Apley Wood Primary School, Telford

The Day The Zoo Escaped . . .

The monkey swung out cheerfully,
The elephant stomped out slowly.

The penguin waddled out slowly,
The frog hopped out quickly.

The crocodile snapped out fiercely,
The tiger roared out loudly,

But the hippopotamus,
Stubbornly
Just stayed where it was.

Josh Kelly (11)
Apley Wood Primary School, Telford

Inside The Horrible House

Inside the horrible house there is . . .
An active aquamarine antelope accepting,
A brilliant beige bat bathing,
A cursing crimson caterpillar crunching,
A dancing damson dracula drawing,
An eccentric emerald elephant electrocuting,
A foreign flaming Frankenstein firefighting,
A great green gorilla gardening,
A hairy hazel hippo hunting,
An impish indigo imp ice skating,
A jaunty jade jellyfish jumping,
A kicking khaki king knitting,
A loony lime lion leaping,
A mean maroon man mopping,
A nutty navy nun nipping,
An outrageous orange owl oozing,
A pretty purple phantom phoning,
A quadruple quicksilver quagga quaking,
A reeling red robin rapping,
A slippy scarlet squid splashing,
A tiny turquoise turtle tapping,
An ugly umber unicorn unwilling,
A violent vampire vibrating,
A whiskery white werewolf windsurfing,
An excitable xanthic exoskeleton exploding,
A yucky yellow yak yelling,
A zitty zinc zombie zapping
In the horrible house.

James Arrowsmith (9)
Apley Wood Primary School, Telford

Elephant

Ear flapper
Tree mover
Food sucker
Loud trumper
Stampede maker
Circus entertainer
Slow traveller
Massive mammal
Water blaster
Disney star.

Ellis Chan (10)
Apley Wood Primary School, Telford

Peace

Peace is like the colour of blue-violet,
It smells like Earth and Heaven are coming together,
It tastes like joy and happiness,
It sounds like people helping each other out.
It feels soft and gentle,
It lives everywhere.

Rosie Thomas (9)
Apley Wood Primary School, Telford

Fear

Fear is black like the night sky,
Fear smells like a wet, cold towel,
Fear tastes like a cold block of ice,
Fear sounds like needles bashing together,
Fear feels bumpy like a mountain,
Fear lives in your body like a shaking machine.

Christian Graham (10)
Apley Wood Primary School, Telford

Hope

Hope is the colour light blue
It smells like fresh spring flowers
It tastes like soft lemon juice running down your throat
Hope sounds like birds singing in the morning
It feels like silk running through your fingers
And hope lives down in your heart.

Zara Purvis (9)
Apley Wood Primary School, Telford

Elephant

Water blaster
Mouse fearer
Bun eater
Ear flapper
Trunk snorter
Jungle roarer.

Alim Khan (9)
Apley Wood Primary School, Telford

Sadness For A Mad House

Sadness is the colour black,
It sounds like screaming and screeching,
It tastes like sour apples,
It's like wet, damp, soggy seaweed from the sea,
It's like you've been stung by a thousand bees,
It reminds me of my mum and dad arguing.

Emma Witty (9)
Apley Wood Primary School, Telford

War

War is the colour of red blood,
It smells like smoke from a cigarette,
It sounds like the bang of a firework,
It feels like getting squashed under an elephant's foot,
It tastes like a nasty bitter medicine.

Akil Allen (9)
Apley Wood Primary School, Telford

Love

Love is a rosy pink shade,
It smells lovely like a rose in the garden,
It sounds soft and quiet,
It feels silky like melting chocolate,
It tastes like juicy summer strawberries,
It lives inside you.

Natalie Sharp (9)
Apley Wood Primary School, Telford

The Fun

Fun is the colour blue,
Fun sounds like a drum, round like a plum,
Fun tastes like chicken nuggets,
Fun smells like candyfloss,
Fun feels like a million pounds,
Fun reminds me of money.

Rashpal Bhakar (10)
Apley Wood Primary School, Telford

Love

Love is a soothing relaxing dark red.
Love is like the sound of birds singing.
Love is a taste of juicy red strawberries.
Love feels like silk trickling down your throat,
Love reminds me of a beach on a summer's day,
Love smells like sweet sugar in strawberry juice.
Love is paradise.

Levan Peart (10)
Apley Wood Primary School, Telford

Love

Love is the colour pink
It sounds like the singing birds
It tastes like creamy chocolates
It smells like red roses
It feels like the soft fur of a kitten
It reminds me of my dog playing with me in my garden.

Luke Hamps (10)
Apley Wood Primary School, Telford

Bone Grinder

Fire breather
Scaly beast
Human scarer
Flesh eater
Spike master
Peace disturber
Wing flapper
Bone grinder.

Nathan Cooke (9)
Apley Wood Primary School, Telford

Dragon

Meat eater
Scale grower
Swift flyer
Fang barer
Egg layer
Hard hatcher
Quick mover
Fire breather.

Suet Lee (10)
Apley Wood Primary School, Telford

Fear!

It is red like the flames in a fire,
It sounds like a volcano erupting,
It tastes like a pepper burning in my mouth,
It smells like a piece of bacon burning in the barbecue,
It feels like a dog digging its claw into your spine,
It reminds me of a boulder whacking my head.

Catrina Yang (9)
Apley Wood Primary School, Telford

Anger

Anger is red like a cooking volcano.
It sounds like a crimson red heart beating rapidly.
It tastes like a bowl of chillies.
It smells like two big bottles of petrol.
It feels like being locked up in chains,
It reminds me of arguing with my parents today.

Charlotte Stone (10)
Apley Wood Primary School, Telford

Anger

Anger sounds like 1000 zombies moaning
Anger tastes like kangaroo fur
Anger smells like rotten meat left in the sun
Anger feels like falling off the moon into nothingness.

Ryan Allen (10)
Apley Wood Primary School, Telford

Love

Love is the colour pink
Love smells like a bouquet
Love tastes like honey
Love sounds like sleigh bells
Love feels like velvet
Love lives in Heaven.

Shannon Edwards (10)
Apley Wood Primary School, Telford

The Monster Who Came
(Based on 'The Sound Collector' by Roger McGough)

A monster cackled this morning,
Coated in green and gooey slime,
Put every sound in his mouth,
And swallowed them with a gulp.

The hissing of a slithering snake,
The roaring of a lion,
The croaking of a frog,
The steaming of an iron.

The screaming of a baby,
The chewing of the baboons,
And the popping of balloons.

The banging of the drums,
Feeling the jungle beat,
The humming of the bird,
The pressure of the beat.

A monster called this afternoon,
He didn't leave his name,
Gave us only silence,
Our life is now changed.

Gerald Ashie (10)
Apley Wood Primary School, Telford

Guess Who?

Lip smacker
Paw padder
Stomach crawler
Ear listener
Tail flicker
Prey stalker
Flesh eater
Long sleeper
Buffalo catcher
Mouth gobbler
Bone rattler
Stare fixer
Ear twitcher.

Brooke Tranter (9)
Apley Wood Primary School, Telford

A Monster At School

Nine-fifteen in the morning,
A snobbish shadow enters without warning,
Leaving people to pick up its mess,
This is what people want to confess . . .

'Dangerous and petrifying,
All who see her are slowly dying,
But teachers are most certainly immune,
To all her singing out of tune . . .'

'She acts like she's all it,
When her nails break, she pulls a fit,
Covering her face with layers of cream,
Which makes the school squeal and scream . . .'

So you see,
She's freak of the week,
Everyone hates her,
Cos she's a swot,
When people stare,
She goes, 'So what?'

Three-fifteen at the end of the day,
She walks home asking people to play
Making anguished faces,
They run away
As fast as a champion of races.

Vanessa Hsieh (11)
Apley Wood Primary School, Telford

The Wind

Swooshing and swirling round and round,
Never ever touching the ground,
Just skidding across,
It keeps on going never stops,
Getting in your hair,
Slowing things everywhere,
Eventually calming,
But never stops,
The wind.

Rhiannon Harris (11)
Apley Wood Primary School, Telford

Love

Love is red like roses,
It sounds like an explosion of laughter,
It tastes like a scrumptious chocolate fudge cake oozing with cream,
It smells like fresh eggs, gleaming in the fridge,
It feels like riding horses,
It reminds me of holding my baby niece for the first time.

Georgina Carter (10)
Apley Wood Primary School, Telford

Love

Love is red like the rainbow red,
It sounds like butterflies fluttering,
It tastes like scrumptious strawberries floating in cream,
It smells like jam oozing in a pot,
It feels like cushions sitting on the sofa,
It reminds you of roses standing in fields.

Jay Edwards-Murphy (9)
Apley Wood Primary School, Telford

Hate

Hate is the darkest black there is
It sounds like an explosion of violins,
It tastes like poison oozing in muddy water
It smells like mouldy dead people
It feels like the gateway to Hell
It reminds me of the tsunami and the people who died in it.

Georgia Williams (10)
Apley Wood Primary School, Telford

Love

Love is baby pink like a love heart
It tastes like your favourite ever chocolates
It smells like Lenor and roses all mixed together
It feels like holding my baby brother for the very first time.

Rebecca Purcell (10)
Apley Wood Primary School, Telford

Happiness, Happiness, Happiness

Happiness is the colour of indigo,
Happiness sounds like the giggle of a baby,
It tastes like a chocolate cake of happiness,
It smells like heated popcorn,
It feels like the petals of roses,
It reminds me of when I held my cousin's baby.

Tom Shepherd (10)
Apley Wood Primary School, Telford

Love

Love is ruby-red like Dorothy's shiny shoes,
Love sounds like plucking the strings of a violin,
Love tastes like sugary strawberries,
Love smells like passion fruit,
Love feels like a smooth waterfall,
Love reminds me of my mum's wedding.

Shannon Onions (9)
Apley Wood Primary School, Telford

Life Stopper

Life stopper
Eye popper
People scarer
Wing flapper
Loud roarer
Fire breather.

Chris Thomas (9)
Apley Wood Primary School, Telford

Penny Pincher

City scarer
Door breaker
Silent sneaker
Heart thumper
Toy breaker
Penny pincher
Night stalker.

Harry Spence (10)
Apley Wood Primary School, Telford

Anger

Anger is red like a fire burning,
It sounds like a volcano erupting,
It tastes like a hot vindaloo,
It smells like a burning chilli HP sauce,
It feels like a sharp spiky spike,
It reminds me of when I get annoyed and get a temper.

Emily Hill (9)
Apley Wood Primary School, Telford

Love

Love is red like roses in the field
Love sounds like you're in the heart of life
Love tastes like ice cream and strawberries
Love smells like fresh red roses
Love feels like you're swaying in the breeze
Love reminds me of red roses that are about to grow.

Katie Stanworth (9)
Apley Wood Primary School, Telford

Beach

I love the beach it's always lots of fun,
When I go there, there is lots of fun sun
I played in the sand once with my bucket and spade
But by noon I was heading for the shade
I was swimming in the sea and I saw a shark
I was scared out of my wits so I ran towards the park.

Ross Mather (10)
Apley Wood Primary School, Telford

Love

Love is a perfect shade of pink
Love sounds like a squeaky mouse
It tastes like scrumptious candyfloss
It smells like strawberry pink shampoo
Love feels like the softest, most beautiful cushion in the world
It reminds me of me and my friends having a good time.

Joe Rose (9)
Apley Wood Primary School, Telford

Love

Love is a deep shade of scarlet-red
It sounds like birds singing
It tastes like chocolate ice cream
It smells like strawberry air freshener
It feels as smooth as a blanket
It reminds me of being loved by my family.

Lewis Sandbrook (9)
Apley Wood Primary School, Telford

I Am Scared Of The Dark

I am scared of the dark
Like the moon is frightened of the sun
Like a shoe is anxious by a muddy puddle
Like a fish is petrified of a shark
Like rubbish is panicked about the bin
Like paper is horrified of writing
I am scared of the dark.

Kulraj Kaur (11)
Apley Wood Primary School, Telford

A Floppy Cap

A floppy cap, soft and thin
Like a thin, crispy pancake
Like a button glued on
Like a bun stuffed in, to make it fat
Like tomato sauce spat out of someone's mouth
Like brown sauce thrown over it
A floppy cap, soft and thin.

Charlie Hammond (10)
Apley Wood Primary School, Telford

The Mouse Muncher!

Four legged
Wall climber
Body licker
Mat scratcher
Chair wrecker
Bird killer
Fur thrower
Mouse muncher.

Ashleigh Fletcher (9)
Apley Wood Primary School, Telford

The Mysterious Beast

It has staring eyes like a cat
Sits there lounging on its mat
Runs, whilst chasing all the bats

Sharp claws to rip through skin
They are as sharp as a pin
Always does his best to win

Bright green in colour
But it is quite poor
And smells like something raw

He has strong feet
But not as strong as his heartbeat
His best food is a large piece of meat.

Ryan Phillips (11)
Apley Wood Primary School, Telford

The Teacher's Pet

Being friends with her is a disaster
She's the teacher's pet
Even with the headmaster
I wish we had never met.

Broad and tall
She doesn't make a sound
Makes us want to fall
She'll follow you around.

We were glad when she moved
And left the school
We were all too rude
Because she was so uncool!

Emily Cheung (10)
Apley Wood Primary School, Telford

Smackdown V Raw

Ray Mysterio born in San Diego
Wrestles after his uncle
He is the flying fury
He is the best.

Batista is an animal
Born in Washington DC
He was a champion
He will destroy.

Kane is a red machine
He was married to Lita
His face was burnt
He is now a champion.

Jordan Davis (11)
Apley Wood Primary School, Telford

Snfinjel

I am a coral in a calm sea,
In the mists of the centre of the Earth sparkling like diamonds.
I am not like danger in the magical cave of dragons,
Snoring like a landslide tumbling down.
As the small pear tree grows,
In the depths of the big city of mantarays.
As coughing leeches sprout,
From the surface of the bark.

Like volcano-destroyed lands,
I rip through the digestive stomach of the terrifying monster.
Mystical sounds like flute and violin,
Softly float like clouds in the air.
Spouting colourful rhythm,
Out of the cool oak tree.
Abandoned like a mansion in a horror story,
I look for a friend.

Elloise Cooper (10)
Ashfield Park CP School, Ross-on-Wye

The Sea

The sea is like a clear crystal,
Always shining, shimmering in the sun,
Sometimes I think, *is it worth a lot of money,*
Is it as heavy as a ton?

The sea is like an angry dog,
Always barking, splashing against the rocks,
The waves are white and cold just like the fog,
Sometimes I wonder if the sea is shaped like a box.

The sea is like a clear crystal,
Always shining, shimmering in the sun,
Sometimes I think, *is it worth a lot of money,*
Is it as heavy as a ton?

The sea is like a big blue house,
It has a lot of creatures living in it,
Sometimes I wonder where the waves end
It covers most of the planet.

The sea is like a clear crystal,
Always shining, shimmering in the sun,
Sometimes I think, *is it worth a lot of money,*
Is it as heavy as a ton?

Jessica Sleeman (10)
Ashfield Park CP School, Ross-on-Wye

When I Ripped My Trousers

I went to school today
And it didn't go so great
It always ends up this way
And this was the time I was late.

I leant down in cooking class
And there was a really loud noise
Then I heard a roar of laughs
I knew I shouldn't have ate those McCoy's.

The worst thing about it was
I had bright pink laced pants
I don't think I will be coming back
But there is a very unlikely chance.

Abi Beddard (10)
Ashfield Park CP School, Ross-on-Wye

I'd Rather Be . . .

I'd rather be asleep than awake,
I'd rather stick than make.
I'd rather be a pond than a lake,
I'd rather give than take.
That's me!

I'd rather be a snake than a frog,
I'd rather be a twig than a log.
I'd rather be a sink than a bog,
I'd rather be a cat than a dog.
If you don't mind!

I'd rather be a fish than a net,
I'd rather ride a plane than a jet.
I'd rather be a human than a pet,
I'd rather bargain than bet.
As I was saying!

I'd rather be thin than fat,
I'd rather be a mouse than a rat.
I'd rather be a carpet than a mat,
I'd rather be a scarf than a hat.
Please!

Lillie Collins (11)
Ashfield Park CP School, Ross-on-Wye

I'd Rather Be!

I'd rather be thin than fat,
I'd rather be a mouse than a rat,
I'd rather be a carpet than a mat,
I'd rather be a house than a flat.
Really I would!

I'd rather run than jog,
I'd rather be a stick than a log,
I'd rather be a cat than a dog,
I'd rather be a sun than the fog,
I would!

I'd rather be still than to be shook,
I'd rather stare than look,
I'd rather eat than cook,
I'd rather be a story than a book.

But that's just me I suppose!

Reanne Hulet (11)
Ashfield Park CP School, Ross-on-Wye

Mountains

As I guessed the towering height,
I shiver in the snow,
Which path must I go?
What a massive sight.

As I climb the steep track,
I wonder to myself,   .
Can I turn and run away?
Can I walk back?

I stand upon the peak,
My journey almost ends,
I have found the view I seek,
But what about my friends?

They died in the cold,
Their bodies shall freeze,
Twenty-five years old,
They fell upon a sneeze.

James Wood (11)
Ashfield Park CP School, Ross-on-Wye

The Great White Shark

The great white shark is a mean, keen,
Eating machine. He glides through
The murky dark water looking
For his prey.

When he catches it, he eats it and
Thinks, *what a fine meal for tea.*

His eye is as black as coal, and looks
As cold, as a winter's day, but he uses it
Well to spot his prey

His teeth are like daggers that are really
Sharp like razors, he uses them well
To catch his tea.

David Cawthorne (10)
Ashfield Park CP School, Ross-on-Wye

Hammy The Hamster

Hammy the hamster is full of laughter,
But he sleeps a lot after,
He is faster than a walking disaster,
And that's Hammy the hamster.

Bridie Hall (10)
Ashfield Park CP School, Ross-on-Wye

My Anger

My blood is raging,
The flames get bigger.
My pulse is faster,
The flames are redder.
As my heart beats,
The flames get quicker.
As my head bursts,
The flames will go.

Is there peace on this Earth?
Or is it just Hell?
Soon I won't be able to take much more.

Have no friends they have all gone,
It is only me left.
And soon, very soon, I will be gone too.

Kim Victor-Trott (10)
Ashfield Park CP School, Ross-on-Wye

The Crashing Sea

Overnight the sea was getting heavier and heavier as the night went past,
It finally became morning, as the waves were crashing against the surface of the water.
The sky was getting greyer and greyer,
It started lashing it down with rain, and smashing against the rocks.
It finally stopped raining,
The gleaming sun came out and the waves were getting calmer and calmer.

Hannah Dobbs (10)
Ashfield Park CP School, Ross-on-Wye

Colour And Noise Of Fire

Flames of red and yellow,
Light the sky,
Red engines, sirens and blue lights
Soon arrive.

Black smoke rising high,
Yellow helmets rush on by,
Silver ladders tower in the air,
Firemen take great care.

The fire is nearly out
Everyone gives a shout
The colour and noise have gone
The birds burst into song.

Kate Williams (11)
Ashfield Park CP School, Ross-on-Wye

Sea And The Beach

The beach, the beach is a place of dreams
Look at the sea it glistens at me.
The water is so clear I can see the wonderful sunset,
It sets in the sky, the colours make me dream.
It is time to go home but I don't want to go,
The moon has come, got to go.

Stacey Beach (11)
Ashfield Park CP School, Ross-on-Wye

The Coral Reef

The fish they are like rainbows
They swim the way the sea goes
The sea anemone gives you a sting
That gives you a little zing.

The clownfish's stripes are like lightning
The light shines through quite frightening
The sea is like the sky
The waves look like they are waving goodbye.

The way we live is harsh
But it could be in the marsh
The seabed is quite bumpy
And it is quite lumpy.

Benjamin Dean (10)
Ashfield Park CP School, Ross-on-Wye

The Dolphin

The dolphin swims without a fright,
It is soft and calm it does not bite.
It likes to play and have lots of fun,
It swims all day in the sun.
It swims back home and goes to sleep,
He does not even make a peep.
He dreams of what he's done today,
In other words, play, play, play.

Amy Ridge (11)
Ashfield Park CP School, Ross-on-Wye

My Little Kitten

My little kitten is such a pain
And my hamster's just the same,
Always watching with those bright blue eyes,
If he doesn't get his tuna, he sighs
If you come to our door
He's laying waiting on the floor
He goes out looking for prey
But that's not where he'll stay
When the hamster's out of his cage
The kitten goes and plays
I put food in his bowl
How it looks like I've got a happy little soul.

Chloe Morgan (11)
Ashfield Park CP School, Ross-on-Wye

The Island

I am an island,
I have calm seas,
As blue as the sky,
And the sapphires that lie
On my sands.

But I am lonely,
So lonely,
So, so lonely.

My sand is hot,
As hot as the sun above,
I have weather perfect for bathing,
And buried treasure lies inside me.

But I am still lonely,
So lonely,
So, so lonely.

Caitlin Oates (11)
Ashfield Park CP School, Ross-on-Wye

The Penguin

Black and white feathers orange webbed feet
What are these used for? Well it's easy
We use them for diving in and out of the water
I have a beak for killing fish, claws for climbing on rocks
The thing we fear most is a killer whale and if they get hold of us
They will kill us, but until that day we have a happy life.

Shane Davies (11)
Ashfield Park CP School, Ross-on-Wye

The Sun On The Sea

When the sun shines on the sea,
It is like a gleaming light.
It really does sparkle,
But it goes dark at night.

In the morning it's like a rainbow in the sea.
It is not that colourful at night.
But in the middle of the day it is really nice
It is a really beautiful sight.

When the sun shines on the sea
The rainbow fish shine.
When the sun shines on the sea,
The scales on the fish really shine.

When the sun shines on the sea
The dolphins are having lots of fun.
The mantaray is playing in the sea,
When the fish shines it knows it is the sun.

George Thomas (10)
Ashfield Park CP School, Ross-on-Wye

Thunder And Lightning

I tell people I am not scared
I tell them that I am brave
But there is one thing that I fear
Something that would send me down to my grave.

Thunder and lightning that's right
Every night when I hear that awful sound
And see that light shooting down
In the pitch-black night I hit the ground.

I'm not scared of heights
I don't find many things frightening
But I am scared of something
Thunder and lightning.

Tom Higgs (11)
Ashfield Park CP School, Ross-on-Wye

The Minotaur

I am a minotaur alone in a maze waiting for flesh to bite.
I wait quietly to ambush my prey.
I cry because I don't have any friends and I
Have nothing to do except kill.

I don't want to rip up people but if I don't
I will be killed by my owner.
I will soon be dead, I feel it in my mind
And in my veins
So goodbye my fellow Earth and Man.

Now my time has come I am old and dying
I am going now
Goodbye my world of love and good doing.

Simon Howells (10)
Ashfield Park CP School, Ross-on-Wye

Four Seasons

Springtime
Daffodils blow in the wind,
While children dance and play
Birds chirping because spring is on the way.

Summertime
Summertime is here, the holidays have begun,
Children laugh and play in the hot blazing sun.

Autumn time
The leaves of red and gold are falling off the trees
The birds fly away to the hot countries
Animals hibernate and the sun starts to dim.

Wintertime
Wintertime is here, as the snow starts to fall,
While we make snowmen,
Children skate on my pond.

Natasha Davies (9)
Bishop Rawle CE Primary School, Cheadle

Up There

Up here is where I leave my clutter
After my cupboard's full and I've blocked the gutter.
It's a place of memory though, freezing cold,
When I'm there I'm only three years old.
I love the scent of wood and dust,
Cardboard boxes and metal rust.
You could call it a loft or even an attic,
But it tells the story of my family's epic.
At this moment it's fun but lifeless
But when I'm not here it fills with brightness.
It's a place where toys can live their lives,
Out of sight from human eyes.

Nicholas Gibbon (10)
Bishop Rawle CE Primary School, Cheadle

My Bedroom

My bedroom as lilac as lavender
My bed as soft as a sheep
Every time I walk into my room
I only wish to sleep.

I see my colourful posters
I see my window view
I see my canopy up high
It reminds me of seeing you.

I can feel my pillow so soft
I can feel the warm breeze
I can feel the fluffiness of my rabbit
As I look at the happy bees.

I can smell cooking from the kitchen
I smell the scent of perfume
I smell the fresh flowers
I'm watching them bloom.

Lydia George (10)
Bishop Rawle CE Primary School, Cheadle

Time For Bed

Mum's cooking tea, sizzling sausages
With wriggly spaghetti like laces on my shoes,
The sausages dance as they sizzle and jump
And the spaghetti wriggles like worms.

As I lie in bed I just about see
The fluttering birds glide,
Like aeroplanes travelling here and there,
As they land on the tree and snuggle into bed
I spot another thing.

The moonlit sky brightens up the dark, black night
Like switching on the light,
The circle-shaped moon changes and moves
As we do every day.

I jump into bed as I bounce once or twice,
I do a roly-poly like a dog wanting a tickle.
I slither like a snake under my covers
And close my eyelids shut.

Bethan Knapper (10)
Bishop Rawle CE Primary School, Cheadle

My Kitchen

I love my kitchen it always smells good
Especially my mum's home-made pud.
I love the sound of the sizzling sausages
At the bottom of the pan it takes ages.
I love the taste of the warm hot chocolate
The chocolatey cocoa at the bottom of the mug.
I love to touch the burning hot water before I eat a meal
And to eat a nice juicy orange and throw away the peel.
I love to look at my family when I start to eat
It's lovely and cosy in the kitchen with the wonderful warm heat.

Lucy Rushton (10)
Bishop Rawle CE Primary School, Cheadle

My Dining Room

It is a waterfall of bubbles,
As clear as the deep blue sea,
Its body slides down the drain
It is a soapy snake slithering down the river.

It is a room of sound,
As soothing as the cool breeze,
It is a magical musical tune
As its voice sings to you.

It is a bulb of light,
As hot as a smouldering fire,
Its hands will burn you like the sun,
It is a blazing, burning ball of light.

It is a burst of flavour,
As tasty as a dream come true,
Its body runs down your throat,
It is a smooth and silky paste that you must taste
For it's lovely rich mixture.

It is a ball of smell,
As scented as a poppy flower,
Its scent flows through the air,
It is a smelling scented candle.

Come into my dining room
Where you can smell, taste, touch and hear,
As if you were on holiday
Walking along the pier.

Jessica Syred (10)
Bishop Rawle CE Primary School, Cheadle

In The Kitchen

It feels bumpy on the outside,
And smooth on the inside
It's hot when heated
And cool when not,
It looks like a tennis racket
And it tastes like metal,
It smells of food that's been cooked
It's a frying pan.

Rhys Green (10)
Bishop Rawle CE Primary School, Cheadle

My Home

When you walk in you feel so cosy,
This is the room to watch television,
The room to relax, and cuddle the fluffy cushion
After coming home at the end of a tiring day,
It is there to comfort you.
When you watch television, it is there,
Listening to the blaring stereo, it is there.
It hugs you warmly with its fuzzy tassels,
The dark brown of the cushion camouflages it
Against the matching sofa, the furry, fuzzy cushion.

They stand on the table, in their frames,
They remind us of some good, some bad memories,
There forever,
They talk to us about old memories,
They store images that have left our minds,
Photographs, the reminders of years gone by.

The ticking clock forever ticks,
Ticking in our days of happiness and sadness.
The clock stands on our fireplace,
Ticking all day, all night,
Tick-tock, tick-tock, tick-tock . . .

Rachel Harrison (10)
Bishop Rawle CE Primary School, Cheadle

Writing A Rhyme

Hi, Teacher, I heard you say,
That we were going to write a poem today.
'So pick up your pencil and start to rhyme,
But remember you only have a bit of time.'

What should I write about let me think,
Mermaids or fairies all pretty and pink.
Mice or rats, cats or a dog,
You could write about anything even a frog.

I think I might write about my school,
Or yet I might write about a ghost or a ghoul.
You may need to give me a bit more time,
Do you know it's really hard writing a rhyme!

Liandda Burnett (11)
Bishop Rawle CE Primary School, Cheadle

Seasons

Winter -
Snow, snow on the ground,
Never ever heard a sound.
Winter is here, watch the snow fall down,
It falls on snowmen and makes a crown.

Spring -
New lambs are born
Children playing nicely on the lawn.
Flowers all beautiful and bright,
Children in the fields flying a kite.

Summer -
The sun is shining nice and bright,
Well it is all hot at night.
Children eating picnics out at the park,
While watching dogs cry and bark.

Autumn -
Children playing in the leaf piles,
Adults on computers looking in files.
There's the cold water dripping down,
While all this is happening, there isn't a frown.

Danni McCormack (9)
Bishop Rawle CE Primary School, Cheadle

Football

Football is the game to play
I would play it every day.
Eleven players warming up,
Training hard to win the cup.
Referee starts the match
What a goalie, what a catch.

We've just scored, it's one-nil
And another, what a thrill.
It's half-time, minutes rest,
I hope we win and do the best.
Oh no! We let one in
We've scored again, we're going to win.

Nearly time for the whistle to go
We played well and put on a good show.
'Come on Ref we're nearly done
Is it true? Have we won?'
It's all over, we've won again
It's a good job we do train.

Billie Burnett (10)
Bishop Rawle CE Primary School, Cheadle

The Tooth Fairies At Night

The children go to bed at night,
After their teeth come out with delight.
Wide awake they toss and turn,
Waiting for the fairy to return.

The fairy takes your tooth away,
And leaves a pound to display
But you don't know when she came,
Or had a chance to play her game.

You might leave a letter,
And think that might be better,
Or perhaps leave a present,
Surely that would be pleasant.

But when you get to a certain age,
The fairy doesn't come again,
The fairy turns into your mum,
You start to feel so glum.

But then you have to think again,
The fairy still thinks about you,
She is true, but there's too many children to go round,
They just want to keep the youngest safe and sound.

Kirsty Maguire (9)
Bishop Rawle CE Primary School, Cheadle

The Bestest Friend

Slowly, slowly
He travels along
Looking, looking
For a meaning
With his shell dull but gleaming.
Danger, danger
All around
He hides his face in shame.
Although he's not the same
He's special to me you know
That snail Jumbo.

Amy Brough (10)
Bishop Rawle CE Primary School, Cheadle

Tiger

Running, I'm running,
Pouncing, I'm pouncing,
Dodging, I'm dodging,
I try to look vicious
I'm scared,
I try to bare my teeth.

Run, I run,
Pounce, I pounce,
Dodge, I dodge,
Rain pouring down,
Pouring down rain,
Down pouring rain.
I turn my anger down.

Running, I'm running,
Pouncing, I'm pouncing,
Dodging, I'm dodging,
I get hit by branches,
I get tangled in weeds,
I try to escape, I can't,
I try more, I do,
I rest, rest I do until morning.

I carry on running,
I'm still scared,
Other animals hate me,
Other animals are chasing me,
Running, I'm running,
Pouncing, I'm pouncing,
Dodging, I'm dodging.

It's me who has to leave,
I can stay no more.

Jenny Ansell (8)
Braunston CE Primary School, Braunston

Loppy

Loppy is my bunny
I love him very much
He's big and round
And grey and white
With floppy ears too

His lick is warm and scratchy
His feet are long and wide
His little nose goes up and down
Loppy is my bunny.

Robert Ansell (10)
Braunston CE Primary School, Braunston

Tiger

The jungle is stormy,
The jungle is stormy,

The tigers are getting sleepy,

The jungle is stormy,
The jungle is stormy,

The tigers are getting creepy,

There is the lightning,
Crash, crash.

There is the thunder,
Rumble, rumble.

There are the trees
Swaying, swaying.

There are the bushes,
This way, that way.

The tiger is now asleep!

Stephanie Young (8)
Braunston CE Primary School, Braunston

Tiger!

In a jungle far and near,
I heard something
I saw something very deadly
In a jungle far and near.

In a jungle far and near,
I saw an eagle
I heard a bear roar
In a jungle far and near.

In a jungle far and near
I
Heard
I
Heard
A tiger
Run!

Christopher Pearson (9)
Braunston CE Primary School, Braunston

Tiger

Here is my home, the jungle of course,
And here is me roaring for my life.
As the lightning nearly strikes, my *tail, tail, tail,*
I'm pounding through the *bushes, bushes, bushes.*

Finally I found a hole deep down inside a bush,
And slept there for the rest of the night.
The morning came, I was vicious for a while,
But when I came out of the hole it was quite *sunny, sunny, sunny.*
    The end.

Angel Aspinwall (8)
Braunston CE Primary School, Braunston

Tiger

It's raining and the twisted branches sway
And the tiger whips its tail as it goes past.

The tiger runs the marathon and leaps,
All the tigers are everywhere,
Tigers' claws dig right in.

Full of noise, then quiet . . .

Everything is silent, you only hear the crickets
Jump!

Charlotte Lyon (9)
Braunston CE Primary School, Braunston

Tiger

Pouncing tiger ready to pounce,
His teeth are as sharp as blades,
And white as lightning.
A leaf falls from a tree
Suddenly some lightning strikes,
Dust and mist fall from the sky,
Tiger does not know what to do.
The tiger runs,
So scared of the noise and the dark.
His legs are so tired,
He can't run anymore,
He hides under one tree and curls up into a ball,
He feels safe
And he falls asleep.

Thomas Wright (9)
Braunston CE Primary School, Braunston

Tiger

The tiger hiding in the long, wavy grass,
The wind and the lightning frightening,
The tiger and the plants cowering,
The long sharp teeth.
The blood dripping on the sharp claws,
And the trees waving side to side.
The tiger crawling through the long, wavy grass,
The blowing of the grass,
The tiger is eating, eating,
The lightning and the rain dripping,
The tiger saw something,
Roar!
Roar!
Roar!

Daniel Burton (8)
Braunston CE Primary School, Braunston

Tiger

In the jungle we have animals
Running,
Pouncing,
Vicious creatures.

Sleeping, crunching on branches
The tiger is his name.
He runs through . . .
Thunder, lightning and rain.

Never stops, never scared,
He goes past a waterfall,
And has a drink at last.

The king of Australia's jungle
Sharp, vicious teeth
Orange and black stripes.

Here in the jungle, out at sea,
We make new friends
Like you and me!

Aleesha Choda (9)
Braunston CE Primary School, Braunston

Cat - Haiku

Cat, cute, dull, jumpy
Lazy, soft, fast and silky.
She is two years old.

John Walvin (8)
Braunston CE Primary School, Braunston

71

The Magic Box
(Based on 'Magic Box' by Kit Wright)

I will put in my box . . .
The taste of freezing cold ice cream,
The sound of music booming in my room,
The sight of the lovely, beachy Atlantic.

I will put in my box . . .
The scent of a round pretty peach,
The sound of my cat purring,
The taste of chocolate running down my throat.

I will put in my box . . .
The sound of a punk band,
The lovely sight of Majorca,
The nice smell of my mum!

I will put in my box . . .
The taste of yummy pork,
The sniff of the fresh countryside,
The sound of the wind.

My box is fashioned from gold, bronze and silver,
With moons and stars on the lid and glitter in the corners,
The hinges are made from a firework.

I will float in my box
On the blue, roasting-hot sea with tiny waves and gentle sounds,
Then wash up on a little beach with no traffic or houses,
Just a beach, the colour of the sun.

Jacob Wright (8)
Braunston CE Primary School, Braunston

Tiger

A vicious, hungry, orange, stripy thing,
Pouncing through the crunchy leaves of the jungle with razor-sharp teeth.
I don't know what it is.

A vicious, hungry, orange, stripy thing,
Creeping through the tall grass of the jungle,
With sharp claws,
I still don't know what it is.

A vicious, hungry, orange, stripy thing,
Walking towards me,
I know what it is,
It's a . . .
Tiger!

Philippa Bricklebank (9)
Braunston CE Primary School, Braunston

The Magic Box
(Based on 'Magic Box' by Kit Wright)

I will put in my box . . .
My cat Marble's face.
A colourful spark from a firework.
The autumn colours in the trees.

I will put in my box . . .
The taste of chocolate melting in a pan.
A sip of the purest lemonade in the world.
The spicy taste of chilli.

I will put in my box . . .
Water dripping from a tap.
My cat purring.
Children splashing in puddles.

I will put in my box . . .
The feel of my furry slippers.
The feel of the soft golden sand on the beach.
The slimy feel of jelly.

My box is fashioned from ice and gold and frost.
Snowflakes on the lid.
And its hinges are made from mini bananas.
I shall dance in my box on Mercury and end up in a sparkly cave.

Olivia King (8)
Braunston CE Primary School, Braunston

Tiger

A vicious horrible tiger
He's scared
He's scared
A pouncing vicious tiger.

He's scared
He's scared
Roaring through the rainforest.

He's vicious
He's vicious
Banging down in the leaves,
He's vicious,
He's vicious,
He's ready to fight another animal,
He's vicious,
He's vicious,
He's scared of the lightning, of it hitting him.

Kieren Bennett (9)
Braunston CE Primary School, Braunston

The Magic Box
(Based on 'Magic Box' by Kit Wright)

I will put in the box . . .
The bluest dolphin,
A pleasant sniffy flavour on my tongue,
And my best picture of Mum and Dad at a wedding.

I will put in the box . . .
The most chocolatey cake I've ever eaten,
The most fruity, lemony sweet I've ever eaten,
And the sweet nibble of toffee.

I will put in the box . . .
The pong of yucky mud,
My favourite Elvis song 'Blue Suede Shoes'
And the revving engine of a BMW.

I will put in the box . . .
The most delicious cake mixture I've ever eaten,
The feel of a really smooth soft centre of a pony's fur,
The first crawl of my cousin's baby.

My box is fashioned with bronze and gold and silver
With a moon on the lid and stars in the corners
And the hinges are like the ends of pasta.

I shall ride in my box
On the biggest T-rex in the big jungle
One person is with me on the T-rex, he is Harry.

Ashley Fisher (7)
Braunston CE Primary School, Braunston

My Goldfish

I have a little goldfish
Who's grown big and golden white.
She swims around the fish tank
And eats up the plants.
She swims through the air bubbles,
And floats to the top.
I've called her Sally because
She's always happy and never sad.

Samantha Griffiths (11)
Braunston CE Primary School, Braunston

My Magic Box

(Based on 'Magic Box' by Kit Wright)

I will put in my box . . .
A gleaming crystal that never stops shimmering,
A glamorous fish with a pimply, shiny tail as long as a ruler,
And a flower whose petals are yellow and pink.

I will put in my box . . .
The flavour of wonderful cheese and onion crisps,
And a peach yoghurt with flavour that never gets out of my mouth,
The gulp of a chocolate crisp Promise chocolate going down to my throat.

I will put in my box . . .
The feel of a smooth, grey, huge rock down by the beach,
A little crab pinching my feet as I walk in the sea,
The gentle touch of when I'm putting lipstick on.

I will put in the box . . .
The pong of my dad getting washed in the shower in the morning,
The sniff of lavender perfume on a summer's night,
The gaze of a man going past my brown house.

My box is fashioned from bear fur so fluffy and soft, I've never forgotten about,
With glitter fur and scorching suns on the lid,
And melting minty chocolates in the corners,
My box's hinges are made from a human's bendy tooth.

I shall fly to the sizzling, boiling, scorching sun in the world,
On my black, bright, shining horse that flies, then fall into the coldest iciest water
in the world.
The colour of a pure lightest blue in the world.

Maddie Gough (7)
Braunston CE Primary School, Braunston

Tiger

It is a windy night,
In the dark, dark jungle,
It is a windy night in the dark, dark jungle.

As the tiger jumps, I jump,
As the tiger eats, I eat,
As the tiger roars, I roar.

As the tiger dies, I die.

Lewis Mazzone (8)
Braunston CE Primary School, Braunston

The Magic Box
(Based on 'Magic Box' by Kit Wright)

I will put in the box . . .
When I first saw Paddy my Irish bull staff
The lemony taste of my first water melon
A fox cub jogging up the field at the airport
The waves crashing on the rocky cliff
The wrecked old castle on the cliff.

I will put in the box . . .
The scent of a lemony sweet going round my nose
The feel of Paddy's ear.

I will put in the box . . .
The racket of Paddy barking at the birds twittering
A splash of a baby pilot whale.

I shall swim with sharks in the box
Wriggling their pointy tails
I will end up in their black cave
The colour of chocolate.

My box is fashioned from ice and gold and steel
The lid is made of candyfloss and stars
The hinges are mini bananas.

George Crozier (7)
Braunston CE Primary School, Braunston

Drawing

Drawing is fun
Drawing is great
You can do it alone
Or with your mate
In the garden
Or by the school gate.

Flowers, animals, birds or trees
You can draw any of these.
Big or small
Short or tall
Drawing is great
You can do them
All!

Victoria Bennett (10)
Braunston CE Primary School, Braunston

My Magic Box
(Based on 'Magic Box' by Kit Wright)

I will put in the box . . .
A gooey jar of strawberry jam,
A hot bowl of roasted potatoes,
A huge pot of colourful sweets.

I will put in the box . . .
A slice of sour oranges,
A piece of melting chocolate,
A whole spongy chocolate cake.

I will put in the box . . .
The squeak of a squeaky swing,
A slippy road with the swish of cold air,
The tail of a cat licking its paw.

I will put in the box . . .
The sound of babies crying,
The first sight of a Chinese dragon,
A row of people standing in a stormy night.

My box is fashioned from
A gold, sparkly, stone with three silver stars placed on the lid,
Rosie flowers in the corners,
The hinges are made from a bendy pen.
I shall fly to the top of the hill to meet my favourite fairies
And end up in a hot place called Barbados.

Ellë Osborne (8)
Braunston CE Primary School, Braunston

Karate Man

Karate man you've passed your dan,
And now you're teaching me.

And if I can I'll pass my dan
And a teacher I shall be.

Karate man you jump so high, it's like you fly,
Among the birds I see.

Karate man you touch the sky, so quick and sly,
You're a real hero to me.

Emily Cooksey (10)
Braunston CE Primary School, Braunston

The Magic Box
(Based on 'Magic Box' by Kit Wright)

I will put in my box . . .
A sparkling crystal I saw in Warwick,
My lovely cousins in the boiling country of Australia,
A pretty pink stone made carefully.

I will put in my box . . .
A sip of the warmest melted chocolate in the pan,
Hearing the waves crashing on the beach,
The sweetest sweet in my mouth.

I will put in my box . . .
My family and friends,
A beautiful carved stone,
The biggest rainbow in the world.

I will put in my box . . .
The biggest snowman I've ever built,
The most scorching sun I've ever felt,
The fresh smell of rain.

My box is fashioned from stars, gold and smooth silk,
With hearts on the lid and whispers in the corners,
Its hinges are the toe joints of leopards.

I will fly in my box
Far away where I meet fairies,
Then ride away with unicorns to a land
The colour of the rainbow.

Jessica Smith (7)
Braunston CE Primary School, Braunston

There Was A Young Girl Named Sue

There was a young girl named Sue
Who didn't know what to do
She walked to the park
Where she heard a dog bark
Then something got stuck on her shoe.

She hurried back home
Rang her mum on the phone
And told her what happened just now
Her mum said, 'Don't be mad
It could have been bad
Thank goodness, it wasn't a cow!'

Matthew Hurley (11)
Braunston CE Primary School, Braunston

The Magic Box
(Based on 'Magic Box' by Kit Wright)

I will put in the box . . .
The appearance of the purest white tigers at West Midlands Safari Park
And the richest scent of hot chocolate
With the awesome sight of Star Wars films.

I will put in the box . . .
The soft sound of cats purring
With the smooth touch of my blanket
The crispy taste of barbecue chicken.

I will put in the box . . .
The creamiest milk I've ever tasted
The picture of medieval people jousting at Warwick Castle
And the sound of chocolate melting on a stove.

I will put in the box . . .
The aroma of orange shower gel
And the flavour of savaloy sausage
The racket of me wrestling.

My box is fashioned from titanium, steel and gold
With silvery chocolate on the lid
And dinosaurs in the corners.
Its hinges are the sharpest cats' teeth.

I shall ride a sabre-toothed tiger on the freezing, icy cold planet of Pluto
And then end up on Mars in a huge crater.

Lucas Porter (8)
Braunston CE Primary School, Braunston

Sausages

Sausages are really yummy,
Sausages fill my tummy.
Sausages come from a pig,
Sausages can be really big.

Sausages are big and fat,
And I am grateful for that.
Sausages are scrummy and yummy,
They go straight to my tummy.

Sausages on my plate,
Put a smile on my face.
Cumberland, pork or beef,
It doesn't matter which,
When they are on my plate,
I feel rich.

Gregory Blundell (10)
Braunston CE Primary School, Braunston

The Magic Box
(Based on 'Magic Box' by Kit Wright)

I will put in the box . . .
Exploding fireworks
And a twinkling rainbow
And a star right in the sky.

I will put in the box . . .
Pungent taste of marmite
A crunchy breadstick
The touch of glittering roses.

I will put in the box . . .
The aroma of perfume.

I will put in the box . . .
The sound of waves crashing on the rocks
I can sniff the chocolate melting on the rocks.

My box is made from cardboard with roses on it
With magic in the corners
And fireworks on the lid.
The hinges lift up like a desk.

I open the box
And there is a fairy's wand in it
And it magics a doll.

Maisy Cooksey (7)
Braunston CE Primary School, Braunston

My Magic Cat

My cat is *brown,* now it's *blue!*
When it was a kitten it got flushed down the *loo!*
Oh! It's *purple,* oh! It's *red!*
It always acts like it's never been fed!
It's *pink,* it's *green!*
My cat was born without a spleen!
White, *black!*
Now it's growing spikes on its back!
Oh! *yellow!* Oh! *orange!*
Did you know my cat is from Norwich!
This is my cat you see!
I am even stranger . . . would you
Love to meet *me!*

Lucy Martin (11)
Braunston CE Primary School, Braunston

The Magic Box
(Based on 'Magic Box' by Kit Wright)

I will put in the box . . .
The bright autumn colours in the trees,
A sip of rich creamy chocolate,
The velvety, smooth, soft surface of a party dress.

I will put in the box . . .
The cheep of robins in the treetops,
Cobwebs sparkling in the sunlight,
The scent of wild roses outside my bedroom window.

I will put in the box . . .
A mouth-watering mouthful of my mum's home-made fudge cake,
The sea sparkling in the moonlight,
A rainbow on a rainy day.

I will put in the box . . .
Olivia's cat, Marbles,
A spark from a firework on a moonlit night,
Some square jelly that won't wobble.

My box is fashioned from moons, glitter and ice,
With sparkling moons and stars on the lid.
Multicoloured mysteries in the corners and
The hinges are made from Roman shields.

I will swim in my box,
With baby dolphins, the size of dustbins,
And wash ashore on a beach the colour of molten lava.

Rosie Haynes (7)
Braunston CE Primary School, Braunston

In My Garden

In my garden the trees stand tall
In my garden the grass is green
In my garden the leaves rustle when I kick or jump in them.
In my garden the flowers are pretty and the vegetables are lovely.
In my garden the butterflies are pretty,
In my garden the birds sing beautifully.

Katie Ronch (11)
Braunston CE Primary School, Braunston

There Was A Young Man From Stoke . . .

There was a young man from Stoke
Who brought a big bottle of Coke,
It was too fizzy to drink
So he started to shrink
And then he started to smoke!

Bryn Tallett (8)
Braunston CE Primary School, Braunston

There Once Was A Big Hairy Bear . . .

There once was a big hairy bear
Who gave everybody a scare
He gave a big growl
And made everyone howl
And then he went back to his lair!

Thomas Mullaney (7)
Braunston CE Primary School, Braunston

Dog - Haiku

My dog is a boy
Ben likes going for a walk
He jumps at the door.

Joshua Cooper (8)
Braunston CE Primary School, Braunston

Snow - Haiku

Delicate, freezing
Sparkly, white, icy and rough
Shivery snowball.

Daisy Snelson (7)
Braunston CE Primary School, Braunston

Dogs - Haiku

Dogs: waggy tail, smooth
Sharp claws, rough paws, fluffy, sweet
Bark loud, sleepy, rest.

Hattie Lewington (8)
Braunston CE Primary School, Braunston

My Dog - Haiku

A four-legged dog
Warm, cuddly and fluffy
Very sharp, long claws.

Emma Dawson (7)
Braunston CE Primary School, Braunston

Snow - Haiku

Snow: sparkly and white
Make snowballs and soft snowmen
Freezing and melting.

Hannah Osborne (7)
Braunston CE Primary School, Braunston

Cats - Haiku

Beautiful, furry
They play with a lot of wool
They get chased by dogs.

Rachel Sullivan (8)
Braunston CE Primary School, Braunston

Dog - Haiku

Mischievous and fun
Molly has black and white fur
Sharp-clawed, soft, jumpy.

Rachel Barnwell (7)
Braunston CE Primary School, Braunston

Monday's Child

Monday's child plays in the sand,
Tuesday's child is in a band,
Wednesday's child is full of joy,
Thursday's child has loads of toys,
Friday's child is full of sin,
Saturday's child plays with a pin,
The child that is born on the Sabbath day,
Is as bad as the others,
But that's OK.

Jack Skitt (11)
Brookside Primary School, Brookside

The Spell From Hell
(Based on 'Macbeth')

'Double, double toil and trouble,
Fire burn and cauldron bubble.'

A tail from a fat snake,
In the cauldron boil and bake.
A dog tongue, a fish's tail,
A fin of a whale,
A gooey frog, a hairy hog,
A spider's leg, a wasp's sting,
A frog's leg, a bat's wing
For a hell broth, boil and bubble.

'Double, double toil and trouble,
Fire burn and cauldron bubble.'

Shannon Upton (10)
Brookside Primary School, Brookside

The Writer Of This Poem
(Based on 'The Writer of this Poem' by Roger McGough)

The writer of this poem,
Is as warm as the sun,
As keen as a runner,
As nice as a bun.

As loud as a volcano,
As quick as a lick,
As sweet as sugar,
As clever as a tick.

As silly as can be,
As small as a mouse,
As sour as a lemon,
As strong as a house.

The writer of this poem,
Never ceases to amaze,
She's one in a million, billion
(or so the poem says!)

Lauren Bond (10)
Brookside Primary School, Brookside

The Writer Of This Poem
(Based on 'The Writer of this Poem' by Roger McGough)

The writer of this poem,
Is as smelly as my dad's socks,
Is as silent as a cat,
Is as red as a fox.

Is as hot as a grill,
Likes to drink milk,
Is as dark as night,
Is as soft as silk.

The writer of this poem,
Never ceases to amaze,
She's one in a million, billion,
(or so the poem says).

Charlie Griffiths (11)
Brookside Primary School, Brookside

The Spell Of Doom
(Based on 'Macbeth')

'Double, double toil and trouble
Fire burn and cauldron bubble.'

Mouldy eyes,
Dead squashed flies,
Fatty frog's belly,
With snotty jelly,
The fin of a fish,
A terrible haunted wish,
Pig nose,
Dead black rose,
Dirty toes with lots of spots,
Browning orange gungy pots.

'Double, double toil and trouble,
Fire burn and cauldron bubble.'

Rachael Bradford & Gabrielle Warrilow (10)
Brookside Primary School, Brookside

Footie Rap
(Inspired by 'Gran, Can You Rap?' by Jack Ousbey)

Gran was at her mirror combing her hair
When I said, 'Nan, can I give you a dare?
Can you play football without a care?'
She dropped her brush and jumped to her feet
And said, 'Right I'm going to put on my beat,
I'm the best footballing gran you've ever seen,
I'm a tip, tap, fit, foot footballing queen.'

She put on her kit and went downstairs,
Picked up the phone and called the three bears.
Asked if she could play centre mid
'Because I'm going to make them look a kid.
Get ready boy we're going to the woods
I'm the best footballing gran you've ever seen,
I'm a tip, tap, fit, foot footballing queen.'

On the pitch we were forty minutes in
When Gran got the ball and scored with her chin.
They had two minutes left and she scored again,
And then she celebrated like a hen.
And there you go she won them the game
I'm the best footballing gran you've ever seen,
I'm a tip, tap, fit, foot footballing queen.

Matthew Stuart & Ryan Raper (11)
Brookside Primary School, Brookside

Monday's Child

Monday's child is very dull,
Tuesday's child looks like a bull,
Wednesday's child is very funny,
Thursday's child has a pet bunny,
Friday's child plays in the sun,
Saturday's child likes having fun,
But the child that was born on Sabbath day,
Is as bad as the rest,
But that's OK.

Abby Thompson (9)
Brookside Primary School, Brookside

The Witch's Spell
(Based on 'Macbeth')

'Double, double toil and trouble,
Fire burn and cauldron bubble.'

Fillet of a fatty frog,
In the cauldron boil the bog;
Paw of lion and eye of cat,
Wool of sheep and wings of bat,
Smelly sock and leg of hog,
Skin of snake and bark of log,
For a charm of powerful trouble,
Like a hell-broth boil and bubble.

'Double, double toil and trouble,
Fire burn and cauldron bubble.'

Tempany Wynn & Rebecca Burton (10)
Brookside Primary School, Brookside

The Writer Of This Poem
(Based on 'The Writer of this Poem' by Roger McGough)

The writer of this poem is
As fast as a mouse
As sneaky as a snake
As strong as a house.

She likes to bake
And is pretty as a flower,
And as tall as a tower.
Is as bright as the sun
Likes hot cross buns,
And is fuzzy as a cat.

The writer of this poem
Is as noisy as a parrot
She's one in a million billion
(or so the poem says).

Sophie Purcell (10)
Brookside Primary School, Brookside

Monday's Monkey

Monday's monkey has a funny face,
Tuesday's turtle has a water race,
Wednesday's walrus is a fat load,
Thursday's toad sleeps on the road,
Friday's fish is a sushi dish,
Saturday's snake wants a wish,
But the spider that's born on the Sabbath day
Is creepy and freaky, I'd just like to say
Argh!

Rebecca Waterman (10)
Brookside Primary School, Brookside

The Writer Of This Poem
(Based on 'The Writer of this Poem' by Roger McGough)

The writer of this poem,
Is small as a mouse
As white as snow
As strong as a house.

As soft as silk
And is like a barrel of milk
As nice as a bun
As loud as a gun.

As pretty as a flower
Isn't as tall as a tower
As clean as white
As sly as night.

The writer of this poem
Never ceases to amaze
She's one in a million billion
Or so the poem says!

Lucy Fewtrell (10)
Brookside Primary School, Brookside

Happy

Happy is tasting the smell of jam cake,
Happy is looking at my friends when I love to play with them.
Happy is hearing birds sing in the morning.
Happy is feeling like yummy sweets.
Happy is smelling my cheese pizza.
Happy reminds me of my favourite teachers.

Chloe Palmer (6)
Brookside Primary School, Brookside

The Writer Of This Poem
(Based on 'The Writer of this Poem' by Roger McGough)

The writer of this poem,
Is as boring as a teacher,
As scary as a shark,
And as still as a picture.

Is as white as a ghost,
As cold as ice,
As tall as a lamp post,
As spotty as a dice.

As friendly as a dog,
As bold as a knight,
Swims like a frog,
And won't go without a fight.

Scott Driscoll & Thomas Morris (10)
Brookside Primary School, Brookside

Footie Rap

We go to the pitch and have a laugh,
David says he needs a nap.
This is all part of the footie rap.
Liam says with a giggle,
'My meat pie's not cooked in the middle!'
As the player kicks the ball,
The crowd start to call,
'This is the best footie
Rap of them all.'

Liam Johnson & David Naylor (10)
Brookside Primary School, Brookside

Happiness

Happiness is when I'm at the beach
With my family.
Happiness is when I see the hot burning sun.
Happiness is when I hear fireworks.
Happiness is when I smell my tea.
Happiness is when I start surfing.

Grace Walker (6)
Brookside Primary School, Brookside

Happiness

Happiness is when I am at my auntie's
Because she has a game to play with.
Happiness is when I see ice cream at my auntie's house in a cone.
Happiness is when I hear toast popping up waiting for me.
Happiness is when I swing on my auntie's swing to and fro.

I love happiness.

Chloe Hancox (7)
Brookside Primary School, Brookside

Happiness

Happiness is when I am playing football with my team.
Happiness is when I see the yellow sun in the blue sky.
Happiness is when people cheer like lions.
Happiness is when I smell fresh air.
I am happy when the ball is in the back of the net.

Ben Szehofner (7)
Brookside Primary School, Brookside

Happiness

Happiness is when I am at football and soccer with my friends.
Happiness is when we gaze up to the stars at night by a grey and blue tent.
Happiness is when I smell my mum cooking my tea.
Happiness is when I hear people cheering for me.
I am happy every time I score a goal.

Jack Nadin (7)
Brookside Primary School, Brookside

Afraid

Afraid is like a hedgehog curled in a ball.
Afraid reminds me of a piece of furniture,
A bath because I always think I will go down the plughole.
Afraid would be a pencil sharpener because it might chop me up.
When I am afraid I yell and run to my kind nan's house.

Zoe Pearson (7)
Brookside Primary School, Brookside

Happiness

Happiness is when I am playing basketball.
Happiness is when I see people swimming in the pool.
Happiness is when I hear the water crashing on the tide.
Happiness is when I smell hot chips and cold ice cream.
I love happiness when I am with my family.

Kyra Leneveu (7)
Brookside Primary School, Brookside

Happiness

Happy is tasting a creamy chocolate cake.
Happy is looking at shark teeth because it reminds me of my favourite holiday.
Happy is feeling like it's your birthday.
Happy is smelling chocolate cake.
Happy reminds me of when I'm with my family.

Joshua Bowker (7)
Brookside Primary School, Brookside

The Moonlight

The moonlight shines and dries up under the sun.
The moonlight shines like a daffodil from Heaven.
The moon is as round as a balloon.
The moonlight is wonderful, but don't look at it because you will go blind.
The moon is like a wonderful piece of gold.
The moonlight is beautiful like a diamond.

Cherie Harris (9)
Brookside Primary School, Brookside

Seven Stages Of My Life

Born on a Sunday in the USA
Flying on a Monday to the UK
New house on Tuesday unpacking today
Off to school on Wednesday ready to play
Visit Nan on Thursday special treats today
Packing on Friday on my holiday
Injured on Saturday hurt my knee at play.

Joseph Porton (8)
Brookside Primary School, Brookside

The Moon

The moon awakes and the stars are bright
Just like a great banana in the twinkling sky.

The moon is like a boomerang
Swishing and soaring through the wind and rain.

The moon will come out at night but not in twilight

The moon is a floating kite flowing through the night sky.

The moon is beginning to go away and the sun will begin to come out.

Jessica Ball (8)
Brookside Primary School, Brookside

A True Story

Born on a Sunday in Mexico.
Flying on a Monday had to go.
New school on a Tuesday, lots to play.
Happy on a Wednesday laughing all day.
Went to Nan on Thursday
Got a big mug
With my family on Friday
I love a big hug.
Went shopping on a Saturday
Bought a new rug.

Leyla Al-Ashaab (9)
Brookside Primary School, Brookside

Monday's Child

Monday's child enjoys a laugh
Tuesday's child has fun in the bath
Wednesday's child is always sad
Thursday's child is never mad
Friday's child is in a muddle
Saturday's child gets in a fuddle
But the child that is born on the Sabbath day
Will be your friend every day.

Louise Cummings (7)
Brookside Primary School, Brookside

The Moon

The moon is like a spinning boomerang swirling in the night sky,
The moon awakes the stars so bright in the night sky,
The moon comes out when the sun sets in the bright sky,
The moon is like a dolphin splashing in the sea,
The moon is bright like the shining sun in the sky.

Amy Stubbings (8)
Brookside Primary School, Brookside

What Is Pink?

What is pink? Candyfloss is pink,
Fluffy wool, soft as mink.

What is red? Blood is red,
Ruby red is often said.

What is blue? The sea is blue,
And the waves go washing through.

What is white? Clouds are white,
In the morning light.

What is yellow? Bananas are yellow,
Eating bananas when you're mellow.

What is green? Mints are green,
Eating mints when you're mean.

What is violet? Violets are violet,
Seeing violets when you are a pilot.

What is orange? Carrots are orange,
Just like an orange.

Bethany Johnson (9)
Brookside Primary School, Brookside

The Moon

The moon awakes
The stars flash
Like fireworks
In the night sky
The moon bounces around
Like a football
The moon shrieks
Into clouds for the morning.

Ryan Johnson (7)

Brookside Primary School, Brookside

Winter

Winter has taken over autumn,
Bringing with her, glitter-like snow.
The grass has turned to tinsel,
And the leaves have turned to paper.

As the old man shuffles up the road,
The snow crunches with every step.
The children are playing outside,
And balls of snow are being thrown,
From side to side.

Every now and again the gritter,
Salts the roads.
Stopping cars from slipping,
And sliding down the streets.

The Christmas lights are as bright as stars,
Hanging off snowy trees.
At the front of a door, a painted sign says
'Santa, please stop here!'

Harry Rogers (11)
Captain Webb Primary School, Dawley

Storm

The sea smashed onto the seafront wall,
The sky was as black as night.
The wind blew the rain across the shore.
Not a person or thing was in sight.

The lightning's fingers
Came down in flashes
Which cast a dark shadow
On the shimmering seashore.

The thunder crashed like a big bass drum
Over the dark and raging sea.
The lighthouse stood alone
Throwing its light into the thundery sky.

When dawn broke, the thunderstorm had gone
The sky was clear and blue.
The seashore was no longer empty,
But once again was full.

Nicole Broomhall (11)
Captain Webb Primary School, Dawley

My Pets . . .

As Jazz watched the washing machine rumble its tummy,
Her multicoloured fur stood up like a porcupine.
When my kitten's confused she looks really yummy
And that's most of the time!

As Sally lounged in front of the baking oven,
She snored like an electric drill.
Those lazy old dogs you just got to love 'em
And she's lazy most of the time!

As Sasha spun faster and faster in her wheel,
Her teeny tail bobbed like a tiny see-saw.
My super fit hamster works hard for her next meal
Most of the time!

Gemma Mansell (11)
Captain Webb Primary School, Dawley

Christmas Day

Snow began to fall
From the dullness
Of the sky

The clouds were as
White as the glistening
Snowflakes

Rooftops started to form
Patterns
Snow scattered across
The long layered tinselled grass

The sun started to beam
Through the glistening trees
Making shapes onto
The sparkling snow that lay heavily on the ground

The sun started gleaming
Onto the glistening pond
Whirling ripples shaped like pearls
Were formed onto the frozen water

The bird bath had
Pointy silver icicles dangling
From it

The sight of it was just beautiful.

Jessica Mathars (10)
Captain Webb Primary School, Dawley

Tripping In My Envy

As I think about the other side of the world,
I'm tripping in my envy,
For the rest of the world enjoys the sun,
Lying on hot, hot beaches.

The cold, cold wind,
Forms a frozen layer of skin,
On my soft bright cheeks,
As I know, it's winter.

As I think about the other side of the world,
I'm tripping in my envy,
The blazing sun sends a ray of heat,
Directly at the people.

The winter breezes tear through my skin,
Sending their icy winds around me,
The wind hits my freezing forehead,
As I know, it's winter.

As I think about the other side of the world,
I'm tripping in my envy,
The others enjoy their heat,
I despise our breezes.

Michael Drummond (10)
Captain Webb Primary School, Dawley

The Night

It was a cold dark night
And the wind was shaking the trees,
As the rain hit the roof of the cold hard house,
But inside all was silent and calm,
The fire was burning red, yellow and gold,
And the warmth spread through the room like a flowing river.
The quiet peaceful room filled with fun and laughter.

But outside it was as cold as an iceberg
And the trees groaned as they stood there
Frozen cold looking at the warm house.

Callum Shropshire (10)
Captain Webb Primary School, Dawley

My Meandering River

A muddy bog in the mountains is how my river begins.
Seeping through grasses and mosses.
Trickling over rocks and into a stream.
More and more water drains into my mini river,
Faster and faster, scraping away at the rock!

Wait, what's this? It's a paw, it's a sheepdog,
Interrupting my stream's flow,
He laps up my water and bounds up the mountain again
To a high-pitched whistle.

I go on my way as rapids approach me,
Pebbles bashing together breaking, turning to dust,
My first waterfall only small but my water still goes down,
My river becomes fast-flowing where salmon leap.
I meet a soft muzzle drinking my swirling soothing water,
My water carries on meandering towards me . . .

Daisy Ruse (9)
Clifford Primary School, Clifford

Christmas In The Eyes Of A Hamster

Twelve o'clock Christmas Eve
　　　　It's up to you and me to believe.

　　　　Tawkwin snuggles in his bed,
　　　　　　Popping up his chubby head.

And then he rests his dancing paws
　　　　There he is, it's Santa Claus!
　　He's got a sack tied with holly,
　　　　He's very big, red and jolly.

'Hello you little thing,' he said,
　　　　'You do look comfy in your bed!'

　　　　Seeing the twinkle in Tawkwin's eyes
　　　　　　When Santa gave him such a lovely surprise.

Bella Ferros (9)
Clifford Primary School, Clifford

The Boggy Mountain

High up in
The boggy
Mountains a
Tiny trickle
Of pale blue
Water running
Out of a damp
Patch, getting
Wider and
Wider picking
Up stones as
It goes along.
Starting to make
Tiny grains of sand.
Every minute the
Little river gets
Bigger, it begins to
Pick up speed, the
River meanders
Down the hill
Getting very close
To the sea. Seaweed
Comes in sight
And meets the tide.

Alice Venables (9)
Clifford Primary School, Clifford

Bob The Dog

Bob's head is nice and wide
His ears are ginger and fluffy inside.
He is full of fun and very happy
Well behaved and never snappy.

He really likes his lunch
Eating with a *munch, munch, munch.*
His tail is nice and thick
And he runs very quick.

Thomas Williams (11)
Clifford Primary School, Clifford

Australia

I wish I was in Australia,
At a hot and sunny beach,
The warm sand in-between my toes
It'd be too good for speech.

A chocolate ice cream in my hands,
The waves whispering around me,
Children playing with buckets and spades,
A sailing boat far out at sea.

Robyn Collins (10)
Clifford Primary School, Clifford

My Cat Scamp

My cat is called Scamp,
He's a fantastic champ,
He's very speedy,
And I think he's greedy.

Sofas he scratches,
And he has two patches,
His fur is so soft,
And he sleeps in a loft.

I love him dearly,
Though he is really,
A big fusspot,
And he gets very hot.

Ella Sutherland (10)
Clifford Primary School, Clifford

Oyvee

I loved Oyvee
My British Blue
I really did
That is true.

But one fateful night
My poor little cat
Died with a fright
Eating a poisoned rat.

The strange thing is
When I'm in bed
I still see her
Even though she's dead.

Raphael Garland (9)
Clifford Primary School, Clifford

My Cats Elwood And Jake

My cats Elwood and Jake
They like playing with the rake.
String, mice and birds
They make my cats go absurd.
My cat Jake has lost a bit of weight
Now he's decided to eat off his plate.

Elwood, Elwood, he likes eating grapes
And when he hides, he hides under capes.
They're so fluffy, cute too
And they miaow at the door when they need the loo.
They dribble on me and make me giggle,
Then they tickle me and make me wiggle.
They're the best cats in the world, I see
I love them and they love me.

Mir Spreckley (9)
Clifford Primary School, Clifford

Me, Mitsy And Sindy

Me and Mitsy go to play
We go to play every day
Around the garden everywhere
And all the way up the stairs.

Me and Sindy run around
We always skid on the ground
Jumping, bouncing up and down
She never really makes a sound.

Mitsy and Sindy play all day
They have so much fun on holiday
Mitsy normally chases Sindy
All around when it's windy.

Kirsty Rea (9)
Clifford Primary School, Clifford

Registration

'Puss in Boots?'
'Miaow, Miss.'

'Jack Black?'
'Breaking the law, Miss.'

'Basil Brush?'
'Ah ha ha ha boom boom! Miss.'

'Thomas the Tank?'
'Smoking, Miss.'

'Homer?'
'Doughnuts *mmm* . . . Miss.'

'Piggy?'
'Moya ya, Miss.'

'Crazy Frog?'
'Ding-ding, Miss.'

'Gingerbread Man?'
'Run, run as fast as you can, you can't catch me
I'm the Gingerbread Man, Miss.'

'Hell Boy?'
'Mission, Miss.'

Jordan Brookes (8)
Cradley CE (VA) Primary School, Cradley

Registration

'Dr Who?'
'Just came back from the past, Miss.'

'Elvis Presley?'
'I'm caught in a trap, Miss.'

'Yoda?'
'May all the force be with you, Miss.'

'Spider-Man?'
'My spider senses are tingling, Miss.'

'Hulk?'
'Getting angry, Miss.'

Patrick Morgan (8)
Cradley CE (VA) Primary School, Cradley

Registration

'Tweety the bird?'
'I thought I saw a putty cat, Miss.'

'Bugs Bunny?'
'What's up, Miss?'

'Willy Wonka?'
'Want a golden ticket, Miss?'

'Basil Brush?'
'Boom, boom! Miss.'

'Nanny Mcphee?'
'I'm Nanny Mcphee, Miss.'

'Mary Poppins?'
'Supercalafragilisticexpialadotious.'

'The boy who cried wolf?'
'Wolf! Wolf! Miss.'

'Crazy Frog?'
'A ring-ding-ding, Miss.'

'Sylvester?'
'Sacker a sukertaron, Miss.'

Laura Hazlewood (8)
Cradley CE (VA) Primary School, Cradley

Registration

'Barry White?'
'Yes, Mam.'

'Milk Tray Man?'
'All because a lady loves Milk Tray, Miss.'

'Elvis Presley?'
'Thank you, thank you very much, Miss.'

'Man in the Moon?'
'Still in space, Miss.'

'Wayne Rooney?'
'Goal! Miss.'

'Bugs Bunny?'
'What's up, Doc, I mean, Miss?'

'Daredevil?'
'Oh that must hurt, Miss.'

Louis Boffy (8)
Cradley CE (VA) Primary School, Cradley

Registration

'Willy Wonka?'
'Too much eating, Miss.'

'James Bond?'
'Shooting people, Miss.'

'Basil Brush?'
'Aah aah ha ha boom boom, Miss.'

'King Kong?'
'Grrrr, Miss.'

'Dick and Dom?'
'Creamy muck muck, Miss.'

'Crazy Frog?'
'Ding ding, Miss.'

'Tweety Bird?'
'Naughty cat, Miss.'

'Sonic?'
'Super fast, Miss.'

Kurt Poppleton (7)
Cradley CE (VA) Primary School, Cradley

Registration

'Tom Jones?'
'Singing on the stage, Miss.'

'Mozart?'
'Playing for the Queen, Miss.'

'Michael Jackson.'
'Plastic surgery, Miss.'

'James Bond?'
'Brandy on the rocks shaken not stirred, Miss.'

'Red Riding Hood.'
'Running from the wolf, Miss.'

'Paula Radcliffe?'
'Still going, Miss.'

Henry Henderson (8)
Cradley CE (VA) Primary School, Cradley

Registration

'Daffy Duck?'
'I can't stop talking, Miss.'

'Willy Wonka?'
'Making chocolate, Miss.'

'Bugs Bunny?'
'Going berserk, Miss.'

'Dick and Dom?'
'We've got too much creamy muck muck all over the place, Miss.'

'Mary Poppins?'
'Flying on my umbrella, Miss.'

'King Kong?'
'Grrrrrrr, Miss.'

'Sonic the Hedgehog?'
'Running around the school, Miss.'

Benjamin Fullagar (8)
Cradley CE (VA) Primary School, Cradley

Registration

'Spider-Man?'
'Climbing up a big wall, Miss.'

'Daffy Duck?'
'Shooting Bugs Bunny but missing, Miss.'

'Willy Wonka?'
'Chocolate for you, Miss.'

'Elvis Presley?'
'Singing, Miss.'

'David Beckham?'
'Playing football, Miss.'

'King Kong?'
'Massive feet, Miss.'

Robbie Watts (8)
Cradley CE (VA) Primary School, Cradley

Registration

'Yoda?'
'Fighting droids, Miss.'

'Jack Black?'
'Shooting dinosaurs, Miss.'

'Wayne Rooney?'
'Scoring goals, Miss.'

'Willy Wonka?'
'Eating chocolate, Miss.'

'Harry Potter?'
'Casting spells, Miss.'

'Basil Brush?'
'A ha ha ha ha boom boom, Miss.'

'Mary Poppins?'
'Upur, Miss.'

'James Bond?'
'Killing bad people, Miss.'

'Scooby Doo?'
'Late, Miss.'

'Mum?'
'Here, Miss.'

'Nanny McPhee?'
'1, 2, 3, 4, soon, Miss.'

'Todd Smallwood?'
'Yes, Miss.'

Todd Smallwood (7)
Cradley CE (VA) Primary School, Cradley

Hope!

I hope I live tomorrow,
If I don't I will feel sorrow.
I'm sad, I miss my dad,
If I hear my tum I miss my mum,
And if I see a black cat,
I think I'll see many more rats.

Zak Lawrence (9)
Cradley CE (VA) Primary School, Cradley

Registration

'Aslan the lion?'
'Battle for you, Miss.'

'Tin Man?'
'A little bit rusty, Miss.'

'Bugs Bunny?'
'What's up, Miss?'

'Daffy Duck?'
'Can't stop trying to shoot Bugs Bunny, Miss.'

'Robin Hood?'
'Arrows for you, Miss.'

'Willy Wonka?'
'Chocolate for you, Miss.'

'King Kong?'
'Beating his chest, Miss.'

'Dumbo the elephant?'
'In the air, Miss.'

'Spider-Man?'
'Spinning, Miss.'

'Mary Poppins?'
'Supercalafragilisticexpialadotious, Miss.'

'David Beckham?'
'Kicking the ball, Miss.'

'Mr Incredible?'
'Saving the world, Miss.'

'Dash?'
'Running, Miss.'

'Elasticgirl?'
A bit stretchy, Miss.'

'Superman?'
'Saving the world, Miss.'

Isaac George (8)
Cradley CE (VA) Primary School, Cradley

Registration

'Obi?'
'Fighting, Miss.'

'Yoda?'
'Fighting a droid, Miss.'

'Scooby Doo?'
'Yaba-daba-doo, Miss.'

'Bugs Bunny?'
'Eating a carrot, Miss.'

'Robin Hood?'
'Firing arrows, Miss.'

'TL?'
'Plane, Miss.'

'Freddy?'
'Driving, Miss.'

'Guss?'
'Eating gum, Miss.'

'Willy Wonka?'
'Golden ticket, Miss.'

'Randle?'
'Snitch, Miss.'

'Kim?'
'Getting a bath, Miss.'

'Ron?'
'Eating, Miss.'

'Rufus?'
'Bit, Miss.'

'Duck?'
'Quack quack, Miss.'

'Beckham?'
'Kicking a football, Miss.'

'Theirry?'
'Fantastic goal, Miss.'

Joshua Davies (7)
Cradley CE (VA) Primary School, Cradley

Registration

'Puss in Boots?'
'Miaow, Miss.'

'Jack Black?'
'Breaking the law, Miss.'

'Basil Brush?'
'A ha ha ha boom boom, Miss.'

'Thomas the Tank Engine?'
'Choo, choo, choo, Miss.'

'Homer?'
'Doh, Miss.'

'Bart?'
'Ay carumba, Miss.'

'Donald Duck?'
'Oh boy.'

'Lisa?'
'Bart!'

'Bugs Bunny?'
'What's up, Miss?'

Kieran Dean (8)
Cradley CE (VA) Primary School, Cradley

Registration

'Doctor Who?'
'Killing aliens, Miss.'

'Garbage Man?'
'It's garbage time, Miss.'

'McFly?'
'My guitar is out of tune, Miss.'

'Postman Pat?'
'Where's my cat, Miss?'

'Thomas the Tank?'
'Chugging down the track, Miss.'

Cameron Dunnett (8)
Cradley CE (VA) Primary School, Cradley

Pebble

Pebble is my friend he is,
My very best friend in fact,
He's round and black,
Smooth and soft,
But he'd blow up on impact.

Pebble is my friend he is,
My very best friend in fact,
He's hard as rock,
Tough as nails,
And if he's naughty then he's smacked.

Pebble is my friend he is,
My very best friend in fact,
He can be as hot as the sun,
Or as cold as ice,
And from his last job he was sacked.

Charlie Brookes (11)
Cradley CE (VA) Primary School, Cradley

Registration

'Aslan the lion?'
'Battle for you, Miss?'

'Robin Hood?'
'An arrow for you! Miss.'

'King Kong?'
'Beating my chest, Miss!'

'Tin Man?'
'A little bit rusty, Miss.'

'Bugs Bunny?'
'Underground, Miss.'

'Willy Wonka?'
'In the factory, Miss.'

'Dumbo?'
'In the sky, Miss.'

Jack Bilby (7)
Cradley CE (VA) Primary School, Cradley

Gobbledeegoo

The land of boggles a terrible place,
In it lives the Gobbledeegoo,
It has four legs and it has no arms
And it eats its lunch from a shoe.

If its shoe went missing it wouldn't eat,
And it would grow very fat,
Or if it felt quite clever,
It would eat its lunch from a hat.

If the Gobbledeegoo was tired,
He'd go to Gobbledeesleep,
And if he wanted a holiday,
He'd go to Googly Gleep.

Googly Gleep's the opposite
Of the land called Boggles here,
I'm Googley Glephers fluffy cheer
In Boggles there's mouldy deer.

The land of Boggles is a terrible place
In it lives the Gobbledeegoo
It has four legs and it has no arms
And it eats its lunch from a shoe.

Jacob Scott (10)
Cradley CE (VA) Primary School, Cradley

Hope And Belief

Hope is good, hope is great,
People who hope are people who believe.
Belief is good, belief is great,
Putting hope and belief together makes the ultimate dream team!

Christian Dandy (9)
Cradley CE (VA) Primary School, Cradley

Registration

'Dumbo?'
'Big ears, Miss.'

'Professor McGonagall?'
'Such a wizard, Miss.'

'Homer Simpson?'
'I love doughnuts, Miss.'

'Pinocchio?'
'He's only wood, Miss.'

Freddy Charters (8)
Cradley CE (VA) Primary School, Cradley

Hope

Hope is a patch of white on a black page,
To hope is to believe,
Hope is a white sheep in a herd of black sheep,
To hope is to believe.

Hope is a candle flickering in the darkness,
To hope is to believe.
Hope is love, in a world full of hate,
To hope is to believe.

Hope is the sun, gleaming behind the clouds,
To hope is to believe.
Hope is everything good in this world,
To hope is to believe.

Fred Van Vuren (9)
Cradley CE (VA) Primary School, Cradley

Hope For The Homeless

Justice is needed
Hearts are broken, no place to stay.
Medicine is needed for those that need it
Comfort for the people that have no one.
Little food,
I need a good life
I hope I can get a little transport.
I'm lonely, but I'm free.
Living on the street with no meat.
One little charity bank could change their lives.

Charlie Rankin (9)
Cradley CE (VA) Primary School, Cradley

The Life I Hope For

All I have is hope
All I hope for is a good education
All I hope for is warmth
All I hope for is food and water
All I hope for is a bit of money
All I hope for is some clothes
All I hope for is shelter
All I hope for is happiness
All I hope for is a bed
All I hope for is companionship
All I want is hope!

Josh Banner (9)
Cradley CE (VA) Primary School, Cradley

Hope

Poor people on the street.
Lots of people they want to meet.
They sometimes picture a great big steak.
When they don't want their heart to break.
They want and need to have a good future.
But they don't want a friend that's immature.
Please let them stay, don't charge them anything to pay.
These people need love and laughter.
They want to have a happily ever after.
If you recognise their face,
Please get them out of the dreaded place.
They want and need a life.
But second of all, the men want a wife.

Peter Bennett (9)
Cradley CE (VA) Primary School, Cradley

The Jora

A Jora went sailing in a matchbox,
'You can't go sailing in a matchbox, you'll sink!'
So he went to the Isle of Boat and set off.
On the way there he sang a little song,
In sight came Suncream Valley.
He jumped out of his box.
Where shall I stay?
He said to himself,
I might as well leave.
Off he went back to the jungle,
And had a nice cup of tea!

Sarah Walker (11)
Cradley CE (VA) Primary School, Cradley

Jersey

Look down on the beach in Jersey, waves splash.
Fun is happening, coffee is drunk.
You are never far away from the sea.
My bored sister watching me bodyboard.
Eating fish and chips in the restaurant.
Look down on the beach in Jersey, waves splash.

Tom Boldry (11)
Cradley CE (VA) Primary School, Cradley

Anfield

Football has not anything to show more fair;
No other ground is such a beautiful sight.
A sight no other supporter can dream of.
The pitch is as green as a piece of green grass.

If you go there you can see the players' shirts;
Anfield is the Champion's League winner's ground.
All the shirts and mugs you can buy at the shop.
Our main sentence is 'you'll never walk alone'.

William Brown (10)
Cradley CE (VA) Primary School, Cradley

Waterfall

I can see my gleaming hair rushing down,
The beautiful butterflies flying round and round,
The trees staggering over my splash,
The sun reflecting over me,
I can feel the slimy touch of the fish,
The lovely heat of the sun's blanket,
I can feel the seagull's peck, peck, pecking at me,
I can see the bright colours of leaves,
Dropping down, down, down.

Lydia Parkhill (10)
Cradley CE (VA) Primary School, Cradley

The View Of Western Australia

Earth has not anything to show more fair:
Dull would he be of soul pass by
A sight so fantastic as Western Aus
The Alps has its snow, its trees and its breeze:
The Caribbean has its sand and its seas,
But none are as gorgeous as Western Aus!
With its sandy beaches and clear blue seas.
Not to mention the beautiful WACCA.

Joe Watts (10)
Cradley CE (VA) Primary School, Cradley

Haiku Poem

When the sun comes out
A rainbow forms in the sky
And it's fine again!

Splashing in the waves
Doing cartwheels on the sand
Having a good laugh!

TV is a blast
Watching a colourful screen
I won't budge a bit!

PS2 is cool
My hands' own entertainment
Playing on and on!

Little Britain fans
Cannot get enough of it
Watching and watching!

X-Factor is great
Singing live and loud is fab
But Chico is cool!

Jade Allard (10)
Cradley CE (VA) Primary School, Cradley

Haikus

Football
Running down the pitch
Passing the ball to teammates,
And scoring a goal.

Animals
Hamsters like to climb
Even cats can climb higher,
But birds are the best.

Cars
Most cars go quite fast
But some zoom above the rest
Like the Bugatti.

Weather
Lightning flashes bright
Thunder roars powerfully
Floods are a danger.

William Cooper (10)
Cradley CE (VA) Primary School, Cradley

Hope!

Hope is a little lone star
In the sky watching homeless people.
Hoping for a home and food and water and a warm blanket.
Lots of people sitting in the street,
In one dark corner,
And hope is the word!

Thomas Bridges (9)
Cradley CE (VA) Primary School, Cradley

Hope

H ave some thought that's stuck inside your head
O f course they're wishing for warm comfy beds.
P acing up and down a street
E ating pasties, watching us weep.

Amy Barratt (9)
Cradley CE (VA) Primary School, Cradley

Hope

Hope is a bed
Hope is blankets
Hope is education
Hope is family
Hope is travelling
Hope is living
Hope is like a nice future.

Daisy Davies (10)
Cradley CE (VA) Primary School, Cradley

Wandering

Searchlights wandering over the thick muddy fields
of no-man's-land,
Like a yellow-eyed wolf hunting for its prey.
Guns chattering loudly
as they send bullets whizzing through the misty air.
Fear slowly creeps up on me.

Jennifer Lewis (10)
Crudgington Primary School, Crudgington

Winter Wonderland

Frost sparkles in the moonlight like Christmas fairy lights twinkling.
Snowdrops fall like shredded paper landing on soft, fluffy cotton wool.
Children play outside getting soaked from the wet, cold snow.
Icicles hang from window ledges, like dangling frozen spiders' legs.
The oak trees wrap themselves in a blanket of snow, to keep them warm
Through the frosty winter nights.
Bare-branched trees are dancing skeletons, swaying in the wind.
The flames crackle in the fireplace as if they are big fireworks.
Big steaming mugs of hot chocolate with marshmallows
Floating like frozen ice cubes.
Curled up inside little cottage dog, staring at the white snow
That has settled on a window ledge.
Children play games sitting by the warm, open fire,
Drinking some hot milk.
Just come in from the cold winter's snow, children warm up their hands.

Michelle Tozer (10) & Gracie Johnson (11)
Crudgington Primary School, Crudgington

War

You can hear the sound of the bombs dropping into the wet old trenches
Tanks creep one by one through
The muddy wet sandy path
You can hear the guns chattering
Together
A gloomy dark gas moves slowly
Across the spooky field, two by two the soldiers crawl
Through the stick gooey tracks the smell of gassy bombs killing the air.

Jack Eggerton (9) & James Taylor (10)
Crudgington Primary School, Crudgington

Winter Imagination

Now I dream about winter,
My toes are freezing cold,
The trees look like skeletons.

All I think about is winter,
The lovely cold snow;
The cold breeze.
Every night all I do is dream about
Winter.

Paige Sharman (9)
Crudgington Primary School, Crudgington

The Real Winter!

From the looming fog a tree appears out of nowhere,
With snowflakes falling like millions of pins,
Snow-covered trees with white gnarled branches
Waiting to lunge.

Snow crunches under my feet,
Like the land shattering into pieces,
The dying flowers bow down to the daring moon,
Shining icicles hang from the web,
Like glistening daggers.

The days are getting shorter,
Like someone putting their hand over the sun,
The bushes are transforming into ice sculptures.

The frost closes around me
Choking the weakened sun . . .

Kate Coventry (9) & Katy Warner (10)
Crudgington Primary School, Crudgington

Freezing Death

Snowflakes falling like shredded paper,
Covering the ground like a white carpet.
Icicles hanging from cobwebs as if they are watery fingers
Desperately hanging on.
Ice-cold frost assassinating unknowing trees,
Animals hibernating in hollow tree trunks.
The wind playing tag with the frozen debris.
Inside the nice warm house, children sleep
Next to the crackling fire, eagerly waiting for spring.

Harry Osbourn & John-Henry Cooper (11)
Crudgington Primary School, Crudgington

Harsh Winter

Large snowdrops heavily charge down to Earth,
Icicles hang as if they're sharp, silver daggers ready to fall.
Icy waters scream as I carefully tread on the frozen lake.
I see trees and plants shivering as frost creeps and
Covers the world in white, cold darkness.
The snow crunches loudly under my feet like the
Land shattering into pieces.
Thick mist kills the land, destroying everything
Related to summer.

Will we survive the winter . . . ?

Katie Edwards (9)
Crudgington Primary School, Crudgington

Searching For Me

Bullets flying past my ears
So many screams so many fears
The alarm bell rings
The gas is coming
Searching for me.

They come out of their trenches
Across no-man's-land
The sargeant shouts, 'Fire!'
We must follow the command.
We aim and shoot
Knowing this could be our last day,
But we have no choice
So we fire away.

I see the bullets growing closer,
As the gas did yesterday,
It hits my chest,
At last I'm free.
It was searching,
But now it's found me.

Fern Hill (9)
Crudgington Primary School, Crudgington

Winter

The gentle waterfall froze in fear
Of the frost approaching in the mist,
The birds fled to get away
As the running wind sped,
Animals scampered losing the race
Against the rain galloping rapidly,
The sun had gone,
The moon had come
The only light left was the
Moon's purple gleam,
The frozen thorns shot out,
Attempting to plunge into the
Darkness of the storm.

Megan Lewis (10)
Crudgington Primary School, Crudgington

Why War?

The men are ready to leave this trench,
Filled with the sweat of their heads,
With their guns by their side,
And God up above.
They get ready to charge.
The men come forward with a mighty screech,
The guns start to chatter as the men fall,
Like a lion on its prey.
The trenches are in sight,
There is a hope of joy,
But then a cold metal enters my chest,
Like a plunge into dark water,
Light fades away for most of us.
A question enters my head,
Like a last request,
And finally says, *why war?*

Charles Boffey-Rawlings (9)
Crudgington Primary School, Crudgington

War

Searchlights wandering
Over thick muddy fields
Of no-man's-land,
Like a yellow-eyed wolf
Hunting for its prey.

Guns chattering loudly
As they send bullets
Whizzing through the thick, dirty air.

Fear slowly creeps up on me;
Body shaking,
Heart racing,
Blood freezing,
Terrified . . .

Siobhan English, Daniel Ginger (9) & Sebastian Lee (10)
Crudgington Primary School, Crudgington

War

Soldiers trudging along a thin walkway,
Where sludgy grass sprouts up out of the ground,
Searchlights everywhere glaring like a lion,
With its shiny eyes looking for its prey.
The muggy air tearing through your clothes,
The sound of tanks creeping like venomous beetles
Through the dark, misty night.

Wishing I was in a safe, cosy place, knowing I could never be hurt,
And that the war would end.
And we could all be calm and friendly again.

Jessica Cavanagh (10)
Crudgington Primary School, Crudgington

Invasion!

Guns chatter like knees knocking.
Bullets scream like a shot soldier.
Tanks crawl across dead soldiers like men crawling on thick, sludgy mud.
Bombs weep like children crying for their dads.
Searchlights dart across no-man's-land like giant fireflies.
Tanks creep and topple like an injured soldier returning to his trench.
Bombs shatter while soldiers run from gunshots.
Men hurtle back to their trenches bootless.
Soldiers cry for help while guns chatter and bombs weep
But nobody can hear.

Michelle Tozer (10)
Crudgington Primary School, Crudgington

Winter

Frost creeps slowly over the grass causing it to crunch like
Popcorn beneath my feet.
Icicles drip from rooftops as if leaky taps.
Snowflakes float softly to the ground like tiny pieces of torn paper.
The pale silver sun stares weakly over the frosty earth.
The frozen grass turns green again
The pale sun regains its colour
Icicles melt
Snowflakes disappear
It's autumn again.

Megan Glenholmes (11)
Crudgington Primary School, Crudgington

Battling

Bombs like fireworks lighting up the sky
Thousands of men preparing to die.

Cold, wet feet sinking in the mud
Fields of poppies as red as blood.

Guns fire bullets. *Snap! Crackle! Pop!*
Shooting at soldiers who've gone over the top.

Bravely battling through the barbed wire
Men shouting orders, 'Fire! Fire! Fire!'

Long deep trenches cutting through the ground
Young dead bodies left to be found.

Darcie Farnsworth (9)
Crudgington Primary School, Crudgington

Why?

Soldiers trudging by like lost dying people,
Looking how to get back home to safety,
Bang! A bomb explodes causing soldiers to fall to the floor,
I feel sick
Sick of the thought of dying,
Why do we have war?
I'm sick of war,
Why?

Shannon Clewes (10)
Crudgington Primary School, Crudgington

Army Of Black

As I watch men marching in black,
I realise that they have tears of water
And tears of blood upon their pale faces.
As they trudge onto the battlefield,
The searchlights wander into the mist
Like cats' eyes staring upon the darkness.
Men stumble hopelessly into the fog of black
Upon the barbed wire,
I hear bombs squealing and crying,
Whilst the tanks trudge along the bodies of black,
As men scream into the night.

Emma Shepherd (10)
Crudgington Primary School, Crudgington

Winter

Autumn has died,
As winter has approached.
Oak trees cover themselves,
As if putting a white coat on.
The frost appears from nowhere,
As if you are half blind.

The sun is frozen,
As if passing by.
Lakes can't breathe,
As though they are trapped from ice.
Leaves are covered,
As if disappearing.

Icicles drip from rooftops,
As if there is a leak.
Icicles are as sharp,
As sharp as a dagger.
Icicles everywhere,
Biting anything that approaches.

Trees are dancing skeletons,
In the wind.
The wind dances,
Through the damp fog.
Snowflakes are forcing their way down,
Snow and ice groan upon the lakes.

Now the winter dies,
As spring approaches as an army.
Killing the cold,
Bringing friendliness.
Walking calmly,
Winter shall resurrect again and again . . .

Douglas Osbourn (10)
Crudgington Primary School, Crudgington

When Things Go Wrong

When water went on the table our work went all wrong.
When a glue stick went on my jumper, it would not come off.
When the screws came out of the chair it all fell apart!
When Joe flicked his pen lid, it hit Mrs Hughes' glass and it all fell apart,
Then water went on the computer, it soon blew up!
Then the school bell rang at five, so we all ran off!

William Owen (9)
Crudgington Primary School, Crudgington

My Class

Welcome to our cool class,
Where every pupil loves to pass.

Amy's like a big teddy bear and
Lauren does care,
Mollie likes her hair in plaits
And Mrs Hughes loves cats.

M iss Davies is our teacher,
Y ou should come and see her.

C are for one another,
L earn a lot too,
A ssessments here, assessments there,
S pecial tests as well,
S pecial friends to sit next to.

So come and join our class today and
You will never want to go away.

Emma Burgess (8)
Crudgington Primary School, Crudgington

My Class

M essy our class sometimes gets
Y ou and I never get wet

C lever pupils we have in here
L oving everyone so they don't have fear
A ll are never sad
S o that is why we're all glad
S ad? *Never* in our cool class.

Lauren Birch (9)
Crudgington Primary School, Crudgington

In Our Mad Class

In our class
The computer blew up,
In our class
The chairs fell apart,
In our class
The keys in the keyboard popped out,
In our class
The tables fell in,
Out of our class
Nothing mad happened.

James Warner (8)
Crudgington Primary School, Crudgington

But Miss

'John go to the head teacher.'
'But Miss.'
'John no fighting in the playground.'
'But Miss.'
'John can you clean that water off the desk?'
'But Miss.'
'John it's your turn to get the milk.'
'But Miss.'
'John if you eat chocolate in the classroom you will end up like Big Ben.'
'But Miss.'
'Are you all right John? You're very white.'
'Yes Miss.'

Millie Hicks (8)
Crudgington Primary School, Crudgington

Poem About Class 4
(Based on 'Excuses' by Allan Ahlberg)

Welcome to our cool class,
Please Miss, my work went all crooked,
Please Miss, I wrote on the wrong page,
Please can I start
           Again . . .

Please Miss, the computer blew up,
Please Miss, my chair broke,
Please Miss, my writing smudged,
Please can I start
           Again . . .

Please Miss, my heading is crooked,
Please Miss, the table wobbled,
Please can I start again . . .

Georgina Hockenhull (8)
Crudgington Primary School, Crudgington

Excuses
(Based on 'Excuses' by Allan Ahlberg)

I've spilt water on my homework, Miss
I forgot my books are at school
My lunch fell in the bin, Miss,
I forgot I was ill and went in the pool,
My alarm clock forgot to ring, Miss,
So that's why I'm late
My computer turned off too soon, Miss
And now I've lost all my work.

Charley Wainwright (9)
Crudgington Primary School, Crudgington

The Alien Teacher

When our teacher went away,
We had an alien who came to stay.
It wrote some other language,
And took our books away.
It put them on a plane,
That flew all the way to Spain.
Then she took her eyeball out,
And gave the guinea pig a Brussels sprout.
But then I found it was only a dream,
And she got picked for the football team.

Christian Hine (9)
Crudgington Primary School, Crudgington

Is It Haunted?

Is it haunted that house on the hill?
The one with the broken window sill,
The one with shattered glass,
The one which belongs to the past.

Is it haunted that house on the hill?
The house so quiet,
So deadly still,
Where no one lives anymore.

Is it haunted that house on the hill?
The crooked house up there,
The crooked house with so much room to spare,
The crooked house where no one would go, even on a dare.

Yes, that house is haunted,
By the ghosts of gas,
The things that scream and howl,
Yes, that house is haunted, get away now!

Laura Price (10)
Dorrington CE (A) Primary School, Dorrington

Friends

F riends help you when you're down
R eliable friends are always there for you
I nterested in everything you say or do
E ven when you are in a bad mood
N ever judging or criticising
D oing fun things together
S pecial friends are friends forever.

Lisa Sheppard (9)
Dorrington CE (A) Primary School, Dorrington

Macy Is My Dog

Macy is loopy
Macy is fun
Macy has love
For everyone.

Macy is sweet
Macy is pure
Although you'll find she's
Cheeky for sure.

She has five bones
Four squeaky toys
And I really hate it
When she makes loads of noise!

I have a cat
And she'll chase him
No doubt
About that!

Macy is naughty
Macy is bad
But she cheers me up
Whenever I'm sad.

Macy is my dog
And that's that!

Lucy Wilde (9)
Dorrington CE (A) Primary School, Dorrington

Autumn Leaves

Autumn leaves are falling,
From trees,
Softly on the ground,
Everywhere around.

Evergreens stand up tall,
Do you think,
Their leaves,
Ever fall?

Amy Davies (10)
Dorrington CE (A) Primary School, Dorrington

A Recipe On How To Make This Poem

Ingredients:

A drop a time
3 squeezes of varieties of poems
1 pocketful of rhymes
A Scribbler! magazine
A dash of advice from Nessie
5oz of words
A sprinkle of fame from being a poet

Firstly find a drop of time and stir in with the three squeezes.
Next sieve in the advice and magazine.
Crack the words into the pocketful of rhymes and sprinkle the fame on top.
Your poem is complete.

Laura Wilde (11)
Dorrington CE (A) Primary School, Dorrington

Whatever The Weather

Whatever the weather,
Tell me the weather,
I can't wait any longer.

Give me the sun,
I'll run outside,
And enjoy the fun.

Give me the rain,
I'll get my books,
And fix my brain.

Give me the fog,
I'll go in the garden,
And sit on a log.

Give me the snow,
I'll sit on the sofa,
And knit and sew.

Munpreet Chatha (10)
Dorrington CE (A) Primary School, Dorrington

My Parrot

Shut him in a cage and
Lock it up tight
This parrot is an outrage.

Send him to another place
Then give him a fright
See if then he will learn some grace.

In size he is very slight
His personality belongs on stage
But I think he is just right.

I don't think he would like this poem
It's a good thing he is out of sight.

Megan Marshall (9)
Dorrington CE (A) Primary School, Dorrington

The Seasons

Autumn

Autumn leaves fall under the trees
Tumbling down under the leaves
Mummy's calling
Now time to go.

Winter

Winter is cold
In the snow
Now we can play
Timing the weather
Everyone's having fun
Running around in the snow.

Spring

Spring is here
People are waiting
Ripping the leaves
Insides growing
Never waiting
Growing leaves.

Summer

Summer's hot
Under the sun
Making you tanned
Making you hot
Even me
Run, run, run into the sea.

Francesca Purser (7)
Dorrington CE (A) Primary School, Dorrington

Evacuee

A whistle and a bang,
German aeroplanes hang
In the skies,
While everyone cries.
Sirens sound through the streets
My heart often skips a beat,
The shelter, quickly run inside,
Mum wants to send me to the countryside.

I start to cry as I get on the train,
I might never see my parents again.
The countryside is good for me,
Mum said that it would be.
She sent me away for my safety,
So that evil Hitler would not bomb me.
When the war is over, and we're all happy,
I hope there is never a World War III.

Lisa Ruddy (10)
Eastfield Primary School, Thurmaston

Here In School

Here in school
I can taste my delicious lunch.
I can see children wandering about
I can hear the stamp of children's feet
I can touch the swaying grass.
I can smell the damp coats on the pegs.
Here in school.

Samuel Garner (7)
Eastfield Primary School, Thurmaston

At School

Here at school
I can hear some birds singing a delightful song outside.
I can feel my hair swaying side to side.
I can taste fresh grapes tickling my taste buds at the back of my throat.
I can smell my friends' buffet in the dinner hall.
I can see my beautiful sister sitting on a bench outside.
Here at school.

Robyn Dewing (8)
Eastfield Primary School, Thurmaston

The Blitz

A whistle, then a *bang* . . .

The Germans are here

Babies are crying
Children are screaming
Parents are caring.

The Germans are here!

The curtains are shut and the lights are out
Darkness is deadly
Running, shouting
As the glass smashes in.

The Germans are here!

As morning light breaks
A wave of sadness sweeps the city

Are the Germans here?

Scrambling through the wreckage by day
Finding loved ones that had to pay,

The Germans have been!

Trinkets, photos, toys that once mattered they are now all shattered.

Are the Germans here?

Jennifer Collier (10)
Eastfield Primary School, Thurmaston

Death Of A Soldier

His football gathers dust
As his mug does rust
His dinner suit full of holes from moths
His cricket bat disappeared in the loft
Never to be found
His slippers disappear under the bed
Where his head used to lay
The dogs are whining . . .
Where they were laying
When he left
His chair left empty
Where he used to sit
The letters are all for him
Left on the table never to be opened
And there - his pipe, oh his pipe
Hush! Hold your tears.

Myles Brown (11)
Eastfield Primary School, Thurmaston

It's War!

A bomb falls here,
A bomb falls there,
Bombs are falling everywhere!
Children cry
As the bombs fly,
Way up high.

The sirens sound through all the streets,
That's when the children meet,
As they head for the shelter.

I'm now off on the train,
Through the sleet and rain,
Whilst my mum wipes her tears,
For now all my family's fears,
Are gone for me.

My new mum is great,
She cares and acts like a mate,
But deep down inside,
I know I can't hide,
My feelings for my real mum,

Yes I know . . . *it's war!*

Kerry Gallagher & Natalie Johnson (10)
Eastfield Primary School, Thurmaston

Bombs Bang!

Bombs! *Bang!* The sirens have begun
Smoke, dust landing on our land
Squeezing tightly to my sister's hand
Soldiers, running, trying not to get shot
Let this memory be forgot
Tick-tock . . . *bang*
Another one dead!

I can't go another day
Hoping Hitler will come and pay
We're finally there in the countryside
With a caring family by our side
They show us around their lovely house
Flowers, trees, even a mouse!

The war has finished
No more bombs
No more planes
I hope it never happens again.

Katie Smith & Emma Large (11)
Eastfield Primary School, Thurmaston

World War II

The air raid siren is sounding
German bombing planes
Fly overhead
All because of Hitler's pounding
We hurry to our shelters.

We put our gas masks on
To protect us from hazardous gases
It's cold, it's damp, it's dark and cramped
In our shelters.

We're being evacuated tomorrow
Visions of children waving
Their mothers goodbye
Flashbacks of what has happened in the past
As I sit in the shelter.

Stephanie Hopkins (10)
Eastfield Primary School, Thurmaston

World War II

When a soldier won his battle
Long, long ago he said out loud
That he was proud
But wished his friend had lasted to the end

When he arrived home that day
He was very sad to say
That his friend who he had thought
To be with till the end
Had sadly passed away.

Jamie Dewing (11)
Eastfield Primary School, Thurmaston

In School

Here in school.
I can see the foggy mist.
I can taste my lovely school dinner.
I can hear the loud sound of the children chatting.
I love to touch the rough, hard playground.
I love the smell of the freezing fresh air.
Here in school.

Dexter Davidson (8)
Eastfield Primary School, Thurmaston

Memories Of War

The sound of sirens whistling through my ears,
Heart pounding like a galloping horse,
Run to the air raid shelter,
Rustling, bustling, panic,
The chaos, the mad rush,
Crash, bang, boom, another bomb falls.

Cramped, tired and hungry,
We try to keep jolly by singing cheerful songs,
On the gas masks go,
Scared and frightened, I hear the bombs fall,
How long are we going to be here for?

The all clear siren has gone,
A sudden solemn silence lingers in the air,
Our house,
Now a pile of rubble covering the ground,
My life, my memories are never again to be found.

The train has just arrived, it's time for me to go,
Away from everything that I love and know,
Please God why can't it all end?
Why can't we all just be friends?

Danielle Olivant (11)
Eastfield Primary School, Thurmaston

Evacuee

I'm going home on the train,
With lots of memories in my mind.
Looking forward to seeing my family again,
But worrying what I'm going to find.

Sunny skies of the countryside fade,
Grey skies of the ruined city loom.
Sad to be leaving friends I've made.
When I get back it might all be gloom.

The train reaches the station,
Mum and Dad are there.
Guards stand to attention,
Out of the window we stare.

Lots of bombed houses and flats
As we walk home from the train.
Buildings left with gaping cracks,
Life will never be the same.

Laura Fitch (10)
Eastfield Primary School, Thurmaston

The Blitz Bombing

Running, running the people are running,
Into the air raid shelters,
Crying, crying, children are crying,
Leaving their families to go away.

Help us, help us, cry the people of London
To all that is left of destruction,
Dying, dying, people are dying,
From air raids and collapsing.

Soldiers, soldiers they are all dying,
But luckily some are surviving,
Boom, boom! Bombs are exploding,
Over the forgotten soldiers.

Hope, hope is all around us,
Hitler has finally gone,
Dancing, dancing the people are prancing,
Happy that Hitler has finally gone

Rations, rations no more rations,
How we can eat freely,
Soldiers, soldiers, they are reunited,
With loved ones and friends.

Katie Aletras (10)
Eastfield Primary School, Thurmaston

In 1939

While bombs are flying overhead,
Children run from their beds,
Oh no! there goes the siren so,
Down to the shelter we must go.
All around there's so much rubble,
For everyone there's so much trouble,
Will I be an evacuee?
But I don't want to leave my family!
My father is a soldier fighting in the war,
Hopefully soon he'll come through our door.
Will my family survive and will my friends stay alive?
While people are dying,
Families are crying,
For families and friends,
It feels like the war never ends.

Grace Glover & Rosie Lewis (10)
Eastfield Primary School, Thurmaston

War Evacuees

W ake up! What are you waiting for?
A ir raid sirens are on, jump out of the window or the door
R unning towards the shelters underneath the floor

E scaping the war the children go
V iolence here, there, everywhere, they didn't know
A nd leaving their families leaves everybody low
C rying and sobbing makes the streams overflow
U nderstanding why they should go
E xplosions in the dark glow
E nd this nightmare, end this show
S top this war and no more foe.

Hanane Belaroussi (10)
Eastfield Primary School, Thurmaston

Bombs Are Dropping!

Bombs are dropping,
Houses are falling, children are calling,
Planes are flying, as people are dying,
On the street, at your feet.

Rushing and pushing, for their shelter
Tonight's going to be a belter!
Fires so high, they reach the sky,
Smoke so thick, it makes you sick,
You just want to escape this horror . . . quick!

Tyler Wright (10)
Eastfield Primary School, Thurmaston

A Dead Soldier

His shotgun lying unused.
His parrot stressed waiting for Dad.
His bat and cap locked up in a dusty old chest.
His children waiting by the window patiently.
His picture is all the children have of him.
His wife crying in the kitchen,
And there his flute, gloomy and dull.
Hush, hold your tears.

Arron Matharu (10)
Eastfield Primary School, Thurmaston

The Reader Of This Poem
(Inspired by 'The Writer of this Poem' by Roger McGough)

The reader of this poem is . . .
As smooth as a bowl
As scary as a barking dog
As mucky as mud
As hard as a brick.

As soft as a sponge cake
As slimy as a slug
As long as a term
As big as a mug.

As long as Pinocchio's nose
As pink as a pig
As tall as a lamp post
As stupid as a monkey.

As boring as homework
As old as a grandad
As slippy as a snake
As flat as a pancake.

Dan Fitch (8)
Eastfield Primary School, Thurmaston

The War

Bombs coming down,
Blowing up the town,
Soldiers dying,
Planes are flying,
We hear guns,
As the warden runs,
Bombing over, let's go inside,
Mum might send me to the countryside.

Mum's taking me to the train,
I might not see her ever again,
She said I had to go with the evacuees,
To see the animals, grass and trees,
The fighting and danger far away,
With a new family I have to stay,
The war is over, it's 1945,
My family and I are still alive.

Blaize Kerr & Martin Herbert (10)
Eastfield Primary School, Thurmaston

The Reader Of This Poem
(Inspired by 'The Writer of this Poem' by Roger McGough)

The reader of this poem is . . .
As cute as a chick
As creepy as a skeleton's hand
As quick as a flick
As noisy as an unknown band.

As thin as a stick
As round as a ball of string
As graceful as a player's kick
As mad as a cat going
Ting! Ting! Ting!

As wicked as your brother
As fat as a pig
As weird as your mother
As curly as a wig.

As bossy as a teacher
As fizzy as Coke
As still as a feature
As drunk as a bloke

So I hope you can take a joke
Cos it's only me!

Sophie Foston (9)
Eastfield Primary School, Thurmaston

World War II

Rifles are blazing
Bombs are banging
Children are gazing
As the train goes by
Air raids are coming
People at risk
Hopefully the bombs will miss
Soldiers fighting
Some are dying
Dad's at war
Our hearts are crying
The war has ended
Everyone has cheer
Our memories are gone
Along with the fear.

Kirsten Doig (11)
Eastfield Primary School, Thurmaston

War - Hard Times

I was five years old when the war began
Between Germany and England,
Everybody had jobs, every woman, every man,
Shelters were built, some with benches, some with bunks.
Plants on top and vegetables grew around mud chunks.

The best idea was for me to go and live in the country,
Leaving my family behind,
To live in the country with the gentry,
As crowds of children gathered around crying and sobbing
My head was throbbing,
Until the long journey had finished.

Five years later, I'm still here,
I like it.
There's lots of wildlife, even deer.
I feed the pigs, look after the chickens
My family? I haven't a dickens.
Not even a letter or a postcard to say how they're doing.

Another year has passed, no letters, no postcards, nothing
But it's going to be different.
The war has ended, May 8th 1945, VE-Day.
Mum's dead, Dad's dead
I'm going home on the 10th, I will miss it here but I love home.
Hitler's dead
And I'm going home to my lovely warm bed.

Nikki Payne (11)
Eastfield Primary School, Thurmaston

The Reader Of This Poem

(Inspired by 'The Writer of this Poem' by Roger McGough)

The reader of this poem is . . .
As huge as an elephant
As furry as a cat
As tiny as a crawling ant
As colourful as a mat.

As scary as a barking dog
As glistening as the sand
As blind as walking in the fog
As noisy as a band.

Josh Robinson, Brandon Elkington (8), Chloe Coltman & Bronwyn Piggins (9)
Eastfield Primary School, Thurmaston

Life In World War II

How long will this war last?
I wish the bombs would stop their blast.

All around there's dust and rubble,
For everyone there's so much trouble.

With everyone having to manage on rations,
No one can keep up with the latest fashions.

Here comes the air raid warden
Attending to his task,
And making sure that everyone's got
Their gas mask.

'Put that light out,' you hear him cry.
As overhead the aeroplanes fly.

Oh no! There go the sirens . . . so
Down the shelter we must go.

Will I be an evacuee
Living in the countryside with
Flowers and trees?

Finally . . . the war is over21
and everyone is happy.
I hope there won't be a World War III.

Rosie Lewis (10)
Eastfield Primary School, Thurmaston

Making Fun
(Inspired by 'The Writer of this Poem' by Roger McGough)

The reader of this poem is . . .
As dusty as soot
As heavy as a brick
Tut, tut, tut,
As horrible as sick.

As blind as a bat
As flat as a mat
As dark as a mine
As huge as an elephant.

As straight as a tree
As barmy as a bee
As boring as a mat
As wet as a fish.

In the end it's just all me!

Lewis Batchelor (9)
Eastfield Primary School, Thurmaston

Bombs Are Falling

Bombs are falling
Whilst children are crawling
Into the air raid shelter
Oh my gosh what a belter
I hope it's not near our shelter
Oh Mother, Mother, Mother dear,
Are all the other children sharing my fear?
Will we ever get out of here?

So long as we are together
We must remember the lovely weather
So sunny, sunny yesterday
Let's hope it'll make the bombs go away.

Why is he doing this to our lovely land?
He obviously just does not understand
What is this madman thinking about?
Giving this country a painful clout.

Oh Mother, Mother, Mother dear,
You brought us up to trust and obey
But it is like this man is catching his prey,
Destroying people by the hour
I feel we have no power.

Come on, come on, come on my dear
It sounds like the coast is clear
We do not know what we'll hear
We just need to survive
And stay alive.

Morning has come
Dew's on the ground
There is news all around
The bombs have cleared
No more to be feared
As Hitler has gone
With that awful pong
Of the bomb
The bomb!

Hayley Jarvis (10)
Eastfield Primary School, Thurmaston

The Reader Of This Poem
(Inspired by 'The Writer of this Poem' by Roger McGough)

The reader of this poem is . . .
As noisy as a band
As scary as a lion
As magical as a fairy
As hot as an iron.

As spiky as a nettle
As furry as a cat
As steamy as a kettle
As quiet as a bat.

As disgusting as a worm
As dark as a night
As long as term
As bright as a light.

As cool as a swimming pool
As silly as a clown
As helpful as a tool
As glistening as a crown

I just hope the reader of this poem can stand a joke!

Abbie Saunders (8)
Eastfield Primary School, Thurmaston

World War II

Woo, woo the sirens go
Bang, bang, bang, the houses blow
Soldiers fighting
Soldiers dying

We are crying of the fear of Father dying
Hitler, Hitler here he is again
Shoot him down before we go insane

Four years have passed
Hitler has stopped his blast
We are going home to Mum
Yippeeeeeee!

Alex Snart (10)
Eastfield Primary School, Thurmaston

All Alone

We played together,
We were always together,
Not anymore!

We went to the air raid
Shelter together
Not anymore.

Now I'm left
Alone
Forever.

We are not
Together
Not anymore.

We would never
Be scared of bombs
Not anymore.

He would be alive
If not for Hitler
Not anymore.

Keily Munden & Kirsty Mackley (10)
Eastfield Primary School, Thurmaston

All About You!

(Inspired by 'The Writer of this Poem' by Roger McGough)

The reader of this poem is . . .
As small as a mouse
As long as a worm
As wicked as headlice
As horrible as a germ.

As scorching as the sun,
As cold as an icicle,
As loud as a gun,
As fast as a bicycle.

As white as snow,
As light as sweets,
As bright as a glow and
As yummy as meat.

Grace Bennett (9)
Eastfield Primary School, Thurmaston

The Reader Of This Poem
(Inspired by 'The Writer of this Poem' by Roger McGough)

The reader of this poem is . . .
As small as an ant
As smooth as ice
As shiny as the sun,
As scary as a spider.

As big as a bear,
As slimy as goo,
As squeaky as a mouse
While it runs round the house
As flat as a mat
As hot as a chilli.

Liam Baker (9)
Eastfield Primary School, Thurmaston

The Reader Of This Poem
(Inspired by 'The Writer of this Poem' by Roger McGough)

The reader of this is . . .
As black as a hole
As lumpy as jelly
As thick as a pole
As square as a telly.

As cute as a fluffy chick
As naughty as a titter
As big as a clock
That goes tick, tick, tock,
As warm as a mitten.

Jade Wells-Larter (9)
Eastfield Primary School, Thurmaston

What Is White?

White is snow falling from the sky
White is a wall in a house
Plain and boring.

White is everywhere
It doesn't disappear
White is paper on a desk
And it scares me.

Ben Hadfield (9)
Eastfield Primary School, Thurmaston

The Reader Of This Poem
(Inspired by 'The Writer of this Poem' by Roger McGough)

The reader of this poem is . . .
As crunchy as a cracker
As nasty as my sister
As noisy as a bomb
As stupid as a monkey.

As fat as an elephant
As tall as a lamp post
As hard as a tooth
As cool as a motorbike.

As fast as a rocket
As small as an ant
As boiling as the sun
As sharp as an needle.

As slow as a snail
As sloppy as a worm
As brown as a chocolate
As heavy as a house.

As invisible as a ghost
As dirty as a drain
As sneaky as a fox
As sticky as glue.

As yellow as a banana
As green as a leaf
As golden as gold
As bossy as a teacher.

Connor Mitchell (8)
Eastfield Primary School, Thurmaston

The Reader Of This Poem
(Inspired by 'The Writer of this Poem' by Roger McGough)

The reader of this poem is . . .
As funny as a dog
As playful as a cat
As cheerful as a pig
As long as a snake.

As snappy as a crocodile
As sneaky as a fox
As bright as an apple
As red as a rose.

Callum Warrilow (9)
Eastfield Primary School, Thurmaston

The Reader Of This Poem
(Inspired by 'The Writer of this Poem' by Roger McGough)

The reader of this poem is . . .
As spiky as a pin
As big as a bear
As full as an overflowing dustbin
As small as a chair.

As blind as a bat
As dark as a mine
As flat as a mat
As straight as a line.

As heavy as a brick
As big as an aeroplane
As horrible as sick
As fluffy as a lion's mane.

As fun as a swimming pool
As bright as the sun
As helpful as a tool
As nice as a bun.

I hope the reader of this poem can take a joke!

Ben Brown & Max Overton (8)
Eastfield Primary School, Thurmaston

The Reader Of This Poem
(Inspired by 'The Writer of this Poem' by Roger McGough)

The reader of this poem is . . .
As fun as a park
As furry as a mole
As loud as a bark
As long as a pole.

As fast as a cheetah
As cute as a chick
As roasting as a heater
As heavy as a brick.

As cool as a swimming pool
As silly as a monkey
As hard as a tool
As stubborn as a donkey.

Jasmine Leftley (9)
Eastfield Primary School, Thurmaston

My Poem!
(Inspired by 'The Writer of this Poem' by Roger McGough)

The reader of this poem is . . .
As tall as a house
As cold as an ice cube
As small as a mouse
As round as a tube.

As sticky as fudge
As slimy as a slug
As fluffy as smudge
As hard as a mug.

As beautiful as my dogs
As silly as my sister
As hollow as a log
As painful as a blister.

As nice as my mum
As mardy as my dad
As big as a sun
As horrible as being mad.

Paige Baines (8)
Eastfield Primary School, Thurmaston

The Gooey Yellow-Eyed Spell
(Based on 'Macbeth')

'Double, double toil and trouble,
Fire burn and cauldron bubble'.

Frogs' breath and lizard wings
With sticky legs and gross things.
Fish blood and sloppy eyes
With stinky toes and bloody pies.
Poo mix and bogeys on sticks
Sharks' teeth with red blood,
With cranky eyes and blood fries.

'Double, double toil and trouble,
Fire burn and cauldron bubble'.

Billy Carnall & Priyesh Mistry (8)
Eastfield Primary School, Thurmaston

The Reader Is . . .
(Inspired by 'The Writer of this Poem' by Roger McGough)

As pink as a pig
As thin as a worm
As curly as a wig
As long as a term.

As hard as a block of wood
As annoying as a sister
As dark as a cave
As shiny as silver

As rich as gold
As bossy as a teacher
As bold as a bear
As small as a creature.

As lazy as a snail
As heavy as a weight
As sharp as a nail
As hot as a summer fête.

As daft as a clown
As stupid as can be
But at the end it's only me!

Lorrie Sole (8) & Jake Pullen (9)
Eastfield Primary School, Thurmaston

In School

Here in school
I can see the children eating their lunch quietly,
Not a sound.
I can hear the sound of children talking in the playground
Really noisily.
| can feel the roughness of the ball in the playground.
I can smell the smell of dog poo on my shoe.
Yuck!
I taste my lunch, my mum made it for me *yummy*
Here in school.

Joshua Utting (7)
Eastfield Primary School, Thurmaston

Love, Love

Love is like a romantic rose and my heart beating softly
It sounds like church bells ringing for the sound of love.
It feels like you are happy and warm inside your soul.
It tastes like two lovebirds kissing in their happy place.
It smells like chocolate given to you from your secret admirer.
It looks like people getting along and planning marriage.
It reminds me of all the happy things in life.

Nikki Hutcheon
Exeter Junior School, Corby

Love

Love is as red as lips kissing my cheek.
Love feels warm and cosy tucked up in bed.
Love sounds like birds singing in the trees.
Love tastes like melted chocolate dribbling down my mouth.
Love smells of sweet-red roses growing in my garden.
Love reminds me of Ellie, my girlfriend.

Bradley McGinlay (8)
Exeter Junior School, Corby

Love

Love is red like blood going around my body.
It sounds like a sweet melody rising to my ears.
It smells like a sweet rose perfume all around the world.
It tastes like a romantic chocolate melting on my tongue.
It feels like a soft pillow under my head.
It reminds me of love hearts.

Barbara Silva (9)
Exeter Junior School, Corby

Love

Love is red like a scented rose given to me.
It sounds like the flutter of beautiful butterflies from the lovely blue sky.
It feels like I'm in heaven on a big white cloud.
It tastes like sweet sugar tingling in my mouth.
It smells like perfume sprayed in the air.
Love looks like a sweet smelling flower.
It reminds me of my family when they are really happy and proud.

Sarah-Louise Fogell
Exeter Junior School, Corby

Love

Love is red like a glittering, sparkling rose just blossoming.
It sounds like a party where everybody has cream buns and everybody's having fun.
It tastes like a chocolate bar and a couple watching a shooting star.
It smells like a rose and very nice smelling clothes.
It feels like a bed sheet and the cold house with a romantic heat.
It reminds me of a baby being carried and me getting married.
It looks like ice cream, a whole lot,
It tastes good when days are hot.

Amy Pyper (10)
Exeter Junior School, Corby

Love

Love is red like a big bunch of roses blowing in the wind.
It sounds like a rushing river cascading down the countryside.
It tastes like sweet strawberries and cream floating down my throat.
It smells like a luscious smell from my mum's new coat.
It feels like hugging the biggest teddy in the world.

Jade Walker (10)
Exeter Junior School, Corby

Love

It sounds like wedding bells knocking from side to side.
It smells like roses being flung from the bride.
It looks like the groom giving the beautiful golden ring away.
It feels like a warm feeling holding your girlfriend's hand all day.
It tastes like wedding cake running down your throat.
It reminds me of the first time rowing or driving a boat.

Love is wonderful.

Jordan Small (9)
Exeter Junior School, Corby

Happy

Happy is blue like the sea making your feet tingle.
It sounds like a fire with the flames going to a tingle.
It tastes like candyfloss with lots of tingle on your tongue.
It smells like an ice cream flooding to your stomach.
It feels like a big teddy hugging me nicely.
It looks like a big firework going off softly.
Happy can get you friends!

Thomas Dance (10)
Exeter Junior School, Corby

Fun

Fun is beautiful like pretty flowers swaying.
It is like people having fun playing.
It sounds like people laughing so much.
It tastes like lots of sweets to touch.
It feels like you're kicking a football and scoring your first goal.
It looks like children playing and having fun on a pole.
It reminds me of lots of birds singing in the trees.

Grant Homer (10)
Exeter Junior School, Corby

Fun

Fun is purple like a flower swaying.
It sounds like laughter at a school playground with children playing.
It feels like you're learning to tie your lace.
It tastes like melted chocolate running down your face.
It looks like a soft brown horse running around.
It reminds me of a lullaby sound.

Emma Witt (10)
Exeter Junior School, Corby

Love

It is red like a beautiful rose in a flower shop.
It sounds like birds singing in a treetop.
It feels like a warm, cuddly teddy bear.
It looks like a love heart floating in the sky, floating everywhere.
It reminds me of a beautiful place.
It tastes like chocolate running down my face.
It smells like a lovely, lovely, lovely cake.

Nicole Keeling (9)
Exeter Junior School, Corby

Anger

It looks like a red fiery devil.
It smells like dead bodies.
It feels like lightning hitting me.
It tastes like blood.
It sounds like an evil laugh.
It reminds me of a rotten egg!

Tyler Butler (9)
Exeter Junior School, Corby

Love

Love is as red as lips kissing my cheek.
Love feels warm and cosy tucked up in bed.
Love sounds like waves gently lapping the shells.
Love tastes like chocolate running down my chin.
Love smells like fresh-cooked cake ready to eat.
It reminds me of my nanny when she cuddles me tight.

Leah Baines (8)
Exeter Junior School, Corby

Anger

Anger is red like molten lava
Anger sounds like a rampaging bull entering the arena.
Anger feels like a burning fire in my brain.
Anger tastes like rotting cheese.
Anger smells like dark smoke.
Anger reminds me of when my nanny went on holiday,
When I was at school.

Lynton Fleming (8)
Exeter Junior School, Corby

Anger

Anger is red like a mad drummer screaming for a drink.
Anger sounds like lightning crashing down a tall tree.
Anger tastes like Egyptian bread.
Anger smells like rotten cheese.
Anger looks like a river of lava.
Anger feels hot like over roasted chicken!
Anger reminds me of my little brother when he is angry.

Hayden Sutherland (9)
Exeter Junior School, Corby

Sad

It tastes like burnt toast.
It sounds like someone crying.
It smells like the seaside.
It looks like a little lost puppy.
It feels like you have lost your dog.
It reminds me of losing my dog, Buster.

Daniel Thompson (8)
Exeter Junior School, Corby

Fun

Fun is yellow like the sun shining strongly and happily down at me.
It sounds like me playing catch with my friends in the big colourful park.
It tastes like the springy summer waiting for me quietly.
It smells like the morning fresh air spreading all around the Earth slowly.
It looks like the funny clown laughing loudly at me.
It feels like a smile spreading slowly across your face.
It reminds me of my birthday party that's just been.

Milica Novakovic (8)
Exeter Junior School, Corby

Hate

Hate is dark like a dark gloomy cave hollow and shadowy.
It sounds like someone having a paddy.
It tastes like blood running down your lips.
It feels like your house is about to flood.
It smells like a park exploding.
It reminds me of a shark chasing you.

James Brown (10)
Exeter Junior School, Corby

Fear

Fear is black just like midnight scaring me in my bed.
It sounds like the wolf howling 'cause he's not been fed.
It tastes like poisons on a mouse.
It smells like fire burning in my house.
It feels like a big hairy bat.
It looks like a large rat.
It reminds me of a dead deer to just appear.

Tamara Vukosavljevic (9)
Exeter Junior School, Corby

Love

Love is red as a rose growing in a beautiful garden.
It sounds like angels singing a song beautifully.
It tastes like a strawberry ice cream fresh from the freezer.
It smells like blossom growing in the trees.
It looks like a romantic dance in the sparkling moonlight.
It feels like me and my boyfriend kissing.
It reminds me of a twinkling star shining in the night.

Lucia Lemos (8)
Exeter Junior School, Corby

Sad

Sad is as blue as a tear running down your eye.
It sounds like a fly dancing up high.
It tastes like water coming down from the sky sadly.
It smells like candyfloss made by myself.
It feels like lonely crying.

Jorja Dawson (10)
Exeter Junior School, Corby

Love

Love is red like a beautiful crystal rose.
It sounds like a famous, romantic singer doing a pose.
It tastes like melted chocolate running down your face.
It smells like you're just learning to tie your lace.
It feels like a baby being carried.
It looks like me getting married.
It reminds me of something good and hot.
It tastes like ice cream, a whole lot!

Mary Carroll (10)
Exeter Junior School, Corby

Love

Love is pink like a pink fluffy flamingo!
Love tastes like a big box of chocolates to eat.
Love looks like red butterflies flying around me.
Love smells like a big red rose in spring.
Love feels like someone hugging me like they love me.
Love sounds like two birds singing together.
Love reminds me of a romantic song.

Lisa Hales (9)
Exeter Junior School, Corby

Love

Love is red like a rose going straight
Love sounds like two birds singing together in love.
Love tastes like some caramel chocolates.
Love smells like a giant, red, rosy rose in spring.
Love looks like little birds flying around people head and heels in love.
Love feels like someone hugging, like they all love me.
Love reminds me of a romantic song.

Cara Logue (9)
Exeter Junior School, Corby

What Is White?

What is white?
A light is white, so are clouds.
What is blue?
The sky is blue, where the sun lives.
What is red?
A rose is red, like the knuckles on my hand.
What is yellow?
The sun is yellow like a daffodil.
What is green?
The grass is green, like a dragonfly.

Charlie Wyles (7)
Exeter Junior School, Corby

Love

Love is the colour bright red like a rose growing in a garden
It sounds like two lovebirds tweeting in a nest.
It reminds me of me and my boyfriend holding hands.
It looks like my boyfriend looking at me.
It tastes like my boyfriend kissing me.
It smells like my boyfriend is buying me chocolate!
It feels like I'm going to be sick any minute now!

Ellie Macleod
Exeter Junior School, Corby

Anger

Anger is red like a fiery volcano ready to blow its top.
It sounds like an enormous explosion bursting in my brain.
It smells like burning brimstone charging through my nose.
It tastes like a red-hot chilli fireball is burning all my organs.
It feels like a charging bull rushing at full speed and me trying to escape.
It reminds me of a rocket blasting into outer space.

Class 6LL
Exeter Junior School, Corby

Hate

Hate is black like someone knocked out cold on the floor.
It sounds like someone rampaging out of sight.
It smells like someone with no love in their heart.
It tastes like blood from a nose bleed.
It feels like someone dying in the moonlight.

Michael Foley
Exeter Junior School, Corby

What Is Red?

What is red?
A rose is red resting in my vase.
What is yellow?
The sun is yellow burning on my back.
What is gold?
Money is gold, like what rich and famous people have.
What is green?
Grass is green that's tickling my back.
What is blue?
The sky is blue, floating around the world.
What is white?
The clouds are white like flying sheep in the air.
What is grey?
Stone is grey like metal breaking my hand.

Robbie Smith (7)
Exeter Junior School, Corby

What Is Pink?

What is pink?
A beetroot face from working hard in the sun.
What is yellow?
A smiley face in the sun.
What is orange?
A sandy desert.
What is green?
The grass is green, long and sweet.
What is rainbow-coloured?
A rainbow of course.
What is cream?
A lovely wedding dress on a special day!

Molly McCormick (7)
Exeter Junior School, Corby

Hate

Hate is red like a fire in a house burning away.
It sounds like elephants running all over the place.
It tastes like rotten old Brussels sprouts that are burnt
It smells like old eggs in a bin,
It looks like a volcano that has just erupted.
It feels like crashing waves in the sea.
It reminds me of when people fight and get hurt.

Courtney Meakins (10)
Exeter Junior School, Corby

What Is Gold?

What is gold?
A pyramid is gold shining in the sun.
What is blue?
The sea is blue waving up and down.
What is silver?
A TV is silver sparkling in my room.
What is green?
The grass is green with flowers growing in-between.
What is red?
A cherry is red growing on a tree.
What is yellow?
The sun is yellow shining all around.

Daniel Rees (8)
Exeter Junior School, Corby

What Is Blue?

What is blue?
A river drifting through the sea.
What is yellow?
The sun is yellow floating through the sky.
What is gold?
Pyramid is gold standing in the sun.
What is green?
The grass is green swaying on the ground.
What is pink?
The rose is pink like our soft skin.
What is red?
The cloud is red like the summer twilight.

Brittany Chandler (7)
Exeter Junior School, Corby

Fun

Elation is fun like a room of people laughing.
It sounds like people playing football.
It tastes like bubblegum blowing.
It smells like candyfloss at the funfair.
It looks like children splashing in the waves on a golden beach.
It feels like running with the wind in your face.
It reminds me of a holiday in Spain.

Jonathon Pickering (9)
Exeter Junior School, Corby

What Is Gold?

What is gold?
A gold cup is gold shining in the sun,
What is yellow?
The sun is yellow shining in the sky,
What is blue?
The river is blue flooding over the land.
What is black?
The sky is black when it gets to night,
What is silver?
A magnet is metal pulling things of metal.
What is multicoloured?
A rainbow is multicoloured dazzling across the sky.

Srdan Stjepanovic (7)
Exeter Junior School, Corby

What Is White?

What is white?
A cloud is white fluffy like a sheep.
What is yellow?
A sun is yellow shining in the sky.
What is red?
A heart is red beating in my chest.
What is gold?
A metal is gold like a shining star.
What is silver?
A star is silver twinkling in the sky.
What is pink?
People are pink like a rose.

Sinead Cross (7)
Exeter Junior School, Corby

Hate

Hate is red like blood dripping from your mouth.
It sounds like crowds of people shouting at each other.
It tastes like mouldy bread rotting away.
It smells like a bunch of sick.
It looks like a dark rumbling thunderstorm.
It feels like your worst tummy ache.
It reminds me of the first day of school.

Callum Brodie (9)
Exeter Junior School, Corby

What Is Gold?

What is gold?
The sun is gold like a ring in the sky.
What is silver?
A car is silver for driving in.
What is bronze?
A medal is bronze for when you finish 3rd in a race.
What is blue?
The sky is blue first thing in the morning.
What is green?
The grass is green for when you play football.
What is black?
A skateboard is black, I like to ride it.

Joe Holmes (8)
Exeter Junior School, Corby

What Is White?

What is white?
A feather floating from the sky.
What is pink?
The clouds are pink like fluffy candyfloss.
What is yellow?
The sun is yellow shining on us below.
What is orange?
A flame is orange, hot and fiery.
What is cream?
A carpet is cream sitting on the floorboards.
What is green?
The grass is green shining in the sunlight.

Melissa Williams (8)
Exeter Junior School, Corby

Light

Light is pure yellow like the enormous summer sun.
It sounds like the sound of a huge party dancing.
It tastes like the morning bubbly mouse.
It smells like lovely flowers in spring.
It looks like the sun shining on Earth.
It reminds me of the sunrise in the morning.

Bethany-Jane Morgan (10)
Exeter Junior School, Corby

What Is Red?

What is red?
A cherry is red shining like blood.
What is gold?
A chunk of gold shining like the sun.
What is black?
A lunch box for eating.
What is blue?
A sapphire is blue gazing in the sun.
What is hazel?
An eyeball like my eye.
What is multicoloured?
A multicoloured pencil so I can colour.
What is white?
A cloud is white just sitting there in the sky.

Claire Cottingham (7)
Exeter Junior School, Corby

What Is Gold?

What is gold?
Shiny paper glittering in the sun.
What is pink?
A pig rolling in the mud.
What is yellow?
The sun shining in the sky,
Like a yellow ball.
What is red?
Red is your heart and a red dress.
What is blue?
The sky is blue with clouds in it.
What is brown?
A coconut is brown, like a brown table.

Melissa Stedman (7)
Exeter Junior School, Corby

Love

Love is red like red roses planted in the countryside.
It sounds like birds singing in an oak tree.
It tastes like creamy luscious chocolate melting in my mouth.
It smells like roses brought down from Heaven.
It looks like bees buzzing around together.
It reminds me of animals being born.

Thomas Brown (10)
Exeter Junior School, Corby

Hunger

Hunger is brown like burnt dark earth as dry as raisins.
It sounds like a storm rumbling and grumbling in and out through the night.
It tastes like a dry desert.
It smells like all of the good things you can eat.
It looks like a big black hole.
It feels like you haven't eaten for weeks.
It reminds me of a poor family that lives on a street.

Caitlin Holmes (9)
Exeter Junior School, Corby

Sad

Sadness is black like an old wrinkled elephant.
It sounds like a lady screaming in an echoing theatre.
It tastes like fish all burnt.
It smells like rotten eggs.
It looks like the poor children in Africa.
It feels like getting punched.
It reminds me of my dogs running away.

Jamie Wright (9)
Exeter Junior School, Corby

Love

Love is pink like roses from me to you.
It sounds like an angel playing the harp, play smoothly to my ears.
It tastes like champagne chocolate melting in my mouth.
It smells like candyfloss sticking to my fingers.
It looks like two kittens snuggling up to their warm mother.
It feels like it's been raining roses with the smell that's still there.
It reminds me of the sun disappearing beyond the horizon.

Chelsea Scott (10)
Exeter Junior School, Corby

Love

Love is like red roses freshly planted.
It sounds like birds singing in the morning.
It tastes like lush, fizzy, cotton candy melting in my mouth.
It smells like the first day of spring.
It looks like baby lambs bounding in a field.
It feels like soft velvet in my hand.
It reminds me of a newborn puppy's first breath.

Rhiann Colman (9)
Exeter Junior School, Corby

Light

Light is a yellow light lighting up the room.
It sounds like the roar of Old Trafford when that almost silent click clicks
And the light goes on.
It tastes like crispy, luscious, scrummy burgers.
It smells like the first day of spring and summer put together in Paris.
It looks like the sun is rising beyond the clouds to Heaven.
It feels like you're having the best time of your life at your favourite place.
It reminds me of the first Christmas of my life.

Ryan Stewart (9)
Exeter Junior School, Corby

Elation

Elation is gold like huge nuggets polished and shining bright.
It sounds like enormous waves crashing on the golden beach.
It tastes like runny chocolate melting in my mouth.
It smells like the very first day of spring.
It looks like newborn lambs walking by.
It feels like a warm breeze running across my face.
It reminds me of Christmas Eve.

Tee-jay McCulloch (9)
Exeter Junior School, Corby

The Reasons Of Love

Love is like red like roses planted in the countryside.
It sounds like birds singing in an enormous oak tree.
It tastes like creamy, luscious chocolate melting in my mouth.
It looks like bees buzzing around together.
It reminds me of baby animals being born.

Callum Nelson (9)
Exeter Junior School, Corby

Love

Love is red like bright shining roses and hand-picked.
It sounds like red robins singing.
It smells like lavender on the first day of spring.
It looks like people kissing.
It feels like bright, hot, fiery flames.
It feels like pain and pleasure.
It reminds me of Valentine's Day.

Jade Wright (9)
Exeter Junior School, Corby

Love

Love is like a red rose blooming in the garden.
It sounds like guitarists serenading us while we eat.
It tastes like a juicy watermelon.
It smells like lavender scent blowing in the wind.
It looks like a love heart carved out in the sand.
It feels like a newborn kitten all soft and furry.
It reminds me of when my brother comes home from the army.

Beth Abbott (10)
Exeter Junior School, Corby

Hunger

Hunger is green like a person ready to be sick.
Hunger sounds like screams of fear from warriors in battle.
Hunger smells like cut mint tempting you to eat.
Hunger tastes like dry bread drying out your throat.
Hunger feels like a hollow room with a monster waiting to be fed.
Hunger reminds me of a deep hole in the ground.

Justin Chapman (10)
Exeter Junior School, Corby

Dark

Dark is black like a small dull room without any windows.
It sounds like screaming creatures trying to get out.
It smells like dusty cobwebs all around the room that has been abandoned for years.
It looks like bats' fur, ragged and bumpy skin.
I feels like you're in a cold, dirty hole, muddy and scary.
It tastes like burnt coal spread out all over the place.
It reminds me of long-legged spiders crawling on my body.

Vicky Black (11)
Exeter Junior School, Corby

Hate

Hate is black like a long dark tunnel in the middle of nowhere.
You can hear soft whispers like the sound of the Devil's heartbeat.
It smells like the Devil's burnt heart that's been in the furnace for 1,000 years.
It looks like a zombie is trying to eat you.
It feels like you're being captured by shadows.
It tastes like cold soup with a rotten eye in it.
It reminds me of being stuck in a cobweb where loads of small spiders eat you.

Sandro Moreira
Exeter Junior School, Corby

Anger

Anger is red like your blood bubbling making your worries stay in its place.
It sounds like a kettle screeching and breaking glass.
It smells like a burning fire on Bonfire Night.
It looks like two people fighting after a drink.
It feels like you can see all the strength coming to your arms.
It tastes like a rotten apple crunching in your mouth.
It reminds me of choking on a sweet.

Nicola Pringle (10)
Exeter Junior School, Corby

Anger

Anger is burgundy like vintage wine.
Anger sounds like a cat crying and rat dying.
Anger sounds like thunder and lightning.
It feels like tainted love.
It's like dying men in Hell.
It smells like rotten flesh.
It smells like rotten cabbage or smelly fish.
It reminds me of Hell on the darkest day.

Ryan Veasey
Exeter Junior School, Corby

Love

Love is like red roses millions of baskets full.
Love sounds like the angels singing softly in the wind.
Love smells like a stream full of silky pink petals
Floating down the crystal lake.
Love tastes like Valentine's chocolates imported from Paris.
It feels like the softest teddy in the world.
It reminds me of him - the boy I love.

Shelley Mills (10)
Exeter Junior School, Corby

The Snail Trail

Snails are slimy, snails are grey
Snails sleep all through the day.
They slither and crawl along the floor
They always bump into the door
As people walk trying to catch the thief
He goes to get another leaf.

Leah Shackman (8)
Fulford Primary School, Fulford

Stinking Steve's Toilet

In stinking Steve's toilet
It is covered in slushy muck.
There's half a pack of bubblegum
And loads of disgusting books.

A sticky sweet,
A dead duck,
A spider
And they are swimming in muck.

There's a dried up snail
And a sliced old worm
And a squirrel's tail
And a little squirm.

So if I were you
I would hold it a little longer
As it will make you sick
So think, be careful, don't wander!

Tom Cannon (9)
Fulford Primary School, Fulford

A Peaceful Dream

In a peaceful dream I met a fairy,
She was the princess of night,
Kind, generous and loving with,
A beautiful face and gown.

A white silken dress flowed down,
Swishing in a light breeze,
Leaving a trail of lilies,
As she quietly walked through deep valleys.

Her eyes bright yellow like glistening stars,
Her mouth was a crescent moon,
Her hair curly and shimmered like a diamond,
A golden crown upon her head.

In a peaceful dream I met a fairy,
She was the princess of night,
Kind, generous and loving,
She will sprinkle sleepdust in your eyes.

Emily Goodwin (10)
Fulford Primary School, Fulford

The Old Miner

There was an old miner
Who lived in a hole
He slept under layers of toilet roll,
With a mound of soil for his bed,
And a pillow of bags
Under his head.

There was an old miner
Who wouldn't die.
He lived on worms and the odd butterfly.
Crunching and munching the wings and the feet
He had no friends
Except a spider called Pete.

There was an old miner
Who ended in time
Being silly and jumping in grime
He never did what his doctor had said
He hardly ever
Went near his bed.

There was an old miner
Who suddenly leaned back
Unfortunately it was a fatal heart attack
The words on his tombstone said: 'Dig your way out'
His grave was a goldmine
Now, that's all,
Amen.

Jakob Garner (10)
Fulford Primary School, Fulford

Snail Poem

With horns out the top
He moves in a flop
He slithers so slow
It's a wonderful show
He's a brilliant spy
As he moves slowly by
He is a big thief
As he hunts for a leaf
He moves with a trail
A silver piece of mail
I love the great snail
In a race he would fail
He has a great shell
It is shaped like a bell.

Hannah Condliffe (8)
Fulford Primary School, Fulford

The Bloodthirsty Demon

Be afraid of the bloodthirsty demon,
That cunningly skulks in wait,
To haul you to its perilous pit,
Your remains he'll mutilate.

His blood is inky and deadly hot.
He hurls out menacing flames,
He'll cook you in his scolding pot
With your head will play gruesome games.

He'll snap your arms, he'll crack your legs
And squash you to a pulp.
Then gobble you like scrambled eggs
Gobble, gobble, gulp.

So watch your steps when next you go,
Upon a refreshing hike.
Or you might perish in the pit below,
With something you don't like.

Rebecca Roe (10)
Fulford Primary School, Fulford

Snail Poem

Noiseless snail creeps in the night
Under the bright street light.
Into the garden to find a leaf
He is a big juicy leaf thief.
Then he sees feet coming by
Black big shoes move slyly by.
Run under the hedge
Right to the edge
Till suddenly the car comes on
But it's only Uncle Don.

Sarah Dakin (9)
Fulford Primary School, Fulford

Autumn Riddle - Haiku

They are drifting down
They twirl around in the wind
They swoop in the air.

What am I?

Jodi Garner (8)
Fulford Primary School, Fulford

I Found At Dawn

I found at dawn a lonely witch,
But soon found out she was treacherous.
She was the soul of night (that horrid thing)
Wicked, cruel and vicious.

Her face was full of blackened greed,
Her eyes like grey rivers,
Her heart had turned dark with hate,
The air around her shivers.

Her black cloak sways in the breeze,
Around her stolen dress.
Stitched by the tiny hands of angels
(Once white) now black with death.

One leg is wooden, one of flesh,
Clonking along she comes.
Bats guard her steps at night,
Glowing in the light of the moon.

Her home is a forest of darkness,
Is a house made of the dead.
Evil, dark and black (like her),
Outside stands a fountain of blood, crimson-red.

Peter Goodwin (10)
Fulford Primary School, Fulford

I've Written On The Wrong Page, Miss

I've written on the wrong page, Miss!
I didn't know what to do
My paper blew out the window, Miss,
And I really needed the loo.

The legs broke off my chair, Miss,
My pencil went all blunt.
You've given me the wrong paper, Miss,
My book was back to front.

I really needed a drink, Miss,
And the work slipped out of my mind,
You didn't give me the sheet, Miss,
I was trying to shut the bind.

I was cleaning up the pallets, Miss
And they wouldn't come clean.
My paper was all smudged, Miss,
So can we try again?

Kimberly Frost (9)
Fulford Primary School, Fulford

My Funky Monkey

I have a magic monkey
And he's very funky.
His arms are long and hairy
And his teeth are sharp and scary.
He eats bananas
In his pyjamas.
When he plays chess
He makes quite a mess.
And that's why I have a monkey
Because they're funky!

Aiden Bray (11)
Glenfield Primary School, Glenfield

The Mix Max

The Mix Max with its two heads of a cat
A fire-breathing creature with smoke like a dragon.
The Mix Max has a tail of a snake with wings on it
The teeth that's can tear through anything
Muscles that kill anything and break anything
And a diamond heart that glows when enemies are near.

Michael Howard (11)
Glenfield Primary School, Glenfield

Snake

If there's an animal that lives in a lake it's a snake.
Its terrible tongue
Is loopy and long.
It slithers and slides,
And gloriously glides.
If there's an animal that I wouldn't like to take
It's a snake.

Stefan Wells (11)
Glenfield Primary School, Glenfield

The Kitten!

She needs:
Eyes like shining stars!
Fur like soft cotton wool!
Teeth like a white, sharp comb!
A collar like a blue rubber ring!
Paws like a beautiful fluffy toy!

Angelmae Long (9)
Glenfield Primary School, Glenfield

The Toowoo

I saw a wearied and funny living thing,
I named him the Toowoo,
He had one eye and one wing,
Across the sky he flew.

The Toowoo was now standing in the zoo,
Right near a tattered tree,
He made a row, he made a moo,
And simply growled at me.

And at that moment he lost his leg,
But soon it grew back,
He sat down and laid his egg,
And hatched it with a *whack!*

The Toowoo can never die
Or never damage himself,
And if you're thinking or wondering why,
Because he's in super health.

So when you see the Toowoo,
My advice is for you to conceal,
Or you will get a Toowoo flu,
And all this is real!

Louise Pye (10)
Glenfield Primary School, Glenfield

The Red Kite

Soaring high in the sky,
The red kite,
Searches for some prey,
It dives,
Down, down, down,
It has caught its prey!

Kate Martin (11)
Glenfield Primary School, Glenfield

Ponies

I have a little pony called Little Miss Rosy,
Brown and white like chocolate milk,
Beautiful and thin as silk,
Nice and big and eats little figs.
When you see Rosy the little pony,
You feel relaxed and secure.

Leyla Sezer (10)
Glenfield Primary School, Glenfield

Icarus And Daedalus

Daedalus built a labyrinth
It was for the king.
'Thank you,' said King Minos
'The maze will hide that thing.'

'No,' said the guard, 'You must not leave Crete.'
'But why?' said Daedalus, 'did I fail?'
'Theseus has killed that beast
Now you'll be put into jail.'

'How can we escape?' asked Icarus,
Daedalus had a plan.
'We'll make some wings and fly away,'
Said Daedalus, the clever man.

Icarus and Daedalus worked hard
To put the wings together,
They used some wax to make them stick
And glued on every feather.

'Beware the sun,' said Daedalus.
'It's hot so stay near me.
The wax will melt if you go near,
And you'll fall into the sea.'

But Icarus didn't listen,
He flew up far too high.
The wax, it then began to melt,
And he fell from the sky.

Daedalus saw his son fall down,
And knew that he had died,
Because he didn't listen
At least they both had tried.

Lisa Hampson (11)
Glenfield Primary School, Glenfield

Butterflies Are Beautiful

Butterflies are beautiful,
Soaring in the air,
Their colours so bright
And their wings so fair.
They fly through the sky
With great ease,
These marvellous creatures
Bring great peace.

Abigail Norman (11)
Glenfield Primary School, Glenfield

Funky Monkey!

Deep in the jungle hiding in the grass
I saw a monkey sitting in his class,
What was he doing? Nobody knew
He was sitting in the grass where the plants all grew.

He swings and swings till the sun drifts down
Waits for another day all safe and sound,
He loves his bananas that he eats so fast,
All the animals stare when they run past.

Through the forest the monkey goes
Swaying his body from his head to his toes.

So whenever you go to the zoo
Look out for the funky monkey
With his hip hop class too!

Amelia Colver (10)
Glenfield Primary School, Glenfield

The Dragon

He needs fire like the breezy, glazing sun.
He needs a head like a rock hard statue in a museum.
He needs eyes like glowing green emeralds in the sun.
He needs horns like a shark's teeth, razor-sharp.
He needs cars like the top of mountains covered in snow.
He needs a body like a humpback bridge.
He needs a mouth like a crocodile's snappy mouth.
He needs a roar like rolling thunder.

Jennifer Merrell (8)
Glenfield Primary School, Glenfield

The Dragon

It needs:
  A long neck like a dotty giraffe.
It needs:
  Fire like hot, burning lava.
It needs:
  Wings like black, creepy shadows.
It needs:
  A beak like a dangerous pteradactyl.
It needs:
  Claws like thick needles.

Stephanie Norman (8)
Glenfield Primary School, Glenfield

A Recipe For A Warm Winter

Ingredients

One large rug to keep you warm and snug.
Two cups of steaming hot chocolate to warm you from the inside to out.
Three glasses of red wine to keep Mum and Dad warm inside.
Four logs placed on an open fire which helps the flames dance in its grate.
Five little apples cooked in a blanket of warm, tasty pastry.

Instructions

Place logs on an open fire, light well.
Get large rug from the bedroom.
In a large bowl add steaming warm chocolate, dip apples in.
Stir in the red wine, place apples into pastry blanket.
Put into warm oven.

Lucy Hickenbotham (10)
Glenfield Primary School, Glenfield

Dogs

If there's an animal cooler than a frog,
It's definitely my dog.

I have a dog named Jess
She's always in a marvellous mess.

She's a husky cross German Shepherd,
She's faster than a leaping leopard!

I've got a dog named Harvey too
They play all day through!

Harvey is an Alsatian
He barks at condensation.

It was his birthday just last week,
It was a day for lots of treats.

Kurt Ledger (11)
Glenfield Primary School, Glenfield

The Cat

She needs:
Claws like thick, long, hard nails.
Fur like a soft, furry hairbrush.
A head like a furry rock with thin, warm points on top.
A tail like a thick, fat, short, furry rope
And paws like small, strong, thick, waterproof winter gloves.

Charlie Statham (8)
Glenfield Primary School, Glenfield

Red Kite

There was a great bird
A vicious raptor
It soars through the sky
As fast as flame
It's like a jet plane
Its wingspan is 2 metres.
It lunges for its prey
It never misses.
It's a scavenger
It's a predator
It's chestnut-red
With a pale grey head.

It's a powerful bird
It is incredibly large when it's attacked.
It gets very aggressive
When it strikes, it never stops,
Drifting as light as a feather through the sky.

Zack Foster (10)
Glenfield Primary School, Glenfield

The Brilliant Red Kite!

R ed as a fiery flame
E ver drifting through the air
D oing its best to

K ill its prey
I ts body so small with
T wo metre-long wings
E xpanding them for evermore!

Ashley Ross (11)
Glenfield Primary School, Glenfield

Red Kite

R eally rare birds
E very day illegally killed by hunters
D eadly but kind birds.

K illing its prey
I ts tail like a fork
T imidly flies through the sky
E merging out from behind the clouds.

Shannon Evans (10)
Glenfield Primary School, Glenfield

Red Kite

Red kite, red kite,
What an amazing sight.
We hear your cry,
As you glide through the sky.

Red kite, red kite,
You fly so light,
You're streamlined and fat,
You never come last.

Red kite, red kite,
You're magic like night.
You're the king of the air,
None can compare!

Charlotte Barnacle (11)
Glenfield Primary School, Glenfield

The Dragon

The dragon needs claws,
Claws like long razor-sharp blades
And teeth like long sharp needles,
And wings like long silk sheets
Oh and a tail like a long thin whip
And the eyes, oh the eyes like
Enormous sea-blue sapphires,
And that is what a dragon needs.

J A Batty (9)
Glenfield Primary School, Glenfield

Red Kite

Red kite soaring through the sky
Will never die.
He lunges for his prey
Day by day.
He slashes,
And splashes
Until his prey is dead,
Then he will go to bed.

Shaun Fairbrother (11)
Glenfield Primary School, Glenfield

Red Kite

There was a bird,
A great long bird,
Flapped his wings really fast,
He is really great,
What could it be?
It is a vicious raptor.

The red kite is as long as a car,
It goes through the sky as fast as a jet,
Drifting through the sky,
Drifting round the bends,
When it lands it is never out of breath.

The red kite it drifts through the sky for hours,
It lunges for its prey,
It's a scavenger,
It's chestnut-red
With a pale grey head.

Daniel Moss (10)
Glenfield Primary School, Glenfield

Red Kite

Flying in the sky very high.
Swoosh, down it goes very fast flying past.
Chestnut-red,
And grey head.
A breast of white,
Flies at the speed of light.
A wingspan of two metres long,
That support your weight,
So it will never be late.
The kill you do not make,
But scavenge you will take.
The prey from other's kill
You will eat until your fill.
Your beauty and your fork-tipped tail
Help you grace the skies like a sail.
What a joy to see
One of God's creatures as graceful as thee.

Sarah Warner (10)
Glenfield Primary School, Glenfield

Space Boys

Bang! There goes another -
I'm getting just as good as my brother.
Alert! Alert! Incoming comet,
Darn it, there goes my bonnet!
Wait, where's my brother and his rocket?
Oh, I've got a tracker in my pocket.
My brother's crash-landed on Mars,
I'll catch a ride on those stars.
Oh, I'm here and so are the Martians
They talked to me, at first they said, 'Lartians.'
I got out the high tech communicator,
They'd swap my brother for a calculator,
So, the deed was done,
We went home to lie in the sun.
So all we wanted to do was to shoot some comets,
But an adventure started and I lost my bonnet.

Emily Mason (10)
Glenfield Primary School, Glenfield

My Day At The Sea

Playing in the light blue sea,
Is so much fun for you and me.
Walking on the soft warm sand,
With an ice cream in my hand.
Seagulls screeching in the sky,
It's as if they're trying to say, 'Hi!'
Going to the restaurant on the shore,
Then we go to the ice cream store.
Lying in the shining sun,
Thinking of this day of fun.
Now it's time to have my tea,
I have to say goodbye to the sea.

Sophie Ellerton (10)
Glenfield Primary School, Glenfield

A Panther

He needs:
A tail like a thin black piece of silk.
Sharp teeth like the blades on a chainsaw.
Sharp claws like silent daggers.
A black cloak as dark as burnt wood,
And finally eyes as yellow as amber.

Elliott Richards (8)
Glenfield Primary School, Glenfield

Animals

Hairy shoulders soft and smooth.
Jiggly mouth full of teeth.
Tails waggle from side to side.
Claws sharp, horns spiky.
Eyes are glowing in the dark.
Ears twisting on the head.
Wiggly stripes.
Tiggly legs.
All the animals go to bed.

Adam Cato
Glenfield Primary School, Glenfield

The Leopard

He needs:
Fur like a bristly sea urchin shooting out its spikes.
Some teeth like a monstrous sharp razorblade.
Claws like a shiny bright chainsaw.
A head like a strong marble sculpture.
Some legs like a strong, hairy piece of wood.

Jovan Gordon (9)
Glenfield Primary School, Glenfield

Heaven On Earth

As I looked over the tall chalky cliffs,
I saw seagulls swooping in the breezy air,
The dazzling, deep, crystal-blue sea sparkled,
As colourful rainbow fish splashed around like shimmering stars from outer space.
My dad shouted, 'It's time to go!'
I jumped in the car and drove off,
Leaving the lush green grass blowing in the fresh air.

Alice Bourner (10)
Glenfield Primary School, Glenfield

The Shark

He needs:
Water really deep, see-through blue
Warm, like sparkling in the sun.
Teeth that are spiky, pointy, hard like a rock.
A nose like a black small button.
A head like a sharp, strong, hairy blanket.
Eyes that are small, like a star.

Kieran Meredith (9)
Glenfield Primary School, Glenfield

Solar System Surprise

Mercury zipping as fast as cheetahs,
From the sun a billion metres.
Comets zooming throughout space,
Keeping a quick and steady pace.
Asteroids whooshing to and fro,
Some are speedy and some are slow.
Look on Mars, there's some life,
An alien husband and his wife.
And there's Jupiter biggest of all,
It looks like one gigantic ball,
And here's Venus, that's really hot,
It's hotter than others by a lot.
Now home I zoom back to my room,
I rest my head in my comfy bed.

Kirsty Naismith (9)
Glenfield Primary School, Glenfield

Coastal Paradise

Feel the wind push against you,
Hear the waves crash against a cliff,
See the seagulls gracefully fly up above,
Smell the salt from the deep blue sea.

Feel the fish circling your ankles,
Hear the small children having fun,
See the reflection of the sunset,
Smell the seafood from a distance.

When I go to the sea, this is what I feel,
Every time, I smell the salt,
Feel the wind blowing and
That is a great adventure for me.

Sophie Leach (9)
Glenfield Primary School, Glenfield

Swooping Through Space

The sun is as hot as a ball of gas,
Whilst two thirds of the Earth is covered in sea.
Space is vast, splashed with planets and asteroids,
The sun is shiny, spitting fire all day every day.
On my journey round the sun,
Circling through outer space,
Leaving not a single trace.

Arron Howard (9)
Glenfield Primary School, Glenfield

McDonald's

Smell in the air makes me hungry
Looking at milkshake makes me dribble
Cheese is hot it melts in your mouth
Chips I love to nibble
Eggs drip out of buns
Lettuce is crunchy in your mouth
Ronald McDonald - his red bow!

Glen Speight (11)
Glenfield Primary School, Glenfield

The Panda

He needs:
A head soft and hairy like thick cotton wool.
Sharp claws like metal combs.
Eyes yellow like amber.
Big paws, strong like rocks on each other.
A fierce growl like rumbling thunder.
Strong enormous teeth like boulders.

Shannon Burrows (9)
Glenfield Primary School, Glenfield

The Cat

She needs:
A head like a hard, circular rock.
A tail like a thick, fat, short, furry rope.
Sharp claws like long, sharp, pointed, fake nails.
Lots of fur like soft, furry material stuck on top.
Paws like small, strong, thick, waterproof winter gloves.

Katie Berwick (8)
Glenfield Primary School, Glenfield

The Red Kite

The red kite soars through the sky like an aeroplane.
The red kite eats its prey like a lion in the jungle.
The red kite is as red as a chestnut.
The red kite's voice is like a mouse.
The red kite's wings can spread as long as a two metre stick.
The red kite's feet are yellow as a sun.
The red kite's beak is as yellow as a light bulb.
The red kite's weight is light as a rabbit.

Yvonne Ma (10)
Glenfield Primary School, Glenfield

Wet Whale

If there's one thing that can't fit into a pail
It's the whale.

They're big and fat,
I'll tell you that.

They're a little bit dodgy,
And a little bit podgy.

They make funny sounds,
And swim around.

They live in packs
They constantly snack on fish that live in the sea.

Gabby Mundin (11)
Glenfield Primary School, Glenfield

Macbeth

Go around the saucepan now.
Then chuck in a liver from a cow.
Now throw in a lizard's eye,
Then chuck in an animal's thigh.
Now throw in a chicken's head,
Then throw in a spider's leg.

Connor Heathcote (10)
Glenfield Primary School, Glenfield

Super Space

I get into my spaceship, *kerplonk!*
Off we go into space, *whoosh!*
We're up and away! *Whoo!*
We're on the moon, moonwalk, *stomp!*

Another spaceship! *Zoom, zoom!*
They want to scare us. *Bang, bang!*

Danielle Pinney (9)
Glenfield Primary School, Glenfield

Stars

S tars up in the night-time sky, maybe one will whizz right by.
T urning planets go really fast, Pluto is the very last.
A steroids come from far away, we don't see them any day.
R ockets zoom in outer space, leaving behind them not a trace.
S aturn's rings shining bright, look at them shine with silvery light.

Bernadette Bates (10)
Glenfield Primary School, Glenfield

The One Chance

The kid had a dream in a team . . .
The day came for the match,
He played amazing against scheme,
The scouts came, he latched.

The kid dreamed he played Stoke . . .
He dreamed two scouts got him,
'You are the best,' the scout spoke,
'You are fit and very slim.'

Then the kid chose to play for Stoke,
'You are playing Plymouth.'
Then he realised that he could cope,
He now plays for Portsmouth.

Yet his true dream, to play in Spain,
Barcelona his aim,
This is really where he wanted it,
It really was a pain!

He played so hard, never gave up,
And all his work paid off,
With his dream team, he lifted the cup,
'Player of the Year!'

Liam Haycock (10)
Gnosall St Lawrence CE Primary School, Gnosall

A Dream In My Palm

My dream, to be a TV presenter
My dream, to be pretty and clever
My dream, to be looked up to by children
My dream, to see my heroes, to be with them.

My job, I will find out great news
My job, I will be watched by you
My job, not to be a great loss
My job, to be paid by the boss.

My life, I will be a success
My life, I will not be a mess
My life, I will have my goals
My life, I will fill those holes.

A TV presenter is what I want to be,
And in my future, that is what I see.

Phoebe Smart (11)
Gnosall St Lawrence CE Primary School, Gnosall

The Three Billy Goats Gruff

Once there were three goats,
They were all called Gruff,
They wanted to cross the deep moat,
But thought it was too rough.

There was only one problem:
To get to the nice grass,
A troll was there to clobber them,
'Perhaps we should run fast?'

Trip, trap, trip, trap, went the goat's hooves,
Bridges he didn't like,
Suddenly he heard his feet move,
The troll gave him a fright.

'I'll gobble you up,' said the troll,
'Not me,' said the scared goat,
'There is a bigger goat,' Gruff called,
So he crossed the moat.

Trip, trap, trip, trap, came the second goat.
Soon the troll jumped out,
'Will I ever cross this moat?'
'There's another,' he did shout.

So on came the last goat, *trip, trap,*
Up came the evil thing,
The stupid troll began to laugh,
'I'm going to soon sing.
After you're in my very large tummy.'
So the goat attacked him,
He fell in the river, 'What a dummy!'

Samuel Watts (10)
Gnosall St Lawrence CE Primary School, Gnosall

The Four Seasons

The four seasons we have every year, make the world extremely beautiful.
Like the first lamb in spring or the first flower that opens in summer,
Or the first snowflake in winter, or maybe even the first red leaf in autumn.
But each season is beautiful like winter is freezing,
Yet fun making snowmen and having snowball fights.
In spring you look around and you see rabbits and lambs just born.
In summer it is very warm with the sun blaring away,
So all you can do is sunbathe outside.
Last of all is autumn, this season is lovely with different coloured leaves every
                                    direction you look,

So those are our four magnificent seasons;
Snow, rain, sun or gale.

Siân Barron (11)
Gnosall St Lawrence CE Primary School, Gnosall

The King Of The Kings

Close the windows,
Lock the doors,
The dragon is coming
With terrible claws.

Razor-sharp teeth
Ferocious jaws
Blazing eyes
And deafening roars.

Soaring high in the icy air
Swooping from its mountain lair
Stealing the sheep and the cattle
Soldiers fighting a losing battle.

Burning houses, bringing death
All with one fiery breath
He has the power to destroy
Every human girl and boy.

Shining scales of black and red
A pointed tail and fearsome head,
With his bellowing wings
He's definitely the king of the kings.

Thomas Pennack (8)
Gnosall St Lawrence CE Primary School, Gnosall

Goldilocks' Demise

Three bears,
One girl,
You know the story don't you?
But this one has a twist.
There is one girl,
There are three bears,
But where does the wolf come in?
Ah well, he came in at the end.
You did not hear,
But now you have.
He came in,
When Goldilocks ran out,
And he said, 'I say, I say, dinner's come quick,'
And gobbled her up, every bit.
So now you know how,
She never came
To the three bears house
Ever again.

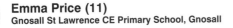

Emma Price (11)
Gnosall St Lawrence CE Primary School, Gnosall

Billy The Dragon

There once was a dragon named Billy,
Who was green all over;
His face was all small and silly,
From the cliffs of Dover.

At times he was a great skater,
But sometimes he would bail;
His favourite food was 'potater',
He never used to fail.

Then one day he went off alone,
Billy felt rather sad;
His mum and dad weren't on his phone,
So he didn't turn bad.

Billy the dragon was done for,
He had lost his way back;
Billy wanted a dinosaur,
To protect him from black.

He couldn't have what he wanted,
So Billy turned angry;
He liked some care from Toronted,
He hated sanctuary.

But then he saw a glimpse of light
His town home he could see;
He was so thirsty for some Sprite,
So then he jumped for glee.

Joe Rhodes (9)
Gnosall St Lawrence CE Primary School, Gnosall

Street Life On A Monday Morning

This morning as I was on my way to school,
The world outside started behaving badly.
The next-door neighbour's bike brakes started screeching and scratching loudly,
Like young babies crying.
Yellow leaves cackling as they raced each other through the wind.
Like yellow-skinned witches howling,
Little brown starlings trying to be Rachel Stevens.
How childish, how childish.
Later on things calmed down.
But just as I got into the playground . . .
The bell called me into the classroom!
You wouldn't believe all this could happen on
My Monday walk to *school!*

Kathryn Hallt (10)
Gnosall St Lawrence CE Primary School, Gnosall

The Worst Winter

I stepped out the door.
Straightaway daggers hit me.
The wind blew down my spine.
The trees, colourless.
Goosebumps went up my arm and down my spine.
Cooking smelled all around me.
My hands and fingers were tingling.
I heard voices behind the trees.
My teeth chattered.
I heard the traffic humming, coming closer and closer to me.
The fog got duller and greyer, I couldn't see my own hand.
The wind whistled all around me.
Behind me I heard stamping like elephants.
My hair blew gently in the cold wind.
I turned around, I saw the leaves frozen on the ground.
Not a bark, not a miaow, one twit, one bird in the sky.
The wind blew up my coat and down my trousers.
Behind an oak tree, a mysterious shadow.
I felt strange in the dark creepy field.
The colour of my hands changed to a blue.
My nose changed to red.

Rachael Hackett (9)
Gnosall St Lawrence CE Primary School, Gnosall

The Misty Night

Standing at the bus stop,
Fingers cold as ice
There's loads of scurrying
It's just a gang of mice.
Trees rustling their branches in the misty fog,
What was that noise? It was just a freaky frog.
Finally, is this the bus that I've been waiting for?
No it's just a car with two spooky-looking doors.
What is that smell? It smells familiar.
Aah it's the burger shop, I could do with a warm burger.
Oh look, it's the bus at last.
But that wasn't that fast.
The bus driver says in a spooky voice, 'Two fifty please.'
I give him the money, I'm not that pleased
At last the bus stops and the bus driver tells me to get off.
I get off the bus with a mysterious cough.

Francesca Marston (10)
Gnosall St Lawrence CE Primary School, Gnosall

Winter Days

Evergreen trees in-between trees with no leaves on them.
It looks like trees are waving goodbye;
It feels like daggers are stabbing us in the chest.
The wind is whistling around the trees.
The echoes of voices, traffic humming away.
We feel like a solid brick of ice,
With the birds flinging about like elastic bands.
The dampness is like some soggy towels.
Leaves flying about on the ground.
Frozen in the cold wind, everyone.
Birds flying about.
Streams of sunlight peeping through the clouds.
Creepy noises coming from the wood,
With fog and trees in the background.

James Till (11)
Gnosall St Lawrence CE Primary School, Gnosall

Fog

Streams of bright sunlight, peeping through the grey clouds.
Brown, crisp leaves rustling as the wind
Whistles through swaying gently.
Frozen in the cold wind, our fingers are cold as ice.
Shivers up my spine, stamping feet.
The echo of the traffic in the distance,
Circles around my frozen ears.
As we walk in the coldness, we can
See the swishing of the bare trees.
Squelch, squish as my frozen feet become muddy.
Oh, to be home snug as a bug
Having a hot chocolate in a mug.

Emily Simpkin (11)
Gnosall St Lawrence CE Primary School, Gnosall

Robots

Hello my name is Jerky Joe,
Now pick up the pen and go with the flow.
When some people see me, they start to cry,
And I want to know the reason why.
A cardboard box I live in,
Which has been dumped in a bin.
My body is made of aluminium,
I cost six pounds at the minimum.

William Doherty (9)
Gnosall St Lawrence CE Primary School, Gnosall

Winter Scene

The air was crisp like crispy leaves,
The voices echoing through the trees,
The cars in the distance you can hear,
A drop of water came like a tear,
As the birds sang high in the sky,
I looked around for their cry,
It was a frosty day,
When the sky was grey,
With gloomy shadows all around me,
Suddenly a gust of wind
Blew down my spine
Chilled me right down,
Could it really be the wind?

Nikki Craven (10)
Gnosall St Lawrence CE Primary School, Gnosall

A Cold Day

Another dull, grey day.
A slight glimpse of sunlight
Peeping through the clouds.
A cold, gentle wind
Biting at tender hands.
Hands as cold as ice cubes,
And feet too.
Huddle up,
Oh so very cold.
Is it time for home yet?

Joe Tunnicliffe (11)
Gnosall St Lawrence CE Primary School, Gnosall

Love Is In The Air

I have a question just for you
Someone must love me
I don't know who
I love my mum
I love my dad
My aunt, my uncle
And my gran too.
Someone must love me
It could be
You!

Lauren Allcock (10)
Gnosall St Lawrence CE Primary School, Gnosall

Josh Johnson

There was a boy who had some skill,
He played for Stafford Town;
Then he got seriously ill
His father was a clown.

He dreamed he played for Liverpool;
His idol was Owen.
He thought his name was really cool,
But he wasn't showin'.

'Oh my he's great!' said a scout,
On a Sunday morning.
'Let's go and give him a shout,'
But he was ignoring!

They came back a few weeks later
They went to Rowley Park,
They saw the kid Daniel Slater
And asked him where to park.

'Do you want to play for City?'
He gave a little frown.
'It may be a pity,
You can live in a town.'

Daniel accepted the deal,
'You will play today.'
They went for a McDonald's meal,
'Get in,' said little Faye.

Josh Johnson (9)
Gnosall St Lawrence CE Primary School, Gnosall

The Foggy Field

Frozen in the cold wind, fingers as cold as ice,
Not time to stand still, goose pimples aplenty.
Crisp, brown leaves rustle as the wind rushes by.
The wonderful smell of food
Drifts past our ruby-red noses.
Muffled sounds of traffic, circling round our ears,
Children's distant voices, reaching across the void.
Streams of bright sunlight
Peeping through the dull, grey clouds.
We squelch through the mud, shoes all muddy.
Oh to be home,
Warm and dry,
Fire burning,
Having a mince pie!

Jessica Bird (11)
Gnosall St Lawrence CE Primary School, Gnosall

Sleeping Beauty

Sleeping Beauty had long blonde hair,
Her hair was wavy blonde,
Sleeping Beauty liked to play fair,
As she sang by her pond.

Sleeping Beauty's loving mother,
Was married to a king,
She had no sister or brother,
And lived with fairies that could sing.

She was cursed when she was a child,
By an evil black witch,
When she was older she smiled,
She was very high-pitched.

She was playing hide-and-seek,
One day she ran along,
She found a hidden door and peeked,
The witch was singing songs.

She asked if she wanted a spin,
She pricked her finger and it bled,
She shouted out loud, 'Yes I win!'
All I could see was red.

Her parents carried her to bed,
One hundred years she slept,
While she was sleeping her prince said,
'I will ride over steps.'

She woke with the kiss of her prince,
After one hundred years,
They married and hadn't kissed since,
The day she woke in tears.

Lucy Cupit (10)
Gnosall St Lawrence CE Primary School, Gnosall

All Animals

Cats and dogs are very hairy,
But dragons and beasts are very scary.
Parrots are clever and can talk,
But most babies can hardly walk.
Snakes and snails are very slimy,
But rabbits sit on laps very kindly.
Chameleons can camouflage into its background,
But beware! Leopards can pounce!
Giraffes' necks are very tall,
But humans are cleverest of them all.

Lui McMahon (8)
Gnosall St Lawrence CE Primary School, Gnosall

A Foggy Day On The Field!

All around us were branches of trees,
Rustling and waving in the cold icy wind.
The mud was as sticky as quicksand trying to pull you down.
When the cold icy winds hit the trees,
The leaves whistled and rustled.
It sounded like loads of children shaking tambourines.
I heard cars zooming past in every direction.
My toes were frozen and numb.
As the cold winds flew past me my hair went all in my face.
The cold icy floor all slushy and full of wet mud.
My fingers were frozen stiff.
I could not move my arms they were so cold.
All the small creatures were hiding from the icy fog.
I felt so miserable and unhappy
Because it was so cold.
I felt like a huge ice cube being broken in two,
It felt like my legs were big
Frozen icicles.
I had a shiver down my spine.

Holly Rounds (9)
Gnosall St Lawrence CE Primary School, Gnosall

The Icy Day

The wind was frozen
In the icy sky.
Trees were swishing
My fingers were like ice.
My face was like snow
The sky was cold
And grey.
Shivers were down
My spine
The echo of traffic
In the distance
I could not move
So cold.

Jessica Land (9)
Gnosall St Lawrence CE Primary School, Gnosall

The Wooden Horses

The army of Greece prepare a fleet,
To defeat the army of Troy,
To save Helen from terrible defeat,
With a strong wooden toy.

The plan to defeat terrible Troy,
Set off with lots of wood,
They started to make their new toy,
For Troy to die they should.

A horse they built with all the wood,
And left it by the gate,
The Trojans thought it looked so good,
And pulled with all their weight.

The men crept out on their tiptoes
When the doors were closed,
After they'd been to Moe's,
And had at least one cup.

Euan Hill (9)
Gnosall St Lawrence CE Primary School, Gnosall

Dick Whittington

Poor Dick, from Gloucester he came,
To seek lots of fortune,
He came with a cat which was tamed,
By the light of the moon.

He found a girl he loved so much,
So she got him a job
She had a very gentle touch,
She travelled with her father, Bob.

Lazy Jack was jealous so he stole
The necklace that her father
Was going to let her hold
So he lost it in the pocket there.

The jewel had gone the next day
Everyone looked in shame.
Found it in the pocket, 'Hey, hey, hey
It was him, it wasn't me!' he blamed.

Jake Jones (10)
Gnosall St Lawrence CE Primary School, Gnosall

Jack And The Beanstalk

One sunny day Jack's mother's orders were,
'Sell the cow at the market.'
Jack angrily stuck his tongue out at her,
The market was his target.

He met a very old and wise man,
Jack traded for magic beans,
He raced home and found a pan,
His mother saw the beans.

She threw them into the garden,
Angrily she sent him to bed,
He woke and found that the ground had hardened,
He had a very bad head.

But still he got out of his bed
He went outside to see
That what had grown over his head
'I want to go and see.'

'My life is going round the bend,
When is this streak going to end?
I will see what is at the end
My grass is on the mend!

Up I go to the high sky
Here I am, now to see
I have a feeling I will soon die,
Now this castle must have a key?'

And the rest is all history.
In the end Jack did fine.
If you want the end to this mystery . . .
Go and read the rhyme.

Christopher Pearson (10)
Gnosall St Lawrence CE Primary School, Gnosall

Who Am I?

They move deadly for their prey,
Getting fiercer day by day.
They rip other sea creatures' guts apart,
Their teeth are deadly sharp.
They send so much fear from the Pacific Ocean
All the way down to Brighton Pier.
Oh sharks no one likes you very much,
Is that because of your deadly touch?

Connor Pezzaioli (9)
Gnosall St Lawrence CE Primary School, Gnosall

George's Marvellous Medicine

There was a farm with lots of cows,
A boy called George lived there,
Whose parents have hundreds of rows,
George used to stop and stare.

He ran to the old dusty shed,
And grabbed a pot and spoon,
He was strong so he put in a bed,
His granny was an old loon.

He stirred it round until it went brown,
Then it went purple, then blue,
He was happy but also had a frown,
This gloop was like sticky glue.

He scooped it out into a medicine tube,
He got a spoon for it,
She slurped it down her big fat cube,
Her belly amazingly lit.

She started to grow up and up,
She was going through the roof,
She wanted more in a big cup,
Even though she was in youth.

His dad came back with a big shock,
He dropped the shopping bag,
His mum came back to this lock,
The old granny looked like rags.

They gave it to their pigs and cows,
They had massive products,
They were bigger than snow or field ploughs,
Their eggs bigger than ducks'.

Oliver Perry (9)
Gnosall St Lawrence CE Primary School, Gnosall

Swan

See the elegant swan, gliding past the mud,
Dancing, dancing all day long,
Wings flutter fast and slow,
Feathers flap up and down, up and down they flow,
Huge webbed feet, flip, flop, flick,
Bodies waddle all day long,
Watch their fine and fluffy neck,
Majestic on a lake like they own it.

Megan Bradley (8)
Gnosall St Lawrence CE Primary School, Gnosall

The Loch Ness Monster

At the bottom of deep Loch Ness
It is dark and murky;
What on earth lives down there, can you guess?
It is of course Nessie!

It has a great big appetite,
Swallowing loads of fish.
To get fish it would have to fight
Soon there would be no fish!

The monster has scaly skin;
When it comes to the top;
It has a couple of big fins,
And goes back down again.

The Loch Ness monster makes a sound,
The noise is unearthly
Drew people to harm, to be drowned,
The sound is a high wail!

It moves swiftly and silently,
Two hundred metres down;
Nessie lives where it is rocky
And lives there peacefully.

The monster has been caught on film,
Locals all have cameras,
The film would be hot as a kiln,
Documents everywhere!

Sammy Bryan (10)
Gnosall St Lawrence CE Primary School, Gnosall

My Horse

In the stable yard,
All I can see,
Is a horse staring down at me,
She has a mane soft and silky,
And her milk is so milky,
She gallops all night and day,
And rolls in the soft hay,
She sleeps in the old wooden stable,
Jumps over the hurdle which she is able,
The friendly owner is so kind,
I wish a horse I could find.

Rebecca Price (8)
Gnosall St Lawrence CE Primary School, Gnosall

The Firework-Maker's Daughter
(Based on the novel by Phillip Pullman)

The firework-makers they came;
Dr Puffenflash first,
Signor Scorcin next in the game,
Colonel Sparkington cursed!

They practised so hard that they burst,
Then came the rolling drum!
The firework-makers who were first,
Shocked at what was to come . . .

Chulak crossed his fingers in hope,
Hamlet watched at the crowd!
With the pressure, how could they cope?
Everyone cheering so loud!

And soon Lila's display began;
Truly supert it was,
It impressed every man,
Everyone else had lost.

And so it was that Lila won,
And Lalchand was freed,
Despite the hassle it had been fun,
For everyone indeed,

All three gifts Lila had shown,
Razvani would be proud,
As a firework-maker, she had grown,
Luck had won over the crowd!

Charlotte Fenton (9)
Gnosall St Lawrence CE Primary School, Gnosall

Polly My Horse

My horse in the stable,
Polly's her name.
Runs like the wind,
Has a fuzzy mane.

She has a long tail,
That swishes around.
You should see her gallop,
She beats the ground.

Polly is so beautiful,
Her copper coat shines in the sun.
Her ears prick up,
When she's having lots of fun.

Rachael Jones (9)
Gnosall St Lawrence CE Primary School, Gnosall

The Three Little Ducklings

There once were three little ducklings,
They were all ghosts of fright.
They scared their mother with duck-cookings,
So their bums were set alight.

Their mother duck got sick and tired,
Of setting their bums on fire,
So they got hired but then fired,
By their boss McGuire.

So they decided to move away,
'Goodbye,' they said to their mother.
All she said to them was, 'Hooray!'
And gone, like their father.

The first little duckling found some hay,
To make a central-heated home.
In the house of hay he would stay
Or more like a big dome.

So what had the second duck done?
A house made of pure wood.
But the frog was having some fun,
Blowing houses down with a thud!

He saw the first duck's house of hay,
And blew it through the sky.
So the house of hay was away,
And it really went sky high.

And so the ducks' houses were blown today,
All the way to the frog.
And the frog was yelling, 'Hooray!'
He had duck in his pond.

Richard Craven (10)
Gnosall St Lawrence CE Primary School, Gnosall

Lambs

Lambs are white, lambs are fluffy,
They look like a cloud hiding a cute black face,
Their legs wobble as they run,
They drink milk from their mum,
They chase about with one another,
All lambs love their mother.
They are really cute but best of all,
They're really, really, really small!

Trudie Ward (9)
Gnosall St Lawrence CE Primary School, Gnosall

The Three Billy Goats Gruff

Three Billy goats Gruff on a hill,
But they wanted more grass,
So off they set, past the old mill,
A castle they soon passed.

They trotted to the riverside,
The troll was sitting there.
The Billy goats they never lied,
The troll had bright green hair!

First small Billy goat tried to cross
The troll peeked up his head.
He hid behind trees and some moss,
'Who's on my bridge?' he said.

'Eat my bro,' said Billy goat Gruff,
He trotted to new grass,
The next goat saw he'd had enough,
So he came down to pass.

Then the second Billy goat came down,
Then the troll said the thing,
The second biggest goat came round,
Then the troll had a ding.

The troll was weak, big goat was strong,
Troll cried, 'You're easy now.'
The troll thought he was strong, that's wrong,
The Billy goat said, 'Ciao!'

Jonathan Adams (10)
Gnosall St Lawrence CE Primary School, Gnosall

The Legend Of Sqwonk

JP Welling went out one day,
To catch the ugly sqwonk,
He searched through the flowers of May
He passed a friendly monk.

He heard a rustle in the trees,
He got down on his knees,
He saw the sqwonk a-weeping,
And he was a creeping.

The sqwonk was grabbed in his big bag,
By moonlight he went home,
When he got home his bag didn't sag,
He found he was all alone.

Reegan Campion-Westwood (10)
Gnosall St Lawrence CE Primary School, Gnosall

The Three Billy Goats Gruff

Once there were three Billy Goats Gruff
One small, one big, one bigger,
The grass they had was not enough,
A plan, they would figure.

Across a bridge, a field they saw,
Whose grass was green and lush,
They dribbled and wanted it more,
Over the bridge they'd rush.

The small one crossed with a clatter,
When a mean troll jumped out,
'Leave me, the next goat is fatter.'
'Then go!' the troll did shout.

Across the bridge, the next goat came,
And the fat troll jumped out.
Like the first goat, he said the same,
'Then go!' the troll did shout.

Then came the greatest biggest goat,
Across the guarded way.
'Ha, ha!' the mean old troll did gloat,
'I'll eat you up today.'

'Not a chance, I'm bigger than you!'
And with a great big bang,
Over the edge the dazed troll flew,
Three goats, a happy gang.

Caitlin Begley (9)
Gnosall St Lawrence CE Primary School, Gnosall

Rabbits Flying Into The Sky

Rabbits, rabbits hopping by,
As I see them in the sky.
I thought it was a dream at first,
But then I realised my brain had burst.
I wonder how they jump so high,
All my life, I've wondered why.
Those rabbits, rabbits in the sky,
Banks of clouds are drifting nigh.

Chloe Fletcher (8)
Gnosall St Lawrence CE Primary School, Gnosall

Mary-Kate And Ashley It's A Snow Problem

'Do winter sport,' said Mary-Kate,
Trying to do skiing,
'Because everything else is lame,'
Yes, make-up she should bring.

She is crazy about make-up,
She takes it everywhere,
She has the 'Best Make-up' cup,
She does it with a care.

She was signed up for the wrong one,
And was very angry,
She made Cambell pay and told Mum,
Met a boy called Larry.

Said he was doing all the sports,
Then Mary-Kate did too,
The equipment the sisters bought,
But then they heard a moo.

It was the other team's mascot,
Somebody put it there,
Excluded from the games she got,
She went to tell the mayor.

Mary-Kate was disappointed,
She lay in bed all day,
She wailed and cried with her ted,
Then she went outside to play.

Laura Fleming (9)
Gnosall St Lawrence CE Primary School, Gnosall

Untitled

B lackbirds are black
L ong tails
A lert
C lever
K nocking its beak
B lackbirds are stupid
I ndigenous
R ummage for worms
D ive for food.

Ben Holter (8)
Gnosall St Lawrence CE Primary School, Gnosall

George's Marvellous Medicine

Mr and Mrs Kranky left George to
Make Grandma's medicine,
What George was very willing to do,
Was to put Grandma in the bin.

Horrible Grandma shouted to him,
'I want my medicine,
I am coming with a full tin,
It might spoil your din.'

George used many ingredients,
Starting with bad shampoo,
And ending with lots of smelly ants;
Stirred it up with some stew.

George was ready to give it to her,
She drank it down in one,
In a second she said, 'Grrr grrr.'
And sounded like a bomb.

She grew slowly up to the roof,
George shouted, 'Stop growing!'
Grandma stopped at the top of the roof,
She still wanted to be growing.

Mr Kranky ordered a tall crane,
Grandma slept in the shed,
She was tied up with a long chain,
But she would like a bed.

George gave her another medicine,
But she went to the floor,
She almost fell on a sharp pin;
That was the end of her!

Harry Bowers (9)
Gnosall St Lawrence CE Primary School, Gnosall

The Spider

The spider works hard spinning his web of silk.
A trap to other insects,
They become his tea!
His jet-black shadow looms out of the darkest corners,
Scurries across towards his prey,
Frightening anyone in his way.

Aron Payne (8)
Gnosall St Lawrence CE Primary School, Gnosall

My Cat Called Dopey

My cat is called Dopey,
Most people love her very much.
The hay barn, all yellow and flat
Is her habitat.

Thirty centimetres is her tail,
Her purring, quiet as a latch opening.
A cute soft body, she is fluffy,
Once she took a hat.

With pink, soft paws
She sneaks around the farmyard.
She walks about with shaggy fur
Anyone would think she's poor.

While Dad walks around the big, dirty, horrible yard,
Working hard,
We give her food, she's really greedy,
She wants more.

Lorna Winnington (9)
Gnosall St Lawrence CE Primary School, Gnosall

Pod

Pod the guinea pig
Naughty but nice
Long fluffy coat
The colour of spice.
He twitches his nose
Scurries around
He washes his face
Nibbles grass on the ground.

William Hallt (8)
Gnosall St Lawrence CE Primary School, Gnosall

Rooney The Horse

H orses are cute
O ther people love them
R eady to see them every day
S ome people like them, some people don't
E very day they run and play.

Chelsea Marston (8)
Gnosall St Lawrence CE Primary School, Gnosall

My Pet Fish

My fish like to swish
Their names are called Splish,
Splash, Splosh
Their tank is very posh.
I feed them twice a day
Even though they do not pay.
Splish keeps nipping Splosh and Splash,
When we are eating sausage and mash.
When the tank goes murky green,
We quickly give it a spring clean.
Splish is orange, Splash is white
They swim around the tank every night.
But Splosh is black and has a swishy tail,
And goes crazy when the postman delivers the mail.

Georgia Burns (9)
Gnosall St Lawrence CE Primary School, Gnosall

Spiders

Spiders crawl, spiders creep, spiders also live in the deep
If you see them in your house, just remember it's not a mouse.
Ugly and hairy they may be, they never can harm a flea.
So leave them alone let them be free, they're not as bad as a bumblebee.

The webs they spin are shiny and bright, especially in the sunlight.
Never kill a spider that's not attacking,
But for some reason, they're good at tracking.

Cameron Godfrey (8)
Gnosall St Lawrence CE Primary School, Gnosall

My Friend Horse

I have a friend, a horse that is very nice,
Is his name Sugar, is his name, Spice?
He gallops around the field in the night,
And his mane shines in the light.
I don't think his name is any of them,
But his mane shines like a gem.
His eyes are definitely crystal clear,
And I say he has no fear.

Jessica Scott (8)
Gnosall St Lawrence CE Primary School, Gnosall

Beyond The Field

Beyond the field something lies,
It's something full of grace.
You may think it's a cloud or tree,
Or maybe something from outer space.

It might be up in the sky,
Or maybe down below,
It could be oh so super fast,
Or possibly extremely slow.

Is it from Africa,
Or could it be French?
Is it a person like Monet,
Or maybe Dame Judi Dench?

Is it on the Internet,
Or is it in a book?
Is it hidden from you,
Or is it everywhere you look?

It is all of these things,
Plus so much more,
They climb through your window,
But usually through the door.
Children!

Rebecca Crowe (10)
Gnosall St Lawrence CE Primary School, Gnosall

Sea Horse

See them swimming round and round
See them sparkle in the light
They don't live on the ground
But they are very bright
See them bobbing up and down
They hide in the coral
But they don't wear a gown.

Guess what my animal is?
It's a sea horse!

Holly Singleton (8)
Gnosall St Lawrence CE Primary School, Gnosall

Sneaky Cats

With velvet toes sneaking she goes,
Small and nice, she likes chasing mice,
She leaps high, she can nearly fly,
She drinks milk, her coat is made of silk,
Silently she sleeps, round the garden she creeps,
Chasing the birds and gives them a wink
What is the animal do you think?

Paige Jones (8)
Gnosall St Lawrence CE Primary School, Gnosall

Footsteps

Walk through the snow,
To show me where you go,
So just walk through the snow,
And I can see where you go.

Go through the sand,
And it will be a land,
So you'd better go through the sand,
To find a beautiful land.

Walk through the grass,
And you will pass,
Me in the grass
So walk through the grass.

Paul Williams (11)
Great Bowden CE Primary School, Great Bowden

I Wish

I like to look up at the sky,
One day I would love to fly,
Really high I would go,
To a place were no one, no one would know.
I'd go so high, I'd zoom into space,
It would definitely be the best place.
When I'm there I'd look around,
Then I'd go back to the ground.
Now I've just got to wait,
Till I get to that lovely place.

Imogen Tooms (11)
Great Bowden CE Primary School, Great Bowden

Snow

Icicles dripping as the sun comes out
Snow melting just wasting away
Oh the frosty, frosty day.
Snowmen disappearing almost gone,
Jack Frost is hiding tin ton, tin ton
I like the snow ho, ho, ho, ho
Oh do be quick St Nick, St Nick
But when the snow comes again
Thicker next day everybody says,
'Hip hip hooray!'

Alice Mercer (9)
Great Bowden CE Primary School, Great Bowden

Happiness

H appiness is everywhere
A ll around is every day
P eople are happy wherever you look
P ower is happiness
I n the houses on the streets
N ever be unhappy
E verywhere, every street
S o beautiful, so calm
S o we should all be happy.

Bethan Smeeton (10)
Great Bowden CE Primary School, Great Bowden

Food Rap

Fast food, thin food, fat food,
Baked beans especially get me in the mood.
Spaghetti all wormy, slippery and slimy,
Go to the shops and you can buy me.
Bacon, eggs, sausages, fish,
All these make a delicious dish.
Some cheese, smelly, creamy or smoked,
Careful, don't eat too fast you might choke.
Some cheeses are even blue
The smoked ones my favourite, how about you?

Sadie Bromley (9)
Great Bowden CE Primary School, Great Bowden

New School

I stood in the middle of the playground,
Waiting for a new friend to appear.
But no one came
I seemed to be invisible.

I slowly walked into the classroom,
And tried to find a seat.
But no one wanted me next to them
So I sat alone.

Then came playtime,
I tried to join in with the different games,
But no one wanted me around,
I stood, waiting.

But then I saw her,
She was just like me.
I slowly went to stand next to her,
I was no longer invisible.

The bell went for lessons,
We walked in together,
No longer alone,
Best friends.

Emma Wilson (11)
Great Bowden CE Primary School, Great Bowden

Love

Love is something you can't throw away.
Love is something that's there every day.
Love is like air you can't live without it.
      Love, it's always there.

Love makes you happy wherever you are,
Love is like seeing a wishing star.
Love makes you feel like you can fly,
Love is just right for you and I.

Kasia Beacher (10)
Great Bowden CE Primary School, Great Bowden

A Winter Poem

A cold winter's day
When all the children play
And the children say happy day
Hip hip hooray
Come and play on a cold winter's day.

Becki McHugo (9)
Great Bowden CE Primary School, Great Bowden

The Weather Rap

The weather's all around
Rainy, sunny and windy.
In the rain it's all wet and cold
In the sunny weather it's really hot,
And not rainy.
Well actually you get a few rain showers
But that's when you can play and play
All day long outside
It's really fun playing.
In the windy weather all the trees blow, blow, blow
It's a weather, weather, weather rap
So in the summer, drink, drink, drink,
It's a weather, weather, weather rap.

Jade Marshall (8)
Great Bowden CE Primary School, Great Bowden

Maths

Circles, squares, diamonds too,
All these shapes make me and you.
A big round nose so you can sniff
If you have no shapes you might not live.

Triangles, hexagons are 2D
My friend put her hand up and shouted, 'Me, me.'
She said one,
When the question was, 'How many sides in a decagon?'

Esme Bamber (10)
Great Bowden CE Primary School, Great Bowden

Planet Rap

Planets, planets all around
Then I can always hear some sound.
It can be loud, it can be quiet,
But my mum always has a riot.
It's my rap, rap planet rap
I always get a fright.
So I just turn on my bedroom light,
I say, 'It's a rap, rap, planet rap,'
I'll say it again, 'It's my rap, rap, rap, planet rap.'

Heath Stretton (9)
Great Bowden CE Primary School, Great Bowden

Being Bored At School

I am sitting on my chair,
And I don't know what to say.
I am looking at my watch,
Every minute of the day.

Teacher, when's it home time?
May I be excused?
Teacher, I feel ill now
And I don't know what to do!

Suddenly thoughts of ice cream
And food enter my mind,
And all thoughts of reality
Are being left behind.

I'm tucked up in my bed
And my duvet feels all soft.
But really, in reality
I must've drifted off.

Jasmin Piercy (10)
Great Bowden CE Primary School, Great Bowden

Seaside

S wishy wavy sea
E agles flying up above
A ir floating round the sea
S unshine on my feet
I ce cream melting on my hand
D olphins swim in the sea
E verybody playing in the sea.

Siân Dimblebee (10)
Great Bowden CE Primary School, Great Bowden

Dreaming Water

As I listen to the beautiful sound of the silent water,
As I watch the silvery sparkly lake of wonderful dreams,
My mind starts to unfold and float away with the river,
The river of silent happiness,
But the river flows on,
Onto the wide sleepy sea.

Rosa Sulley (10)
Great Bowden CE Primary School, Great Bowden

Fast Food Rap

I really love fast food,
It puts me in the mood!
I bite the burger I chew the chips,
Bring on the sauces, bring on the dips!
As you can guess I am getting fat,
I eat so much I can't help that!

Kebabs and pizzas are my fave,
I have a super, super large crave!
I go gobble, gobble and slurp, slurp, slurp,
I have no time to burp!

Saveloys and fish cake too,
I am like an animal in a zoo.
Day and night I shovel it in,
I even eat things from a bin!
Fast food, fast food, yummy and spice,
Fast food, fast food, man it's nice!

Jessica Cole (11)
Great Bowden CE Primary School, Great Bowden

Mashed Potato Rap

I'm living in an alleyway,
I've got to get some food today,
I've found a full up bin,
Of mashed potatoes and chicken skin.

I threw away the chicken skin,
In exactly the same bin,
I ate the mashed potatoes,
But they tasted like mouldy tomatoes.

I'm living in an alleyway,
I've got to get some food today.
I don't feel very well,
I feel like I'm going to Hell.

And the moral of the story is,
If you're ever in a tizz,
Don't eat trashed potatoes!

Liam Southwell (11)
Great Bowden CE Primary School, Great Bowden

Monsters

There's a monster on my bed,
And I can't rest my head,
There's a very spooky ghost at the door,
And I'm about to prance on the floor,
There's a monster over there sitting right on top of my chair,
And I'm afraid he's gonna chop off my head,
And the goblins in the hall,
Are gonna crawl right up my wall,
And I think I'm going to explode.

McCaulley (9)
Great Bowden CE Primary School, Great Bowden

Love And Hate

Love looks colourful like a parrot in flight
Hate looks like fresh blood after a fight,
Love sounds like bells after a wedding
Hate sounds like bad dreams under the bedding.

Love smells like chocolate or candyfloss at a fair
Hate smells like fear and when nobody cares.
Love tastes like McDonald's - yummy!
Hate tastes like spinach cooked by your mummy.

Love feels like a soft fluffy cushion
Hate feels like being shot with a bullet from a gun,
Love reminds me of flowers in the spring
Hate reminds me of a dark, creeping dementor thing.

Chris Gamble (9)
Greenfield Primary School, Countesthorpe

Hate

Hate looks like darkness in the middle of the night,
Hate feels like rocks, spiky, sharp and jagged,
Hate tastes like mud, brown and wet,
Hate smells like cow dung, rotten and disgusting,
Hate sounds like screams of fear and pain,
Hate reminds me of my darkest, most evil deeds.

Steven Trotter (9)
Greenfield Primary School, Countesthorpe

Good Riddance

Good riddance to the jealousy chasing me
Goodbye to the jealousy not setting me free
Goodbye to jealousy making me wonder why
Good riddance to jealousy making people cry
Good riddance to jealousy turning me cold
Goodbye to jealousy keeping its hold
Goodbye to jealousy making me say bad things
Good riddance to the sadness that jealousy brings.

Goodbye to jealousy that eats you up inside
Goodbye to the jealousy that takes away your pride
Good riddance to jealousy that makes you feel alone
Good riddance to jealousy that always makes you moan
Goodbye to the jealousy that keeps you up all night
Good riddance to jealousy that makes you impolite
Good riddance to jealousy that turns you red with rage
Goodbye to jealousy that keeps you in a cage.

Goodbye to jealousy that makes you weak
Goodbye to jealousy that makes you incomplete
Good riddance to jealousy that hangs in the air
Goodbye to jealousy it's a nightmare
Goodbye to the jealousy that lost me my friend
Goodbye to the jealousy that took me round the bend
Goodbye to the jealousy I don't want to see again
Good riddance to the jealousy that gave me the pain.

Good riddance to the jealousy that wouldn't stop
Goodbye to the sadness and the teardrop
Goodbye to the jealousy I won't ever forget
Goodbye to the jealousy I wish I never met
Goodbye to the jealousy that taught me something
Friends are better than anything
Goodbye to the jealousy that made me plain
I hope I never see jealousy again.

Alice Cassie (11)
Greenfield Primary School, Countesthorpe

Fear Is A Monster

It tastes like mouldy petrol in a bottle.
It feels like a piece of rotten, sour, horrible toast
Stuck with flat sweets.
It looks like a green fairy, cow and half man with steaming nose.
It sounds like a cow eating rubbish in the bins.
It smells like people dipped in stinky old milk.
It reminds me of my nightmares that come every single night.

Joe Webb (10)
Greenfield Primary School, Countesthorpe

Thank You For . . .

Thank you for your smiling face
And bringing chocolates to my place.
Thank you for buying me clothes,
Thank you for that big red rose,
Thank you for smiling at me so I'll be nice to you,
Thank you for bringing me here to see this beautiful view.
Thank you for really cute pets
Thanks for me passing my test.

Thank you for when snow falls,
Thank you for a new football.
Thank you for loving someone,
Thank you for the words 'Come on!'
Thank you for a new puppy that's tame,
Thank you for my new game,
Thank you for coming to my house,
Thanks for getting rid of that mouse!

Thank you for when the sun's out,
Thank you for when there is no doubt.
Thanks for taking me to the beach,
Thanks for buying me a peach.
Thank you for a great big cuddle,
Thanks for having fun in a puddle.
Thank you for the birth of a baby,
Thank you for going crazy.

Thank you for when I'm in love,
Thank you for the beautiful doves.
Thank you for the sky at night,
The orange glow makes my heart feel light.
Thanks for funny songs you sing,
To cheer me up and make a grin.
Thank you for the things you do,
Thank you for just being you.

Sam Mould (11)
Greenfield Primary School, Countesthorpe

Fear Is An Animal

It sounds like a tree in the wind
It tastes like mouldy mud left for a year,
It smells like a tinkling sewer underground,
It feels like a tarantula, hairy and creepy,
It reminds me of a tiger pouncing on me.

Zak Anderson (9)
Greenfield Primary School, Countesthorpe

Thank You For Friends

Thank you for the friends that set me free
Thank you for the friends that made me, me
Thank you for the love that we all share
Thank you for the friends that made life fair
Thank you for the friends that spend time with you
Thank you for the friends that pull you through
Thank you for the friends that warm you up
Thank you for the friends that pick you up.

Thank you for the friends who are always happy
Thank you for the friends who are never snappy
Thank you for the friends who never make you feel alone
Thank you for the friends who never make you moan
Thank you for the friends who make you smile
Thank you for the friends with grace and style
Thank you for the friends who always make you laugh
Thank you for the friends who can be very daft.

Thank you for the friends that make you feel alive
Thank you for the friends who always arrive
Thank you for the friends who look after you
Thank you for the friends who you can talk to
Thank you for the friends who make you do the right things
Thank you for the friends who are better than a diamond ring
Thank you for the friends who put you first
Thank you for the friends who help you overcome the worst.

Thank you for the friends who will always have fun
Thank you for the friends who think you're number one
Thank you for the friends that take time for you
Thank you for the friends that will always be true
Thank you for the friends who you meet
Thank you for the friends who are short and sweet
Thank you for the friends that love me such
Thank you very, very much.

Emma Cooke (11)
Greenfield Primary School, Countesthorpe

Hate Is An Ogre

It looks like a doll with lots of make-up on.
It smells like a bit of mouldy bread that's been left for a century.
It feels like a crocodile that's got lots of scales.
It tastes like baked beans that have gone rotten.
It sounds like a monster crashing into walls.
It reminds me of my brother with make-up on.

Daniel Munn (9)
Greenfield Primary School, Countesthorpe

Thank You For Hugs

Thank you for hugs when you succeed
Thanks for hugs that you need
Thank you for hugs when you celebrate
Thank you for hugs that mean you're a mate
Thanks for hugs that show you're there
Thank you for hugs to show you really care
Thank you for hugs when we've had fun
Thanks for hugs which help you overcome.

Thanks for hugs when you're kind and sad
Thank you for hugs when you're lonely and mad
Thanks for hugs when you're all alone
Thank you for hugs when you're having a moan
Thanks for hugs 'cause you've had a breakdown
Thank you for hugs that calm you down
Thanks for hugs that cheer you up
Thank you for hugs that always make up.

Thanks for hugs that keep you warm at night
Thank you for hugs when you've had a terrible fight
Thank you for hugs that show you understand
Thanks for hugs that whisk you to dreamland
Thanks for hugs when you've been on a scary ride
Thanks for hugs that welcome you
Thank you for hugs when you're really feeling blue.

Thank you for hugs when you're left in the cold
Thank you for hugs when something bad unfolds
Thank you for hugs when you find your one love
Thanks for hugs that make you feel like a dove
Thank you for hugs at Christmas time
And thanks for hugs that are all mine
Thank you for hugs when life gets tough
Thank you for hugs I just can't thank you enough.

Rachel Heggs (10)
Greenfield Primary School, Countesthorpe

Sadness

Sadness smells like rotting cow dung,
Sadness reminds me of a sky without sun,
Sadness feels like you're falling down a big black hole,
Sadness looks like a helpless dying foal,
Sadness sounds like all your worst fears,
Sadness tastes like salty tears,
Sadness is a thing everyone hates,
But you will soon cheer up when you're with your mates!

Kelsi Varney (10)
Greenfield Primary School, Countesthorpe

Thank You For Beauty

Thank you for a ballerina in a gown
Thank you for the sea sparkling as the sun goes down
Thank you for a dragonfly in the sun
Thank you for a tree in the autumn
Thank you for a beautiful brown pheasant
Thank you for a silver half-crescent
Thank you for the beautiful long reeds
Thank you for a sari made with sequins and beads.

Thank you for a tree filled with blossom
Thank you for an ancient fossil
Thank you for a wedding dress pure white
Thank you for the stars in the night
Thank you for fireworks sparkling
Thank you for diamonds on necklaces and rings
Thank you for the glitter on a birthday card
Thank you for a long patterned tabard.

Thank you for the clouds at the tip of a mountain
Thank you for the water spurting out of a fountain
Thank you for a harbour filled with yachts
Thank you for a web filled with dewdrops
Thank you for a butterfly getting pollen from a flower
Thank you for the lights at night on Blackpool Tower
Thank you for a beautiful white swan
Thank you for the dresses you'd see at a prom.

Thank you for a rainbow beaming so high
Thank you for an eagle soaring through the sky
Thank you for the colourful shells
Thank you for the wedding bells
Thank you for a waterfall
Thank you for a colourful dancing ball
Thank you for a moth fluttering in the sky
Thank you for all of this because it's enough to make you cry.

Poppy Owsin (10)
Greenfield Primary School, Countesthorpe

Hunger

Hunger is white like chicken.
It looks like a roast dinner flowing in the air,
It feels like a fork that has been stabbed in my heart,
It sounds like my mum cooking dinner,
It tastes like pasta,
It smells like roast chicken,
It reminds me of me eating a roast on Christmas Day.

Daniel Glover (9)
Greenfield Primary School, Countesthorpe

Thank You For Smiles

Thanks for smiles that make me feel warm inside
Thank you for smiles that give me pride
Thanks for smiles that mean so much
Thank you for smiles that really touch
Thanks for smiles when I'm over the moon
Thank you for smiles that will reach me soon
Thanks for smiles that make life fun
Thank you for smiles that shine like the sun.

Thank you for smiles that set me free
Thanks for smiles that let me be
Thank you for smiles that are always around
Thanks for smiles that pick me up off the ground
Thank you for smiles that are full of bliss
Thanks for smiles that give me a kiss
Thank you for smiles when I go on my holiday
Thanks for smiles that like me my own way.

Thank you for smiles I will never forget
Thanks for smiles when I'm upset
Thank you for smiles that cheer me up
Thanks for smiles that bring me good luck
Thank you for smiles that encourage me
Thanks for smiles that I can see
Thank you for smiles that I receive
Thanks for smiles that never leave.

Thank you for smiles that blow me away
Thanks for smiles I trust every day
Thank you for smiles I always know are there
Thanks for smiles that float everywhere
Thank you for smiles that are in the atmosphere
Thanks for smiles that are always near
Thank you for smiles that are always my friend
Thanks for smiles that love me till the end.

Jessica Widdowson (11)
Greenfield Primary School, Countesthorpe

Fear

Fear is grey like a cloudy day or a teardrop rolling down your face,
It looks like a big red cross in your maths book standing out so bold,
It feels like a bony hand crawling up your back ever so ridged and old,
It sounds like a parrot squawking in your ear,
Like a fire engine or a charging deer.
It tastes like a flaming fire, burning in your mouth,
It smells like smoke in a misty room,
Fear reminds me of a ghostly gloom.

Chloe Oram (10)
Greenfield Primary School, Countesthorpe

Thank You For Friends

Thank you for the friends that help me win
Thank you for the friends that stay with me through thick and thin
Thank you for the friends who stay and listen to me
Thanks for the friends who feel like part of my family
Thank you for the friends whose friendship is pure
Thanks for the friends who encourage me to do things I've never done before
Thanks for the friends who will always make up in the end
And thank you for the friends whose friendship will never go round the bend.

Thanks for the friends who cheer me up when I'm sad
Thank you for the friends who stay with me even when I'm mad
Thank you for the friends I do really need
Thanks for the friends who help me at top speed
Thank you for the friends who share my hopes and dreams
Thanks for the friends who tell bullies to stop being mean.
Thank you for the friends who dry my tears
And thank you for the friends who chase away my fears.

Thank you for the friends who make me want to get up in the morning
Thanks for friends who say well done when I've only done a little thing
Thank you for friends that help me sleep at night
Thanks for the friends who never fight
Thanks for the friends who make me feel confident
Thank you for the friends who get me towards my achievement
Thanks for the friends who can get quite loud
Thank you for the friends who make me stand out from the crowd.

Thank you for the friends who make me feel wanted
Thanks for the friends who give me good thoughts in my head
Thank you for the friends I love
Thanks for the friends that are from above
Thank you for the friends who share fun times
Thanks for the friends that I'm glad are mine
Thank you for the friends who support me and what I like to do
Thank you for my friends and yes that's you!

Holly Whatsize (11)
Greenfield Primary School, Countesthorpe

Excitedness

Excitedness is blue like the sea.
It feels like you're fizzing up.
It tastes like juicy drinks.
It smells like lovely fresh air.
It looks like bubbles bubbling up.
It sounds like fireworks crackling.
Excitedness reminds me of a sunny day at the beach.

Esmé Hill (10)
Greenfield Primary School, Countesthorpe

Thank You For Friends

Thank you for friends who comfort you
Thank you for friends who listen to your view
Thank you for friends who play with you too
Thank you for friends who look after you
Thank you for friends who help you
Thank you for friends who encourage you
Thank you for friends who share
Thank you for friends who treat you with care.

Thank you for friends that never moan
Thank you for friends who never leave you alone
Thank you for friends who share their ideas with you too
Thank you for friends who always believe you too
Thank you for friends who forgive you if you've lied
Thank you for friends who never leave your side
Thank you for friends who make you smile
Thank you for friends who make life worthwhile.

Thank you for friends who never frown
Thank you for friends who don't let you down
Thank you for friends who go with you to town
Thank you for friends who comfort you when you're down
Thank you for friends who go with you to hike
Thank you for friends who don't care what you look like
Thank you for friends who help you ride
Thank you for friends who keep you warm inside.

Thank you for friends who are funny
Thank you for friends who lend you money
Thank you for friends who help you after you've cried
Thank you for friends who stay by your side
Thank you for friends who keep you happy
Thank you for friends who are never snappy
Thank you for friends who cheer you up
Thank you for friends who always make up.

Erica Ferris (10)
Greenfield Primary School, Countesthorpe

Love

Love is thick as a red heart,
It feels like candy sweets falling from the sky,
It tastes of chocolate in my mouth,
It sounds like an angel singing from the sky,
It looks like hearts singing in my ears,
It smells like sweets in a shop,
Love reminds me of love hearts.

Larissa Chamberlain (10)
Greenfield Primary School, Countesthorpe

Thank You For People

Thank you for people who I love
Thank you for the people who are as soft as a dove
Thank you for the people who look like my gran
Thank you for the people who cook like my mam
Thank you for the people who like the kisses
Thank you for the people who like the missus
Thank you for the people who think I'm so great
Thank you for the people who start on a clean slate.

Thank you for the people who are always happy
Thank you for the people who think I'm wacky
Thank you for the people who are always caring
Thank you for the people who are never scaring
Thank you for the people who are always there
Thank you for the people who are up for a dare
Thank you for the people who are always glad
Thank you for the people who are never bad.

Thank you for the people who are very generous
Thank you for the people who are extremely glamorous
Thank you for the people who are very calm
Thank you for the people who are a real charm
Thank you for the people who have a smile
Thank you for the people who are there for a while
Thank you for the people who like a sound
Thank you for the people who are always around.

Thank you for the people who are very proud
Thank you for the people who are very loud
Thank you for the people who like a laugh
Thank you for the people who like a bath
Thank you for the people who are very curious
Thank you for the people who are very notorious
Thank you for the people who like to smirk
Thank you for the people who like to work.

Connor Mason (10)
Greenfield Primary School, Countesthorpe

Love

Love is red like a heart,
It feels like we will never be apart,
It looks like a butterfly,
It tastes like apple pie.
It smells like a gorgeous rose,
Love reminds me of Valentine's Day
Because it's a dream away!

Georgie Douglas (10)
Greenfield Primary School, Countesthorpe

Thank You For Smiles

Thank you for smiles we use every day
Thank you for smiles that take worries away
Thanks for smiles that make me feel happy
Thanks for smiles that are short and snappy
Thank you for smiles when friends and family are there
Thank you for smiles that are everywhere
Thanks for smiles when people encourage you
Thanks for smiles when you're feeling blue.

Thank you for smiles that make us glad
Thank you for smiles when we're feeling sad
Thanks for smiles at a special occasion
Thanks for smiles all around the nation
Thanks for smiles when you need them most
Thank you for smiles that come in the post
Thanks for smiles when you're really scared
Thanks for smiles when we are compared.

Thank you for smiles that brighten up the day
Thank you for smiles all the way even in May
Thanks for smiles that show you care
Thanks for smiles all in the fresh air
Thanks for smiles when your friends make you laugh
Thank you for smiles when you have a photograph
Thanks for smiles when a new family member arrives
Thanks for smiles when you're on a drive.

Thank you for smiles that make you like who you are
Thank you for smiles that make you feel like a star
Thanks for smiles that make you feel part of it
Thank you for smiles when I have a banana split
Thank you for smiles that you will never forget
Thanks for smiles when you're upset
Thanks for smiles that make a day a day
Thank you for smiles that we all got today.

Hannah Allured (11)
Greenfield Primary School, Countesthorpe

Fear

Fear feels like ice cubes crawling down your spine,
Fear looks like spiders, creeping in a mine,
Fear tastes like spices burning in your throat,
Fear smells like dead rats hiding in your coat,
Fear reminds me of a spirit, always lurking near,
Out of everything I don't like, number one is fear!

Rebecca Read (10)
Greenfield Primary School, Countesthorpe

Happiness!

Happiness tastes like chocolate melting on your tongue!
Happiness feels like a warm tingling feeling inside!
Happiness smells like roast potatoes and chicken just out of the oven!
Happiness sounds like birds singing and flitting about!
Happiness looks like smiles and grins on happy children's faces!
Happiness reminds me of a big hug from my mum!

Tim Stokes (9)
Greenfield Primary School, Countesthorpe

Fear Is A Monster

Fear is a monster
It sounds like a snake hissing through the night
It tastes like rotten poison
It smells like garbage dipped in sour milk
It looks like Hell
It feels like rough scales
It reminds me of snakes from nightmares crawling on my flesh.

Allister Fenton-Jones (10)
Greenfield Primary School, Countesthorpe

Sadness

Sadness is dark blue like the sea
It looks like a sea of tears
It feels like you're on your own
It sounds like a sea of waves
It tastes like the salty sea
It smells like the salty sea air
It reminds me of my sister bullying me.

Grace Varney (9)
Greenfield Primary School, Countesthorpe

Fear

Fear reminds me of the dark and lonely corners in my life
Fear feels like a body in a church graveyard
Fear looks like the darkness of the night waiting to pounce
Fear tastes like mud and slime, forcing yourself to eat
Fear sounds like a ghost's footsteps going to my bedroom in the dark night
Fear smells like rotten cabbage, green or brown, or horrid black.

Chloe Bolsover (9)
Greenfield Primary School, Countesthorpe

Anger Is A Monster

It sounds like a man singing in the shower
It tastes like soapy water
It smells like aftershave on his face
It looks like steam in the bathroom
It feels like water off my head
It reminds me of my horrible dreams.

Nicole Hunt (9)
Greenfield Primary School, Countesthorpe

Anger Is A Man

It sounds like a man singing in the shower
It tastes like soapy water
It smells like aftershave on his beard
It looks like steam in the bathroom
It feels like water on my head
It reminds me of my horrible dreams.

Lily North (9)
Greenfield Primary School, Countesthorpe

Happiness

It feels like a hot bath
It tastes like something sweet
It smells like a bar of chocolate
It sounds like my mum and dad speaking
It reminds me of Mum and Dad.

Laura Flude (9)
Greenfield Primary School, Countesthorpe

Sadness

Sadness is like the night sky clouds flowing by
It looks like a river full of tears
It feels like dead flowers falling to the ground
It sounds like echoing screams and tears
It tastes like a dry mouth
It smells like damp gardens
Sadness reminds me of my grandad in Heaven.

Maddie Wheway (9)
Greenfield Primary School, Countesthorpe

Good Riddance To Fear

Good riddance to fear that makes you cry
Goodbye to fear when you can't get shut-eye
Good riddance to fear when you're alone
Good riddance to fear when you're lost with no phone
Goodbye to fear that makes your stomach churn
Goodbye to the fear that seems to burn
Good riddance to fear that you'll never get out
And bye for the fear that just makes you shout.

Good riddance to fear when you're trying to be brave
Goodbye to fear of your loves and their graves
Good riddance to fear of having no friends
Good riddance to fear that drives you round bends
Goodbye to fear that no one can stop
Goodbye to fear when you're at the top
Good riddance to fear of no more fun
And to the fear that makes you run.

Good riddance to fear when you're waiting for news
Goodbye to fear that gives you the blues
Good riddance to fear late at night
Good riddance to fear that something might bite
Goodbye to fear that feels like falling
Goodbye to fear that someone is calling
Good riddance to fear that never goes away
And see ya to fear, fear that no one will stay.

Good riddance to fear of monsters under the bed
Goodbye to fear of being misled
Good riddance to fear of being left
Goodbye to fear of madness and theft
Goodbye to fear that is full of terror
Goodbye to fear that goes on forever
Good riddance to fear that cuts you like a knife
And fear that will haunt you for the rest of your life.

Louise Cosby (10)
Greenfield Primary School, Countesthorpe

Fear Is A Creature

It sounds like a blackbird shrieking
It tastes like a piece of mouldy cheese
It smells like a dead body left for a year
It looks like a black ghostly shadow
It feels like needles and spiky ice
It reminds me of the nightmares I fear every night.

Jayde Stafford (9)
Greenfield Primary School, Countesthorpe

Good Riddance To Pain

Good riddance to the pain of regret
And to the pain of losing a pet
Good riddance to the pain of seeing your blood
And to the pain of losing something loved
Good riddance to the pain of arguments
And to the pain of failed events
Good riddance to the pain of blisters
And, of course, the pain of sisters.

Goodbye to all the pain of loss
And the pain of feeling cross
Goodbye to the pain of Dad's bad jokes
And to the pain of cigarette smoke
Goodbye to the pain of terrible grief
And to the pain of brushing your teeth
Goodbye to the pain of socks that pong
And to the pain of birthdays gone wrong.

Farewell to the pain of illness
And to the pain of great distress
Farewell to the pain of a frown
And to the pain of being let down
Farewell to the pain of bad memories
And to the pain of being stung by bees
Farewell to the pain of bad nightmares
And to the pain of bus fares.

Good riddance to the pain of falling
And to the pain of babies bawling
Good riddance to the pain of a good day's end
And to the pain of saying bye to a friend
Good riddance to the pain of divorce
And to the pain of great force
Good riddance to the pain of tight rings
And to the pain of all sorts of things.

Rebecca Oughton (10)
Greenfield Primary School, Countesthorpe

Hunger

It sounds like a frog croaking in your tummy.
It looks like a skeleton all dried up.
It tastes like cold, dry water in your throat.
It smells like fresh food you cannot get to.
It feels like a volcano about to explode everywhere.
It reminds me of sad starving children in Africa.

Katie Ford (9)
Greenfield Primary School, Countesthorpe

Thank You For Love

Thank you for love when I am all alone
Thank you for love when I'm on my own
Thank you for love when it means loyalty
Thank you for love when it can be
Thank you for love when it means value
Thank for you for love when they are there for you
Thank you for love it proves devotion
Thank you for love it proves emotion.

Thanks for love when you can trust
Thanks for love when it means lust
Thanks for love when it is inspiration
Thanks for love when it is admiration
Thanks for love when you know it is sharing
Thanks for love when you know they are caring
Thanks for love when it is protection
Thanks for love when it makes affection.

Thank you for love when there is a helping hand
Thank you for love when it springs back like a band
Thank you for love for it is at first sight
Thank you for love when there's no fight
Thank you for love when you can admire
Thank you for love when they can desire
Thank you for love when you can adore
Thank you for love when it comes back for more.

Thanks for love where there's no debate
Thanks for love when you find a soulmate
Thanks for love that comes from a book
Thanks for love that gives you good luck
Thanks for love that makes you united
Thanks for love that makes them delighted
Thanks for love that's with me all day
Thanks for love that never goes away.

Sophie Hassell (10)
Greenfield Primary School, Countesthorpe

Happiness

Happiness tastes like melting chocolate
Happiness smells like fresh air
Happiness sounds like a blackbird singing
Happiness feels like your own mum hugging you
Happiness reminds me of my friends and relations.

Chloé Morson (9)
Greenfield Primary School, Countesthorpe

Laughter

It smells like fresh air in the sky
It sounds like cheers from a party
It sounds like a heart beating inside you
It reminds me of when I first smiled
It reminds me of my mum and dad messing about
It looks like melted chocolate cake
It feels like a bird in your hand, fluffy and tickly
It tastes like all my favourite foods and a hot chocolate
Making me smile.

Sophie Hancock (9)
Greenfield Primary School, Countesthorpe

Silence

It reminds me of a small, empty, deserted village
It sounds like nothing but pure silence
It tastes like still water trickling down my lips
It looks like a pale white ghost spiralling me
It feels like a frozen hand swiping across my face.

Luke Parr (10)
Greenfield Primary School, Countesthorpe

Fears

F ear sounds like a deadly scream from down a dark, damp alley,
E verything smells like wet sand with a touch of rotten seaweed in a valley,
A nd fear looks like a mouldy black ball of fire, waiting to burn right through you,
R ound the corner, it feels like your thumb grips tight as someone shouts, *'Boo!'*
S creaming fills the air and that's when you fear and it tastes like a bowl of manky
Brussels sprouts.

Abbey Ford (10)
Greenfield Primary School, Countesthorpe

Horror

It looks like cars in a rush hour, when you're in the middle of a crash.
It sounds like a baby screaming, no mum around.
It sounds like a woman stabbed, all alone, no phone.
It smells like burning ashes, dead bodies underneath or cold chains in prison cells.
It feels like blood and sweat, trickling off your forehead.
Or poison pricks when they hit your skin.
It tastes like metal melted down or fire to burn your tongue.

Sophie Wain (9)
Greenfield Primary School, Countesthorpe

The Cheers Of Happiness

Happiness sounds like cheerful children
Whizzing down a fast waterslide,
In a water park having a fantastic time.
Happiness smells like a delicious, sweet strawberry ice cream with lots of sauce,
Melting in the rays of the burning, hot sun on a relaxing sandy beach.
Happiness feels like swimming slowly over soft waves in the peaceful blue ocean.
Happiness tastes like Cadbury's chocolate melting on my tongue.
Happiness reminds me of a nice, calm sunny day.

Libby Bowler (9)
Greenfield Primary School, Countesthorpe

Darkness

Darkness looks like a dark knight galloping on his black stallion,
Darkness smells like a rotting corpse, murdered by Attila the Hun.
Darkness feels like the shadows eating through my skin,
Darkness tastes like year-old spinach being forced down my chin.
Darkness sounds like a woman with a dagger in her flesh,
Darkness reminds me of an enemy army breaking through the wire mesh.

Dan Greenhill (10)
Greenfield Primary School, Countesthorpe

Surprised

Surprised is yellow like party decorations,
It feels like magic air all around everyone,
It sounds like laughing and having fun,
It smells like love from children's loving hearts,
It tastes like chocolate cake sliding down my throat,
It looks like a sunny day in the grassy hills,
Surprised reminds me of my birthday.

Bethany Rollett (9)
Greenfield Primary School, Countesthorpe

Hate

Hate is an octopus
It sounds like a dragon
It tastes like grease
It smells like rotten egg and blood
It looks like one-eyed Willy
It feels like bristles of a brush
It reminds me of the cat creature.

Kiedis Clay (9)
Greenfield Primary School, Countesthorpe

Fear Is A Dragon

It sounds like a lion roaring his life out.
It tastes like rotten blood dirty as can be.
It smells like an ogre that's not had a wash for 100 years.
It looks like a big, fat pig rotting.
It feels like a snake's skin.
It reminds me of a big snake bigger than a school.

Jake Scott (9)
Greenfield Primary School, Countesthorpe

Hate Is A Devil

It sounds like a lion roaring
It tastes like a rotten egg
It smells like a mouldy lump of mouldy cow poo
It looks like a monster eating
It feels like a crocodile hunting
It reminds me of my sister.

Matthew Lawson (9)
Greenfield Primary School, Countesthorpe

Fear Is A Cheetah

It sounds like a cat scratching
It tastes like mouldy cheese
It smells like dry blood
It looks like red, beady eyes
It feels like rough skin
It reminds me of my nightmare.

Tom Morris
Greenfield Primary School, Countesthorpe

Love

Love is red like a soft bunny
Love smells like a lovely red rose
Love tastes like the sweetest chocolate
Love sounds like birds cheeping everywhere
Love feels like a happy pill running down my throat
Love looks like fields of roses
Love reminds me of a little butterfly.

Sam Jones (10)
Greenfield Primary School, Countesthorpe

Thank You For Dreams

Thank you for dreams that make me satisfied
Thank you for dreams that make me warm inside
Thank you for dreams where I have wings
Thank you for dreams where I'm eating things
Thank you for dreams with a great big teddy
Thank you for dreams that help me to get ready
Thank you for dreams where I'm the boss
Thank you for dreams with an alien called Ross.

Thank you for dreams where I meet a clown
Thank you for dreams that stop me feeling down
Thank you for dreams where I go to places
Thank you for dreams with alien races
Thank you for dreams where I'm in a rocket
Thank you for dreams where I find a locket
Thank you for dreams where I'm over the moon
Thank you for dreams where I eat with a spoon.

Thank you for dreams that make me smile
Thank you for dreams that last a while
Thank you for dreams where I go to the beach
Thank you for dreams where I eat a peach
Thank you for dreams where I rule the world
Thank you for dreams where the bully's lips curled
Thank you for dreams with my pet dog
Thank you for dreams where I sleep like a log.

Thank you for dreams that really inspire
Thank you for dreams with electric wire
Thank you for dreams where I tell jokes
Thank you for dreams where there's no such thing as a hoax
Thank you for dreams with lots of pets
Thank you for dreams where I go to the vet's
Thank you for dreams where no one can weep
Thank you for dreams that help me go to sleep.

Matthew Dale (10)
Greenfield Primary School, Countesthorpe

Fear Is A Monster

It sounds like a roaring troll.
It tastes like a smelly turkey.
It smells like a dead bleeding shark.
It looks like a furry four armed beast, with a murderous roar.
It feels like a garbage of cookies.
It reminds me of a scorpion creeping up to me.

Michael Watson (10)
Greenfield Primary School, Countesthorpe

Thank You For The Memories

Thanks for memories that make me glad
Thanks for memories that make me sad
Maybe a birthday celebration
And when your parents give affection
Thanks for memories that set me free
Thanks for memories of the ice sea
Thanks for memories of the first kiss
And those little moments that were bliss.

Thank the memories when we had fun
Thanks for memories of the bad things we've done
Thanks for memories on the seashore
Thanks for memories that I adore
Thanks for memories of my pet dog
We had so, so much fun in the fog
And all those little things that can touch
And some things we can miss very much.

The glistening stars and moon up way high
And the smell of my mum's fresh baked pie
Thanks for memories for a sticky treat
Thank you for dessert that was so sweet
Thanks for memories that we regret
Thanks for memories that we forget
And some memories set you on fire
And some things are just our heart's desire.

Thanks for memories for you and I
Thanks for the sun beaming in the sky
Thanks for memories for a great day
And when my best friend came round to play
Thank memories confused in your head
Thank God we don't have them in our bed
These are things we cannot touch
But anyway thank you very much.

Megan Fairbrother (11)
Greenfield Primary School, Countesthorpe

My Fear!

Fear is an alien
It tastes like mouldy cream been left for ten years.
It smells like jelly in a rubbish dump.
It sounds like a baby crying in his bed.
It looks like a big purple blob with blue spots.
It feels like thick lumpy porridge.
It reminds me of my bed cover that I snuggle in every night.

Brogan Burley (9)
Greenfield Primary School, Countesthorpe

Thank You For Smiles

Thanks for smiles that are always there,
Thanks for smiles that show you care.
Smiles make you feel so good,
Smile 'cause you know you should.
Thank you for smiles you need more than two,
Smile and the world smiles with you!

Thank you for smiles they make new friends,
When you smile don't pretend.
Smile when you watch a good show,
Smile at someone you love or know.
Thank you for smiles day and night,
Thank you for smiles black and white.
Thank you for smiles across the nation,
Thank you for smiles from every destination.

Sarah Moore (10)
Greenfield Primary School, Countesthorpe

Fear

You can see fear in someone's eyes
As it shivers, as it shines.
Fear feels like a monster moving its hand down your spine.
Fear tastes cold and bitter, it makes you sick to your belly.
Fear smells like rotten chips, vegetables that have not been eaten
And fish that are really smelly.
Fear sounds like people screeching for their lives,
The screams, the shouts, the non-stop screaming nights.
Fear reminds me of the graveyard where a great killer died,
It reminds me of difficult times I remember when I come here,
The past, wars, and fights.

Holly Madden (10)
Greenfield Primary School, Countesthorpe

Happiness

Happiness is yellow like the sun shining on you,
It looks like lots of scampi and chips floating down from Heaven,
It feels like a big warm bath,
It sounds like the sea bashing to the shore,
It tastes like chocolate running down my chin,
It smells like the lush green grass,
It reminds me of my mum cuddling me.

Sophie Beckett (9)
Greenfield Primary School, Countesthorpe

Thank You For Friends

Thank you for friends that do stuff together
Thank you for friends like Mia Mellor
Thank you for friends that dry up your fears
Thank you for friends that dry up your tears
Thank you for friends that hold on forever
Thank you for friends that keep together
Thank you for friends that cheer you on
Thank you for friends that shine upon.

Thank you for friends that really do share
Thank you for friends that really do care
Thank you for friends that make your heart gold
Thank you for friends that really do mould
Thank you for friends that shine on you like the sun
Thank you for friends that get things done
Thank you for friends that care for you
Thank you for friends old and new.

Thank you for friends that give you a chill
Thank you for friends that are kind and loveable
Thank you for friends that are not that dull
Thank you for friends that help and see
Thank you for friends that is the key.

Thank you for friends that really cry
Thank you for friends that sometimes lie
Thank you for friends that really are fun
Thank you for friends that are like the sun
Thank you for friends that get things wrong
Thank you for friends come and now gone
Thank you for friends that long live your life!

Faye Turnbull (11)
Greenfield Primary School, Countesthorpe

Love

Love reminds us of angels, soaps and happiness.
Love gives people pride and joy in time.
Love's like rainbows appearing in the sky.
Love gives us bliss, merriment and delight.
Love sounds like gentle voices coming from the sky.
Love gives us elation, contentment and jubilation.
Love tastes like chocolate, simmering in a pan.
Love ends in words,
A lie, stupidity,
You feel so sad,
Heartbroken and angry.

Luke Andrew Salmon (10)
Greenfield Primary School, Countesthorpe

Thank You For Smiles

Thank you for smiles which set me free
Thanks for smiles that let me see
Thanks for smiles that show you care
Thanks for smiles that show you're there
Thanks for smiles when I've been helpful
Thanks for smiles that make me joyful
Thanks for smiles that make me glad
Thanks for smiles when I'm feeling sad.

Thanks for smiles that make me feel warm inside
Thanks for smiles which means I don't have to hide
Thanks for smiles which make us attractive
Thanks for smiles which keep me active
Thanks for smiles that leave me feeling high
Thanks for smiles that brighten up the sky
Thanks for smiles that cheer me up each day
Thanks for smiles that send me on my way.

Thanks for the smile when I come home at night
Thanks for the smile which shows I'm alright
Thanks for smiles when I'm over the moon
Thanks for our smiles when we listen to our tunes
Thanks for your smile when nothing makes sense
Thanks for the smile which gives me confidence
Thanks for smiles when I get a bug
Thank you for smiles that come with a hug.

Thanks for smiles that are soft and warm
Thanks for smiles that could blow up a storm
Thanks for smiles when I score a goal
Thanks for smiles that make me feel whole
Thanks for smiles when I go to bed
Thanks for smiles when I lay down my head
Thanks for smiles that come from above
Thanks for smiles that show I'm loved.

Nick Hollis (11)
Greenfield Primary School, Countesthorpe

A Fear Of A Sloppy Alien

Fear is an alien
It tastes like mouldy jelly
It smells like mixed food left from three years ago
It feels like thick lumpy porridge!
It looks like a green sloppy blob!
It sounds like a baby shouting for its dummy
It reminds me of a big squelchy patch of mud!

Amberley Vessey (9)
Greenfield Primary School, Countesthorpe

Thank You For Friends

Thank you for the friends we need
Thank you for friends who do good deeds
Thank you for friends when you're on your own
Thank you for friends who never groan
Thank you for friends who give you pride
Thank you for the friends that keep you warm inside
Thank you for the friends that make you smile
Thank you for the friends that keep you calm for a while.

Thanks for the friends who let you play
Thanks for the friends who are there for you every day
Thanks for the friends who never ignore
Thanks for the friends who make you feel cared for
Thanks for the friends who never leave you out
Thanks for the friends who never shout
Thanks for the friends who help you buy new things
Thanks for the friends who give you friendship rings.

Thank you for the friends that stand up for you
Thank you for the friends that see you through
Thank you for the friends who put you first
Thank you for the friends who are there for you at your worst
Thank you for the friends who cheer you up
Thank you for the friends who give you thumbs-up
Thank you for the friends who brighten your days
Thank you for the friends who appreciate your ways.

Thanks for friends who are always there
Thanks for friends who are never unfair
Thanks for friends who are really funny
Thanks for friends who are bright and sunny
Thanks for friends who will dry your tears
Thanks for friends who will be there for years
Thanks for the friends who spend time with you
Thanks for your friends, even if you only have a few.

Amy Newman (11)
Greenfield Primary School, Countesthorpe

Love

Love is red like a love heart.
It feels sweet and warm,
It tastes like chocolate, swilling through my mouth,
It sounds like an angel singing in my ear,
It looks like you can see confetti hearts falling from the sky,
Love reminds me we will never be apart.

Rebecca Warren (10)
Greenfield Primary School, Countesthorpe

Thanks For Smiles

Thanks for smiles on my face
They can be in any place
Thanks for smiles that wake me up
And things make me smile like a pup
Thanks for people who are very smiley
Thanks for people who act happily
Smiles are obviously free
There are smiles as far as the eye can see.

Thanks for smiles that make me laugh
And all of the smiles that I have
Thank you for the smiles I keep
And all of the smiles that make me leap
Thank you very much for my smile
That keeps me happy all the while
Thank you for the smiles so bright
Smiles that stop me from starting a fight.

Thanks for cheerful stuff I say
Like smile in the morning smile all day
Thanks for smiles that make me glad
They keep me happy when I'm sad
They make me relax when I'm stressed
Smiles are really the very best
They show people how you feel
They show some things are a really big deal.

Thanks for things that are funny
That make your day really sunny
They brighten up your day
And makes sadness go away
You're never too tired to smile
There are smiles for billions of miles
No one can steal your smile from you
No matter how much they have or what they do.

Steve Singh (10)
Greenfield Primary School, Countesthorpe

Sadness

Sadness feels like it's the end of the world
Sadness looks like a lost puppy without his mum
Sadness tastes like a Big Mac without the beef inside
Sadness sounds like my relatives' funeral bells
Sadness smells like rotten garbage
Sadness reminds me of an orphan starving on a street.

Ellie Gosling (10)
Greenfield Primary School, Countesthorpe

Thank You

Thank you for my family's laugh
Thank you for my family's path
Thank you for my family, warm like fire
Thank you for my family's desire
Thank you for family's love so pure
Thank you for family's that are for sure
Thank you for my family's love
My family makes me rise above.

Thank you for families that beautifully sing
Thank you for families that love everything
Thank you for families that are definitely fun
Thank you for families that help you overcome
Thank you for families that do care
Thank you for families that try out a dare
Thank you for families underground
Everyone needs a family around.

Thank you for families that want you and need
Thank you for families that do a good deed
Thank you for families that set you free
Thank you for my family that stay with me
Thank you for my family's smile
Thank you for families worthwhile
Thank you for families you can reach out and touch
Everybody's family loves them very, very much.

Thank you for families that help you improve
Thank you for families that aren't on the move
Thank you for families without a doubt
Thank you for families that always help out
Thank you for my family's wishes
Thank you for my family's kisses
Thank you for families that say 'I do'
Everyone needs a family like you!

Melissa Dawkins (11)
Greenfield Primary School, Countesthorpe

Sadness

Sadness feels like tomorrow will never come.
Sadness tastes like the sea without the sun.
Sadness looks like a starving orphan on the street.
Sadness sounds like my sister stamping her angry feet.
Sadness smells like fish without any batter.
Sadness reminds me of my mum in a clatter.

Bethan Grant (10)
Greenfield Primary School, Countesthorpe

Thank You For Waves

Thank you for waves that bring in the shore
Thank you for waves we want more
Thanks for waves sparkling blue
Thanks for waves that shine on you
Thanks for waves gleaming in the sunshine
Thanks for waves relaxing and fine
Thank you for waves swaying in the night
Every night waves are rocking in the moonlight.

Thanks for waves that bring us great memories
Thanks for waves crashing in the great breeze
Thank you for waves a beautiful sight
Thank you for waves they lift up the light
Thanks for waves that bring us friends
Thanks for waves that make amends
Thank you for waves that are in our dreams
These are the waves we really mean.

Thank you for waves that encourage you
Thank you for waves that bring us through
Thanks for waves full of happiness
Thanks for waves that dries up sadness
Thanks for waves ice-cold but great
Thanks for waves that brought my mate
Thank you for waves that bring us smiles
But thank you mostly for waves of love.

Thank you for waves that make us cry
Thank you for waves that stop us to lie
Thanks for waves that rise in the sun
Thanks for waves that make us have fun
Thank you for waves kind and caring
Thank you for waves soft and sharing
Thanks for waves great and mighty
Goodbye to waves that make tsunamis!

Mia Mellor (11)
Greenfield Primary School, Countesthorpe

Fun

Fun is white like snow
It feels like I'm at a funfair.
It looks like I'm on my best rides ever
It tastes like dairy milk delicious chocolate
It sounds like roller coasters
It smells like candyfloss as I lick my lips
Fun reminds me of having a party.

Aysha Sainsbury (9)
Greenfield Primary School, Countesthorpe

Thank You For Smiles

Thank you for smiles that make me cry
Thanks for smiles that make me reach for the sky
Thank you for smiles when you're in pain
Thanks for smiles from people vain
Thank you for smiles from someone loved
Thanks for smiles from the heavens above
Thank you for smiles when your birthday's remembered
Thanks for smiles that look tremendous.

Thank you for smiles when you've just been hugged
Thanks for smiles when you're being bugged
Thank you for smiles that touch the heart
Thanks for smiles when you've got the main part
Thank you for smiles when you're alone in the dark
Thanks for smiles when you're playing in the park
Thank you for when defeated in a game
Thanks for smiles that might look plain.

Thank you for smiles that make me fight
Thanks for smiles that shine bright
Thank you for smiles when you pass a test
Thanks for smiles when you feel the best
Thank you for smiles that don't reach the eyes
Thanks for smiles that make me touch the sky
Thank you for smiles that make me sad
Thanks for smiles that make me glad.

Thank you for smiles that make me complete
Thanks for smiles when you've had a defeat
Thank you for smiles that make me frown
Thanks for smiles that makes me feel down
Thank you for smiles that set me free
Thanks for smiles from you and me
Thank you for smiles that I can't touch
Thanks for smiles we need so much.

Lucy Nealon (11)
Greenfield Primary School, Countesthorpe

Fear

Fear is dark black like the sky at night,
It smells like raw fish,
It looks like a hairy spider,
It tastes like rotten fish from last night,
It feels like someone pulling your hair,
It sounds like nails scraping down a blackboard,
Fear reminds me of people shouting in my ear.

Rhianna Hubbard (9)
Greenfield Primary School, Countesthorpe

Thank You

Thank you for the kisses I see
Thank you for kisses for you and me
Thank you for kisses that burn like fire
Thank you for kisses that inspire
Thank you for kisses that stay with me
Thank you for kisses that set me free
Thank you for kisses that are pure
Thank you for kisses that are for sure.

Thank you for kisses so great
Thanks for kisses that make me faint
Thanks for kisses that catch me when I fall
Thanks for kisses big or small
Thank you for kisses that cheer me up
Thanks for kisses from my pup
Thanks for kisses in my memories
Thanks for kisses from my family.

Thanks for kisses on birthday cards
Thanks for kisses from Frank Lampard
Thank you for kisses that never end
Thanks for kisses from my friend
Thanks for kisses that make me feel good
Thank you for kisses from my childhood
Thank you for kisses that I share
Thanks for kisses that I care.

Thanks for kisses that keep me strong
Thanks for kisses I know were wrong
Thank you for kisses from my mum
Thanks for kisses that send my legs numb
Thanks for kisses that overcome
Thanks for kisses I know were dumb
Thank you for kisses that tingle on touch
Thank you, very, very much.

Molly Baxter (11)
Greenfield Primary School, Countesthorpe

Fear

Fear is white because when you get scared you go all pale
It smells like rotten cheese
It looks like you're all cold and frozen
It tastes like smoke
It feels like a ghost is coming after you.

Fear reminds me of a monster.

Frazer Jones (9)
Greenfield Primary School, Countesthorpe

Thank You

Thank you for love that stays with me through thick and thin
Thank you for love that I need to help me win
Thank you for love that is pure
Thank you for the love that I'll always care for
Thank you for love that is in my memories
Thank you for love in families
Thank you for the love that's in flirts
Thank you for the love that hurts.

Thank you for the love that's in a Valentine
Thank you for the love that grows over time
Thank you for love from the missus
Thank you for the love in hugs and kisses
Thank you for the love that helps me win achievement
Thank you for the love that makes me confident
Thank you for the love that helps me overcome
Thank you for the love from my mum.

Thank you for the love that's romance channels
Thank you for love for the endangered animals
Thank you for the love that overcomes fears
Thank you for the love that wipes away my tears
Thank you for the love for those that care
Thank you for the love that is always there
Thank you for the love from friends
Thank you for the love that mends.

Thank you for the love that keeps me going
Thank you for the love that is showing
Thank you for the love that keeps me warm inside
Thank you for the love you don't hide
Thank you for the love I see
Thank you for the love for me
Thank you for the loving touch
Thank you very much.

Lucy Murray (11)
Greenfield Primary School, Countesthorpe

Darkness

Darkness is black like a pitch-black cave
It feels like you're lost in a dark maze
It looks like the night sky
It smells like a burnt burger
It sounds like a scream in the darkness
It tastes like rotten fish
Darkness reminds me of when I get lost.

Matt Ross (9)
Greenfield Primary School, Countesthorpe

Thank You For Smiles

Thank you for smiles of your friends
Thank you for smiles that will never end
Thanks for smiles that give confidence to you
Thanks for smiles that make you feel blue
Thank you for smiles that let me be
Thank you for smiles that make me feel happy
Thanks for smiles that make me laugh
Thanks for smiles that make me look daft.

Thank you for smiles that make you feel glad
Thank you for smiles that makes you feel bad
Thanks for smiles that make me feel down
Thanks for smiles that make me look like a clown
Thanks for smiles that makes you feel welcome
Thank you for smiles that make you help them
Thanks for smiles that make me feel calm
Thanks for smiles that make me laugh on a farm.

Thank you for smiles off your family
Thank you for smiles that make you live happily
Thanks for smiles that make you feel good inside
Thanks for smiles that give you pride
Thank you for smiles that give you love
Thank you for smiles that come from above
Thanks for smiles that let you pray
Thanks for smiles that never go away.

Thank you for smiles that come when you're on your own
Thank you for smiles that never groan
Thanks for smiles that make you feel good
Thanks for smiles when you're playing in the mud
Thank you for smiles that are never cross or grumpy
Thank you for smiles that never leave you feeling bumpy
Thanks for smiles that make you smile
Thanks for smiles that make you warm for a while.

Charlotte Hanna (11)
Greenfield Primary School, Countesthorpe

Happiness

Happiness is bright red like a love heart,
It reminds me of my beautiful parents,
It tastes like fresh chocolate melting in my mouth,
It sounds like fresh fireworks and church bells ringing,
It smells like fresh candy in the circus,
It looks like a bright red rose,
It feels like the softest pillow in the world.

Joshua Potterton-Orton (9)
Greenfield Primary School, Countesthorpe

Sadness

Sadness looks like somebody about to buy your puppy.
Sadness feels like your dad's about to flush your guppy.
Sadness sounds like funeral music far, far away,
Sadness tastes like guilt after you wouldn't let someone play.

Sadness reminds me of times I never wanted to remember,
Sadness is always there even in December.
Sadness smells like bunnies not cleaned for many days,
Sadness isn't enjoyable, as it hurts in many ways.

Megan Barnes (10)
Greenfield Primary School, Countesthorpe

Darkness

Darkness reminds me of running through a dark, gloomy forest.
Darkness feels like strong fears and destruction in your sore throat.
Darkness sounds like a teenage girl crying and locked in a cellar,
Stamping her bleeding feet.
Darkness looks like oil mixed with acid and blood.
Darkness smells like the burning of rotten heart and gooey liver stew.
Darkness tastes like razor-sharp thistles clinging to your tongue.

Jackson Davis (9)
Greenfield Primary School, Countesthorpe

Darkness

Darkness reminds me of black skeletons dripping with blood,
Darkness looks like giant red explosions and a nuclear bomb explosion,
Darkness sounds like a teenage girl screaming in the middle of a black, gloomy castle,
Darkness feels like all of the bad dreams returning to haunt me,
Darkness smells like rotting mould on someone's toe,
Darkness tastes like Brussels sprouts that I detest.

Josh Salvin (9)
Greenfield Primary School, Countesthorpe

Fear

Fears is black like night
It smells like mouldy cheese
It tastes like black smoke
It feels like a gun pointed at me
It sounds like an explosion near me
Fear reminds me of ghosts riding around me.

George Vellam (9)
Greenfield Primary School, Countesthorpe

Happiness

Happiness is blue like the sky up above.
It tastes like the best food I've ever had.
It feels like a big bag of goodness.
It sounds like kids laughing in the playground.
It looks like a sun as bright as can be.
Happiness reminds me of the fun times I had with my dog Tilly.

Cameron Betteridge (10)
Greenfield Primary School, Countesthorpe

Sadness

Sadness is as black as the big dull sky
It looks like people are leaving me out
It feels like rain pouring down my face
It sounds like people laughing at me
It tastes like mud being shoved in my mouth
It smells like very damp air
Sadness reminds me of my mum and dad fighting.

Danielle Tildesley (9)
Greenfield Primary School, Countesthorpe

Sadness

Sadness is like the dark ocean waves
It looks pale white in the distance
It feels like arrows shooting through my heart
It tastes like the sea of water
It sounds like the wind racing towards me
It smells like smoke rushing by me
Sadness reminds me of getting left out.

Leigha Taylor (10)
Greenfield Primary School, Countesthorpe

Fear

It reminds me of being deserted on a desert island with just water from the sea.
It smells like dead people on the bottom of the ocean.
It feels like I'm the only one hope.
It tastes like the seaweed that washes up on the shore.
It sounds like every morning there's a horn blazing over the world.
I run and see
I yell for help, but they don't see me.
I'll be stuck here for the rest of my life.

David Lennon (9)
Greenfield Primary School, Countesthorpe

Thank You For Memories

Thank you for memories that make me sad
Thanks for memories that leave me feeling bad
Thanks for memories that make me cry
And thanks for memories that leave me feeling dry
Thank you for memories that let me down
Thanks for memories that make me frown
Thanks for memories that I regret
And thanks for memories that I'll never forget.

Thank you for memories that make me proud
Thanks for memories that make me shout out loud
Thanks for memories that really touch
And thanks for memories that I need so much
Thank you for memories that give me emotion
Thanks for memories of the deep blue ocean
Thanks for memories that are so great
And thanks for memories of the first date.

Thank you for memories that leave me in pain
Thanks for memories that put me in vain
Thanks for memories that make life fun
And thanks for memories of me in the sun
Thank you for memories that make me weak
Thanks for memories that we still seek
Thanks for memories that keep me satisfied
And thanks for memories that keep me warm inside.

Thank you for memories for you and I
Thanks for memories that make me shy
Thanks for memories that make me smile
And thanks for memories with grace and style
Thank you for memories that make me complete
Thanks for memories when we've had a defeat
Thanks for memories that come from above
And thanks for memories that I absolutely
Love!

Carolina Sansom (10)
Greenfield Primary School, Countesthorpe

Anger Is A Monster

It sounds like a bull groaning.
It tastes like mouldy milk from one century ago.
It smells like rubbish dipped in poo.
It looks like a green-horned ghost.
It feels like a piece of rotten bread.
It reminds me of the nightmare that comes in the night.

William Parker (9)
Greenfield Primary School, Countesthorpe

Good Riddance

Good riddance to sadness from a baby crying
And good riddance to sadness from someone dying
Sadness whilst watching' Balamory'
Sadness when reading a really sad story
Good riddance to sadness when someone's upset
Good riddance to sadness your birthday they forget
And good riddance to sadness that makes you cry
Good riddance to sadness when you wave goodbye.

Good riddance to sadness when you have a bad dream
And good riddance to sadness when someone's mean
Good riddance to sadness when you're feeling depressed
Good riddance to sadness when you're not at your best
Good riddance to sadness when a beloved pet dies
Good riddance to sadness when you're told lots of lies
Good riddance to sadness whilst watching the rain
And good riddance to sadness when getting the cane.

Good riddance to sadness whilst seeing cruelty
Good riddance to sadness when you have no loyalty
Good riddance to sadness when you are feeling ill
Good riddance to sadness when you want to kill
Good riddance to sadness when you're too small
Good riddance to sadness when you're too tall
Good riddance to sadness when something good ends
Good riddance to sadness when something can't mend.

Good riddance to sadness when you are left out
Good riddance to sadness when you are in doubt
Good riddance to sadness when you have a nightmare
Good riddance to sadness when you're caught in a dare
Good riddance to sadness when there's a world disaster
Good riddance to sadness when you're beaten by the master
Good riddance to sadness when you're at the end of your tether
Goodbye to sadness forever and ever . . .

Lauren Hilton (10)
Greenfield Primary School, Countesthorpe

Love

Love feels like getting a bundle of Easter eggs.
Love sounds like birds singing on a spring morning.
Love looks like a field full of blood-red roses waiting to be picked.
Love tastes like an ice cream sundae.

Amelia Thomas (10)
Greenfield Primary School, Countesthorpe

Water

W aterfalls running and tumbling down
A ctions of sea creatures swimming around
T reasure from under the deep blue sea
E very drop of rain is as clear as crystal
R ivers flowing for miles and miles.

A ll waters pure and infected
N ever dwindle in our perspective
D ifferent coloured fish swimming about.

O ctopus' eight tentacles swivelling around
C oral leaves, green and puffy
E lectric eels stinging sharp
A round the world are different seas
N ever changing, never fading
S ounds of voices muffled underwater.

C atching fish to be eaten
L akes and ponds where ducks and swans swim
E veryone having fun and swimming in the pool
A dolphin splashing and jumping high
R ipples of water where they've been disturbed.

Lauren Smith (10)
Gretton CP School, Gretton

Fire

One spark could lead to an infectious blaze,
That goes on for days and days.

One flicker could lead to a deadly red parade,
Roaring through the streets until the firemen come to aid.

One forgotten cigarette alight,
Could destroy the house within the night.

One tiny flame even has the power,
To destroy the land hour by hour.

One bush fire depriving animals of their homes,
A herd of wandering creatures quietly roams.

One tree blazing away,
The fire passes on day by day.

One fire demolishes trees so tall,
Yet one quick thinking person could save us all.

Esme Troughton (10)
Gretton CP School, Gretton

Fire

Fire is dangerous
Red-hot flames
Fireworks as they bang
Burning ash as you smoke
Sun is bright just like fire
Mist, as the volcanoes blow up
Blazing colours you get from fire.

Fire is warm
Cosy in your room
And soldiers fire at people
You can feel the warmth from your fire.

Beware, your house could be on fire
So get out
And stay out
Ring the fire brigade.

Crackling paper in fire
Sizzling sausages on the barbecue
Hot, warm oven
Different coloured burning fireworks
Boom, boom!
As you set them off
Signs that say no smoking
Beware!

Blazing, warm, hot sun
Beware, don't get sunburnt
Check your smoke alarm every week
Don't get into any danger
Not fire.

Lucy Harrison (10)
Gretton CP School, Gretton

Water Is A Liquid

W ater is waiting and watching when to fall
A fter the action it waits once again
T he tiring tear that trickles
E ach and every drop expands when touching the earth
R ippes in rivers when rain rides down

L iquid lazily lolls about everywhere
I ce-cold lemonade fizzing froth everywhere
Q ueues of drops ready to fill the cup
U p high in the clouds the water cycle continuously goes on
I n the mountains the snow melts to create streams
D ucks that are rubber are a faithful bathtime buddy.

Leigh-Anne Bell (10)
Gretton CP School, Gretton

Fire

As I watch the scorching sun set
Destruction is two miles from here
The fire is on the way
Two fires meet and make a huge fire

Smoke is everywhere
I have to escape
Wait, I forgot, there's a volcano not far away
It might be that

The volcano erupts every 30 years
We've prepared for it and it was this year
I now see lava coming
I try water, but nothing happens, this is strong

What? Where's the fire? It's gone
The lava is still there though
Now the smoke is in my face
I can't see a thing, only red

Now I feel blood dripping off me
There's nothing I can do
Wait, there's a river, I can get to the other side
My mum will probably ring me though

I'm in the middle of the river
I'm heading for the falls
There's lava down there
I need rope, *now!*

Jamie McEwan (10)
Gretton CP School, Gretton

Water

Raindrops fall on the earth, as oceans rise and fall,
Octopi go swimming, while the waterfalls stand tall.
The sunlight skims the lakes, so they all shimmer and glitter,
But unfortunately, as this happens, people throw in litter.

Perhaps the lakes and seas hold creatures we do not know,
But we are down there searching, swimming with the water's flow.
The waterfalls go crashing, down to the sharp, sharp rocks,
While divers go searching, in the deep, deep lochs.

Oceans collect shells and salt, creatures of the deep,
But when people see them, they're usually asleep.
While we all sit down, and have a cup of tea,
I sometimes wonder what happens underneath the sea.

Jack Haworth (9)
Gretton CP School, Gretton

Waterfall

W ater dripping down a mouldy stone
A gushing sound fading away
T rickling from a distance far
E xploding rocks as the water freezes
R ippling drops from a tiny stream
F alling water from up high
A river flowing down and down
L ittle droplets from the misty air
L ast of all it fades away

D ripping splashes falling in
R ainbow colours as the sun shines
O ver and over, the water goes
P lop, plop, that's all I can hear
S lowly the river sways right to left.

Grace Clark (9)
Gretton CP School, Gretton

Water And Ocean

W ater falling off the cliffs
A qua bubbling all around me
T ons of oceans around the world
E very time I go near water I feel happy
R ipples build up on the pond surface

O ver the sea there are many countries
C ould you sail around the world?
E ver carry on across every lake
A qua colour, beautiful sea
N ever stop to see the years going by

B lowing from side to side
L ovely gentle breezes calm the sea
U sing the water for lots of things
E very time I dive into the deep, cold water.

Sophie Ferguson (9)
Gretton CP School, Gretton

Wind - Cinquain

Gentle
Or destructive
It decides what to do
If you can't stop it, nothing can
Beware!

Tom Grisley (11)
Gretton CP School, Gretton

Bravest's Hung

'Twas on the battlefield,
Upon the bloodstained hill,
I took high my shield of glory
And gripped my fearsome will.

I wielded my sword of flame
And felt my courage high,
The blood and slaughter all around,
Then a rough hoarse cry!

'Fall back, fall back, retreat,
We have not won.'
I ran to hide among the trees,
Our massive force was hung.

Emily Arnold (11)
Gretton CP School, Gretton

Ten Naughty Dragons

Ten naughty dragons standing in a line,
One fell down, then there were nine.

Nine naughty dragons waiting for a date,
One didn't get one, then there were eight.

Eight naughty dragons going to Heaven,
One fell out and then there were seven.

Seven naughty dragons stole a Twix,
One choked to death, then there were six.

Six naughty dragons got stuck in a beehive,
One was allergic to a sting, then there were five.

Five naughty dragons fighting the Minotaur,
One of them died, then there were four.

Four naughty dragons using a gun, hee hee,
One shot himself, then there were three.

Three naughty dragons living in an igloo,
One got frozen, then there were two.

Two naughty dragons using a gun,
One shot himself, then there was one!

One naughty dragon being a hero,
He ran out of gas, then there was zero!

Jordan Addison Phillips (9) & James Cooke (8)
Hanley Swan Primary School, Hanley Swan

The Minotaur

I know a Minotaur who is very fierce,
I know a Minotaur who has his ears pierced.

I know a Minotaur who is very fat,
I know a Minotaur who thinks he's a cat.

I know a Minotaur who likes to dance,
I know a Minotaur who wears stripy pants.

I know a Minotaur who likes to drink,
I know a Minotaur who is wearing pink.

I know a Minotaur who lives in a cave,
I know a Minotaur who is very brave.

I know a Minotaur who likes to cook,
I know a Minotaur who reads a book.

I know a Minotaur who is very bossy,
I know a Minotaur whose name is Flossy.

I know a Minotaur who went to the beach,
I know a minotaur who ate a peach.

I know a Minotaur who had a baby,
I know a Minotaur who's called Saby.

Jasmine Ravenhill & Eleanor Courtman (8)
Hanley Swan Primary School, Hanley Swan

Enter If You Dare

Enter the witch's room,
You're sure to hear a boom.

Enter the wizard's loft,
Try not to have a cough.

Enter the twilight zone,
You'll never forget the bones.

Enter the mummy's tomb,
She's sure to make a zoom.

Enter the skeleton's corner,
And take a steamy sauna.

Enter the ghost's cellar,
And put up your umbrella.

Now leave the ghost's cellar
And take down your umbrella.

Jacob Matthews (7) & Orlaith Owen (8)
Hanley Swan Primary School, Hanley Swan

Silly Poems

I know a man who has his own fish,
I know a man who is very selfish.

I know a man who lives on the moon,
I know a man who has a baboon.

I know a man who doesn't know the time,
I know a man who has a washing line.

I know a man who hates the sun,
I know a man who has a gun.

I know a man who hates the rain,
I know a man who doesn't have a brain.

I know a man whose hair is red,
I know a man who doesn't like bread.

I know a man who doesn't have any food,
I know a man who's always in a good mood.

I know a man who is very quick,
I know a man who has a chick.

I know a man who's got 20 toes,
I know a man with an enormous nose.

I know a man who has a pool,
I know a man who is very, very cool.

I know a man who likes to skate,
I know a man who hates cake.

I know a man whose name is Cash,
I know a man who takes out the trash.

I know a man who is a cow,
I know a man who has a row.

Jessica Rawlings & Harriet Lloyd (9)
Hanley Swan Primary School, Hanley Swan

I Wonder What It's Like In Heaven?

I wonder what it's like in Heaven,
Is it like Devon?
Do animals hop, skip and play,
Day after day after day?
Do the angels in the sky fly so high?
Are there seasons in the sky
That we can see when we die?
Are there birds singing up high
That dance in the sky?
Are there fairies up there?
I could go there to play.

Chloe Mitten (7) & Amy Whittaker (8)
Hanley Swan Primary School, Hanley Swan

The Funniest Poem

I know a man who loves the loo,
I know a man who sings to you.

I know a man who chews on the loo,
I know a man who likes to moo.

I know a man who runs a van,
I know a man who lives in Japan.

I know a man whose nose is a flare,
I know a man who eats a pear.

I know a man who lives in a shoe,
I know a man who loves shampoo.

I know a man who looks like bamboo,
I know a man who is cuckoo.

I know a man who woke up in the night,
I know a man who had a terrible fright.

I know a man who had a small bed,
I know a man who is very red.

I know a man who loves the telly,
I know a man who wobbles his belly.

I know a man who went off to teach,
I know a man who likes eating a leech.

Dilon Norris-Story-Day (8) & Dan Rawlings (7)
Hanley Swan Primary School, Hanley Swan

The Rhyming Poems

I know a man who goes to bed,
I know a man with shoes on his head.

I know a man who wears smelly socks,
I know a man who thinks he's a fox.

I know a man with toes on his head,
I know a man who thinks he's called Ted.

I know a man whose nose is square,
I know a man who's got red hair.

I know a man who wears a hat,
I know a man who has a cat.

I know a man who has a pink bed,
I know a man who has a silly head.

I know a man who is silly,
I know a man who's called Billy.

Hannah Bown & Harvey Anderson (7)
Hanley Swan Primary School, Hanley Swan

I Know A Man . . .

I know a man who stands on his head,
I know a man who likes to be dead.

I know a man who lives in a sprout,
I know a man who has a hideout.

I know a man who stepped out of a plane,
I know a man who always gets the blame.

I know a man who likes the show Bamzookie,
I know a man who likes to be quite spooky.

I know a man who likes Greece,
I know a man who wants peace.

I know a man who sat on the ice,
I know a man who rolled a big dice.

I know a man who likes to ride a big bike,
I know a man who got eaten by a pike.

I know a man who likes mistletoe,
I know a man who's called Big Joe.

Joe Senior (8)
Hanley Swan Primary School, Hanley Swan

I Know A Man . . .

I know a man who has ears on his toes,
I know a man who makes big UFOs.

I know a man who's learning to drive,
I know a man who acts like he's five.

I know a man who stays in bed,
I know a man called Uncle Fred.

I know a man who lives in a shoe,
I know a man who lives in a loo.

I know a man who killed a frog,
I know a man who ate a bog.

I know a man who wants to be a hero,
I know a man who likes the age zero.

I know a man who likes Greece,
I know a man who wants peace.

Edward Terry (8)
Hanley Swan Primary School, Hanley Swan

Ten Hairy Minotaurs

Ten hairy Minotaurs wanting a Valentine,
One got one and fell in love, then there were nine.

Nine hairy Minotaurs going to a fete,
One smashed a coconut, then there were eight.

Eight hairy Minotaurs wanting to be eleven,
One found a time machine, then there were seven.

Seven hairy Minotaurs giving ice lolly licks,
One of them melted, then there were six.

Six hairy Minotaurs doing a jive,
One turned the music off, then there were five.

Five hairy Minotaurs chewing guts and gore,
One felt sick, then there were four.

Four hairy Minotaurs laughing with glee,
One laughed his head off, then there were three.

Three hairy Minotaurs sick with the flu,
One got better, then there were two.

Two hairy Minotaurs wanting some fun,
One had a party, then there was one.

One hairy Minotaur hiding in a burrow,
The snow came down, then there was zero!

Daisy Collins (9)
Hanley Swan Primary School, Hanley Swan

I Know A Man . . .

I know a man who thinks he's silly,
I know a man whose name is Billy.

I know a man who hates the time,
I know a man who likes to climb.

I know a man who has an apple a day,
I know a man who keeps the doctor away.

I know a man who likes to act,
I know a man who plays Impact.

I know a man who hates to crash,
I know a man who has to dash.

I know a man who lives in the air,
I know a man who thinks he's a millionaire.

Sally Clive (8)
Hanley Swan Primary School, Hanley Swan

Fairies

I know a fairy that stands on a spot,
I know a fairy that sleeps in a cot.

I know a fairy that has a pool,
I know a fairy that likes to stay cool.

I know a fairy that likes to boast,
I know a fairy that likes to host.

I know a fairy that likes to paint,
I know a fairy who's made a complaint.

I know a fairy that swims in a pond,
I know a fairy that likes the colour blond.

I know a fairy that likes a place,
I know a fairy that has won a race.

I know a fairy that has a rose,
I know a fairy that likes to pose.

I know a fairy that plays a game,
I know a fairy that likes fame.

Jade Sheldon (9)
Hanley Swan Primary School, Hanley Swan

I Know A Man . . .

I know a man who flies in a jet,
I know a man who likes to bet.

I know a man who likes to hug a mug,
I know a man who sleeps with a rug.

I know a man who is in the Hall of Fame,
I know a man who likes to complain.

I know a man who lives in a hat,
I know a man who has a big cat.

I know a man whose bottom is bare,
I know a man who is the mayor.

I know a man who has long hair,
I know a man who likes to eat bear.

I know a man who lives by the lake,
I know a man who likes to bake.

Katie Dunwell (9)
Hanley Swan Primary School, Hanley Swan

Father To A Dead Girl

There he stood perplexed and still,
In the darkness of the snowy hill.

Stood on top he saw his child,
Screaming like the call of the wild.

Then she fell to the ground,
With one great big, painful pound.

Rapidly he ran up the slope,
Filled with dread and tinged with hope.

There he saw his sweet child dead,
Lying in a snowy bed.

How could someone kill his child?
A little girl so meek and mild.

He could not bear the pain,
Knowing his life would never be the same.

Alice Henson (10)
Hathern CE Primary School, Hathern

The Dog Kennels

All the sad faces sit and stare,
When adults see and start to care.
You just want to hold them tight,
Through the morning and through the night.

The ears just flop on the floor,
When helpers walk right through the door.
All the dogs are all alone,
So please, please give a dog a home.

Amy Williams (9)
Hathern CE Primary School, Hathern

Spring

The warm spring days will soon arrive,
The bulbs and trees will come alive,
Gentle blue clouds fill the air,
Birds are singing everywhere!

As I dance around the tree,
With a lot of honeybees,
The sunny days,
Have their different ways.

Sarah Innes (11)
Hathern CE Primary School, Hathern

The Cold Morning Air

The sun comes up,
In the cold morning air,
I look out of my window
And the blue sky is there.
The birds fly around,
I watch them and stare,
I like the way they move
In the cold morning air.

I rush downstairs,
I go outside,
I feed the birds in my backyard.
I sit calmly
And wonder why,
We have the morning
Sun and sky.

Lauren Burt (10)
Hathern CE Primary School, Hathern

Animals

Hopping through the summer grass,
Darting, dashing, as happy as can be,
I watch and stare as it plays,
It goes and hides because of me.

Taking a walk in the midsummer heat,
Arriving home, drink, drink, drink,
Snoozing in the cooling shade,
He looked at me as he gave a wink.

Eating bananas all day long,
Swinging from tree to tree in the jungle,
Picking fleas from each other,
Hardly ever take a tumble.

Katherine Thorpe (11)
Hathern CE Primary School, Hathern

Fishing

I went fishing with my dad,
I lost the rod, he went mad.

Then I went and lost the net,
We waded in and got all wet!

Alexander Cobbin (10)
Hathern CE Primary School, Hathern

Teddy Trouble

Do you believe in teddy bears?
How they get up in the night,
They get out of their baskets
And turn on the bedroom light!

They gather all the cushions
And equally give them out,
So each and every teddy bear,
Won't scream and shout!

Then they start to hit each other,
The cushions fall apart,
Feathers are everywhere,
But that was just the start!

They decide to leave the cushions
And just to use their paws,
The teddies pull down the curtains
And slice them with their claws!

So if you're ever planning,
On a visit from a teddy bear,
Make sure your room is cushion free
And your curtains don't easily tear!

Billie Westwood (10)
Hathern CE Primary School, Hathern

Limericks About Animals

There was a female cat from Wales,
Who thought she had two tails,
She wore a green hat,
She took a snooze on a mat
And she loved to flirt with the males.

There was an old duck,
Who always had bad luck,
His name was King Cole,
He fell down a hole
And landed in the muck.

Once there was a frog,
Who liked to live in his bog,
He had a large lump
And he loved to jump,
Then he made friends with a dog.

Joseph Osborn-Grummett (11)
Hathern CE Primary School, Hathern

The Crazy Dog Family

There once was a black dog from Spain,
But there was something wrong with his brain,
As he ate his noodles,
He thought he was a poodle,
But actually he was a Great Dane.

There once was his brother from Wales,
Who was told he had five tails,
He turned around,
He made a weird sound,
As he realised it was a big tale.

There once was their dad,
Who came from Baghdad,
One day,
He ran away,
When he realised his family were mad!

Naomi Davis (11)
Hathern CE Primary School, Hathern

Limericks Around The World

There was an old man from Brazil
Who took a dynamite pill
Turning away, trying to pay
He got his braces stuck in the till.

There was an old man from Spain
Who was a complete pain
He went for a walk, stopped for a talk
Then it started to rain.

There was an old man from Peru
Who just didn't know what to do
He went to the market, came back with a carpet
Then took up the sport of kung fu!

Jack Insley (10)
Hathern CE Primary School, Hathern

The Dolphin

He appears from out of the ocean blue,
The beautiful dolphin comes into view.
The smooth, grey body glides through the calm sea,
How they love to swim so free!

Rowan Davis (9)
Hathern CE Primary School, Hathern

Proudly Potions

Onward, near the darkness
We try our best,
And pour the potions
Sweating in our robes and vest.

Shadows in the moonlit sky
Full of joy we mix our potions,
On our brooms we fly
Taking on the moonlit air.

Keep our cauldrons bubbling nicely
Pouring in our smelly potions,
Tickling our nose and ears
Making faces and emotions.

Claire Walker (9)
Hathern CE Primary School, Hathern

Are You There Or Not?

There was a girl from a lost island,
She was sucked down by the sand.

She was seen by someone,
She was not seen for very long.

Then she disappeared to her graveyard,
She had been scared.

She returned to her grave,
Only to remember she was once a slave.

Was she dead or alive?
She never likes to dive.

Emma Pritchard (11)
Hathern CE Primary School, Hathern

Summer Night

The night is bright,
With the summer night,
The stars shine like gold,
The sun is down, the moon is up.

I'm silently walking down the road,
Then I see a toad,
Jumping up and down,
I just walk past.

I'd better get home,
Because I'm alone.

Ellie Pitchford (9)
Hathern CE Primary School, Hathern

Sweets Galore!

I wish I could eat sweets every day
I wonder what my mum would say.
She says, 'No way, because I'll have to pay.'

I bought some sweets today
But yet I did not have to pay.
The chocolate was soft and silky,
It tasted all sweet and milky.

When I got home,
My mum was mad.
She ranted and raved,
It made me sad.

'But Mum, these are for you!'

Kendra Taylor (11)
Hathern CE Primary School, Hathern

The Blue Lagoon

Through the trees she ran,
Over the hills, under the moon,
There she met a man
And she would be drowned in the lagoon.
Her spirit will roam the wood,
Watching people who do no good,
She will meet the man again
And he will die in awful pain.

Laura Hearn (10)
Hathern CE Primary School, Hathern

Winter's Day

It is a cold winter's day, I'm frozen to the bone,
I'm searching for a warm place to sleep, I'm all alone.

Fighting through the icy-cold snow,
Hardly able to move, my head hanging down low.

Walking through the tragic blizzard I suffered a lot of pain,
As I struggled down the lane.

Looking out into the village street,
I felt empty and could not feel my feet.

So now I know it's not a dream,
As I yelped out a loud scream.

Hayley Dobson (11)
Hathern CE Primary School, Hathern

Deep

Her eyes glisten, her eyes are amazing,
Her name is Ocean Girl,
Her deep, long, magical hair flows in the sea,
The deep blue sea.

Diving and dipping in and out,
Her tail flicks up water
And comes down over her,
Performing a rainbow.

She was my friend, best friend,
Whenever she went into the sea,
She turned up as a mermaid.
Her family got tangled up in a net, a fishing net,
Someone has her family, her family.

Do you want to know who Ocean Girl is?
She is the last mermaid, the queen of the sea.

Kelly Brown (10)
Hathern CE Primary School, Hathern

The Magic Box Dust
(Inspired by 'Magic Box' by Kit Wright)

Inside the magic box
Are some strips of different colours
And a red heart beating fast.
Inside the magic box
Are some lovely flowers
And the smell of yellow roses.
Inside the magic box
Is a rainbow of lovely colours.
Inside is a green-blue sky.
Close the box for another day.

Lois Pritchard (9)
Hinstock Primary School, Hinstock

Loudly

Loudly the leprechaun leaps with joy,
Loudly the dog barks at the boy,
Loudly the elephant blows its nose,
Loudly a person cleans his toes.

Loudly the hail drops on the roof,
Loudly the horse clops its hoof,
Loudly Dad starts the car,
Loudly the people talk in the bar.

Oliver Wakefield (10)
Hinstock Primary School, Hinstock

The Magical Wisdom Box
(Inspired by 'Magic Box' by Kit Wright)

Inside the magical box
Is a secret chamber
That carries 70 wands.

Inside the magical box
There are flying unicorns
They all carry 90 lockets.

Inside the magical box
Is Harry Potter
Flying on his broomstick.

Close the lid gently
Before the magic disappears.

Ruth Gilliand Simon (10)
Hinstock Primary School, Hinstock

Memories
(Inspired by 'Magic Box' by Kit Wright)

Inside the magic box
Is the memory of being locked in the toilet.

Inside the magic box
Is my sister jumping on my belly
And smacking me with my light sabre.

Inside the magic box
Is my dad playing the guitar
And him drinking.

Close the box,
Lock it away,
Save the magic for another day.

Harvey Wakefield (8)
Hinstock Primary School, Hinstock

Scared And Not Prepared!

I'm in the park and it's dark
And I'm getting bullied.
I'm scared and I'm not prepared
And I'm nearly crying and nearly dying.

I'm sad and I'm bad,
Sitting in the park and *it is dark!*
Need someone to love and to hug,
I'm scared and not prepared.

Katie Nagington (8)
Hinstock Primary School, Hinstock

Magic Horrors
(Inspired by 'Magic Box' by Kit Wright)

Inside the magic box,
Are rattling Dementors
And the fearsome Boggarts.

Inside the magic box,
Is the dreadful Adva Kedra curse
And the painful cruitacus curse.

Inside the magic box,
Is terrible Jack the Ripper
And the deathly Grim Reaper.

Quickly, shut the box,
Before anything escapes.

Fern Moore (11)
Hinstock Primary School, Hinstock

Magic Box Of Fears
(Inspired by 'Magic Box' by Kit Wright)

Inside the magic box
There are fire-breathing dragons
And other petrifying monsters.

Inside the magic box
There is the lethal plague
And cunning murderers.

Inside the magic box
There are bloodthirsty vampires
And bloodsucking bats.

Close the lid gently,
Before the magic drains away.

Michael Lyons (10)
Hinstock Primary School, Hinstock

Dying

I feel like I'm stuck up on a shelf,
All alone and all by myself,
My spirit is dying
And I feel like crying.

I think I'm being hit by the cane,
And I'm being thrown down the drain,
If I wasn't dead,
I would have fled.

Luke Pontin (9)
Hinstock Primary School, Hinstock

The Witches' Spell

Double, double, toil and trouble,
Let the cauldron boil and bubble,
Watch the witches cackle by night,
As the skeletons give us a fright.

Eye of a toad, toe of a vampire,
Wing of a bat and tongue of a dog,
Wolf's fang, big and brand,
Unicorn blood and kitten's ear.

Double, double, toil and trouble,
Let the cauldron boil and bubble,
Watch the witches cackle tonight,
Now the potion is ready, ha, ha, ha.

Cerys Lloyd (8)
Hinstock Primary School, Hinstock

Magic

(Inspired by 'Magic Box' by Kit Wright)

Inside the magic box
Are some strips of different colours
And a red heart beating fast.
Inside the magic box
Are some flowers
And the smell of yellow roses.
Inside the magic box
Is a rainbow of lovely colours
In the great blue sky.
Close the box, lock it away,
Save it for another day.

Sophie Robinson (9)
Hinstock Primary School, Hinstock

Slowly

Slowly the tide creeps up the sand
Slowly the shadows cross the land
Slowly the carthorse pulls his mile
Slowly the old man mounts the stile.

Slowly the hands move round the clock
Slowly the dew dries on the dock
Slow is the snail, but slowest of all
The green moss spreads on the old brick wall.

Luke Mathewson (10)
Hinstock Primary School, Hinstock

A Witch's Spell

'Double, double, toil and trouble,
Wood to ashes and cauldron bubble,
Now to make this evil spell,'
Said the witches that came up from Hell.
'Now to make this evil curse,
even worse by . . .

Putting in the head of a bat,
Also the paw of a cat,
Now some spotty eagles' eggs
And jumping, slimy toads' legs.

The rattley rattle of a snake,
Trust me, this poem is not fake,
Come on now, we must be steady,
Oh yes, the curse is ready.'

Charlotte Chapman (8)
Hinstock Primary School, Hinstock

Magic Box Of Mythical Creatures
(Inspired by 'Magic Box' by Kit Wright)

Inside the magic box
Is the scaly, fire-breathing dragon
And the fiery, flying phoenix.

Inside the magic box
There lives a one-eyed cyclops
And an ugly man-eating ogre.

Inside the magic box
Is a muscular centaur
And a goat-bodied faun.

Georgia Smith (9)
Hinstock Primary School, Hinstock

The Witches' Spell

Double, double, toil and trouble
See us brewing up some trouble.
Eye of a newt, toe of a frog,
A dog's tail and the horn of a hog.

Demons pour out of the pot,
Goblins, dragons, all the lot.
The cauldron is so hot,
The brew is finished.

Sam Jordan (9)
Hinstock Primary School, Hinstock

Bloodsuckers
(Inspired by 'Magic Box' by Kit Wright)

In the magic box is . . .
A vampire with sharp, dripping teeth,
Leeches sucking blood from their prey.

Inside the magic box is . . .
A bat swooping down on its victim
And zombies devouring a carcass.

Inside the magic box is . . .
A mummy drinking the blood of a horse,
Ghouls getting ready to have a meal of blood and flesh.

Slam the lid shut before the bloodsuckers *get out!*

Holly Guy (9)
Hinstock Primary School, Hinstock

Alone

There I was all alone,
All I could hear was the street telephone,
Upset, sad, crying like mad,
I felt really bad.

I felt I'd entered the darkness of Hell,
How I wished I had a wishing well,
But then a light came to me
And knelt down by my knee.

She said, 'Can I be your friend?'
I smiled and said, 'Yes,'
And that was the end.

Paige Moore (10)
Hinstock Primary School, Hinstock

Colours

Anger is red
Anger is blood
I am upset
My tears are like a flood
Dripping off my face.

Blue is cold and lonely
Blue is like ice
I am alone
Cold as a stone
On a steep mountainside.

Aaron Pritchard (11)
Hinstock Primary School, Hinstock

Bonfire Poem

B lazing fire at night
O range, red and yellow
N ight is the time when fireworks go off
F ire is ready and fireworks have gone
I n the moonlight
R emember, remember, the 5th of November
E very night is good

N ight is dark and scary
I n the moonlight
G et ready for sparkle and flame
H it the sky and reach up high
T omorrow it's coming!

Ashley Holmes (9)
Hinstock Primary School, Hinstock

Magical World

Inside the magical world
Is the wonderful scaly dragon guarding his cliff
And the fire-breathing phoenix catching his prey.

Then enter the fairy world,
Fairies so fast, flying around collecting flowers
And the pixies, frowning as always.

Inside the magical world
Is a castle with kings, queens and knights
And there is a place where animals are talking and surprising everyone.

Rachel Bromley (9)
Hinstock Primary School, Hinstock

Loudly

Loudly the lion calls for his mate,
Loudly the wind opens the creaking gate,
Loudly the dolphin flips and trips,
Loudly the magical magician does his tricks.

Loudly the traps go *snap, snap, snap,*
Loudly the eggs crack,
Loudly the dragon falls to the ground,
Loudly the children shout at what they've found.

Katie Furber (8)
Hinstock Primary School, Hinstock

Noisily

Noisily the rain falls to the ground,
Noisily the children dig a mound,
Noisily Mrs Hunter plays the piano,
Noisily I think, *what's a liana?*

Noisily Ethan plays in the playground,
Noisily children play around,
Noisily children play the drums,
Noisily I talk to people's mums.

Robert Lee (8)
Hinstock Primary School, Hinstock

Water Poem

The calm current turns into white horses
And races back to shore.
It acts like a brick and smashes on a rock,
Races back to shore and tries again and again.

The heavens' holy hail has no taste, no smell,
Just the boring drops of hail.
It can be helpful,
Like bits of gel dropping on the floor.

Crystal clear drops from the taps.
A whirlpool spinning like a tornado.
Bubbles partying as they pop,
Gives a helping hand to clear up the rain.

Oliver Jeffs (9)
Higham Ferrers Junior School, Higham Ferrers

Water

It seems so endless,
It's so silent,
The crystal clear current
Suddenly turns into an angry, bubbling roller coaster.
 Crash!
It drums heavily on your window,
Making you jump with fear.
You feel you can't escape,
Your windows feel the pulse.
 Splash!

Lauren Hamper (10)
Higham Ferrers Junior School, Higham Ferrers

Water

The calm, smooth water flowing up to the rocks,
As the smooth, crystal current starts playing with the sea,
As the water puts its full weight on the rocks,
As it plays, it wakes up the fish.
    Bash!
The heavens open,
As a pitter-patter hits the window,
As it races down the window,
Crashes of water come flying down.
    Crash!
The shining crystals of the frozen tap,
As the tall, soft bubbles melt in the bath,
As the gleaming gems drop out of the tap,
As the bubbles surround in your depth.
    Splash!

Thomas Longley (9)
Higham Ferrers Junior School, Higham Ferrers

Water

Water loves to play,
It jumps up to grab the boats,
The calm sea transforms into white horses,
As it plunges to shore.
    Splash!
Water, water, coming down like bullets,
The windows and doors jump with fear,
The clouds so angry they change colour to grey,
The rain bites our hands and ears.
    Crash!
Water whispering to clean plates,
Shiny silver taps sweat to give me a drink,
Bubbles parting as they pop,
Drips trickling out of the tap, trying to run away.
    Bash!

Harry Collett (9)
Higham Ferrers Junior School, Higham Ferrers

The Storm Beast

The eye of the sea peered at the boat.
The wind yelled across the sea.
The arms of the sea came out of the water.

Joshua Horam (9)
Higham Ferrers Junior School, Higham Ferrers

Mix Of Water

The clear glass, crystal, shiny current,
Gleaming bright in sunlight,
Then plays happily till midnight,
Skimming roughly.
Bubbling roller coaster swimming peacefully,
Round and round.
Rushing and rushing,
Playful.
Banging and banging,
Then a big wallop.
 Crash!
Slowly the dancers come down
And tap on your shoulder.
You watch the little sugar drops dance,
While they get all the attention.
 Click!
Sweating taps making a humorous party,
While there's a spinning whirlpool
Twisting smaller and smaller.
Gleaming gem drops tapping on my hand,
Cleaning and shining my fingers and toes.

Bronya Creary (9)
Higham Ferrers Junior School, Higham Ferrers

Water

Crystal-clear, playful current seems endless.
The monster crashes all its weight down on the rocks.
Smooth surface like magical ice inside an igloo.
The freezing, frosty water transforms into white, snowy horses.
 Whoosh!
The heavens open,
Mirror of clouds.
Tiny sugar drops start to dance down,
Nipping softly at your face,
Forming little pictures on your window,
Making little petticoats for the plants.
 Snip!
Sparkling, popping, melting bubbles floating,
Spraying hose pipe,
Shiny taps sweating as the gems drop down.
 Snap!

Anya Smith (9)
Higham Ferrers Junior School, Higham Ferrers

Water

The calm body,
Twitching, twinkling in the moonlight,
Playing with the boats,
It plunges angrily towards shore.
> *Crash!*
Drums heavily on your window,
Creating a silvery covering on the plants,
Moving in time,
Getting bent in all directions.
> *Splash!*
Gleaming gems drop out of the tap,
Dripping down to fill the bath,
Bubbles partying as they pop,
Drips exploding as they drop.
> *Smash!*
Cleaning us, dripping out the shower,
Water coming down like very fine powder,
Water's the thing that destroys all boats,
Pushing, then tugging like a herd of goats.
> *Bash!*

Matthew Chambers (10)
Higham Ferrers Junior School, Higham Ferrers

Water

Far out over a blanket of water,
Settled, sleepy, smooth.
Waking up, getting playful,
Smashing its weight on the rocks.
> *Bash!*
Drip, drip, drip, drip,
The sky leaks as we search for shelter.
It thunders down in a million little bullets,
Drumming on your window,
Forming groups to make puddles.
> *Splash!*
Shining crystals drain from the tap
As I pour my bath.
The bubbles pop, melt and disappear.
I pour some glittery, magic spray,
I pull the plug as the domestic waste disappears.
> *Dash!*

Rebecca Medlin (9)
Higham Ferrers Junior School, Higham Ferrers

Water

The beautiful atmosphere,
Strong currents change into short, white horses,
The waves sway slowly left to right,
The waves turn into a calm, clear, crystal atmosphere.
 Crash!
The heavens slowly open,
God turns His shower on,
Lightning streaks across the sky,
Windows rattle and make ghostly sounds.
 Splash!
The flying steam rises and turns into a boiling sweat,
Gleaming gems drop out the tap,
Gives a helping hand to clean,
Spinning whirlpool when pulling the plug.
 Slash!
The flying stream rises and slowly overfills,
The currents toss slowly and steadily over,
As rain streaks down to the ground, the wind loudly howls,
The rain steadily rolls into the drain.
 Whoosh!

Callum Langley (10)
Higham Ferrers Junior School, Higham Ferrers

Water

The water is calm for now
The crystals are clear for now
Suddenly the water turns red
The bubbles are going so fast
A roller coaster couldn't beat it.
 Bang!
Millions of bullets shoot the water down like 1,000 crystals
As it whips the houses
The rain goes so fast
It roars like an alien as it plunges to shore.
 Slam!
Crystals running down the plughole
Dirty water goes down and comes up clean
Bubbles dancing at a party as the foam is playing tig outside.
 Damn!

Holly Surr (10)
Higham Ferrers Junior School, Higham Ferrers

Water

The calm and playful water splashes upon the rocks
Like a pouncing panther.
The water crashes its full weight on the rocks,
Seeming endless.
Water rushing rapidly down the stream.
Seaweed touches the water with delicate fingers.
> *Splish!*
The heavens open.
Lightning streaks across the sky
Like a rocket car zooming down a track.
Pitter-patter, trickling drops shoot down
From the black sky.
I stand out in it, I'm getting drenched,
It feels cold.

Kieran Gilson (10)
Higham Ferrers Junior School, Higham Ferrers

Water

A strange, peaceful noise is singing like a bird.
Bang!
A herd of blue smashes as it claws the rocks.
Crash!
As it whips the rocks, it makes the clouds open with anger.
It roars like a lion.
It's shooting down like spirals as it plunges to shore.
An end was coming.
Shiny domestic droplets coming down like powder.
Bubbles racing with tears.
Lovely, clean blue moves with happiness.
Gently, everything goes back.

Aaron Burdett (9)
Higham Ferrers Junior School, Higham Ferrers

The Sea Storm

The storm was starting to open its eyes.
The mouth of the sea started chomping.
The arms of the sea wobbled the boat
While the horses galloped quickly
Through the strong waves holding them down.
The leg of the sea was splashing.

Kiera Nicholson (9)
Higham Ferrers Junior School, Higham Ferrers

Water

Smooth crystal water
Splashing up against the rocks
Like a seal jumping up for some food.
Water moves slowly with its bubbly water.
Water running rapidly with its frozen, frosty water.
    Splash!
The heavens open as the dark clouds gather round.
A few minutes later the damage starts to take over the Earth.
An hour later the sun comes back out.
But there's not much left of the town.
    Crash!
Smooth crystal bubbles pounce up and pop.
As I jump into the bath the taps start to sweat.
After I've finished in the bath
The bubbles spin round and go down the drain.
The bubbles have gone down
And give a helping hand to clean the bath.
    Bash!

Paige Gartlan (10)
Higham Ferrers Junior School, Higham Ferrers

Water

Water is wavy, the sunshine shows.
It is cold and the smooth water shows.
The bubbly water crashes into the big rocks.
The water is salty under and above.

Water is coming down dancing to Earth.
Tiny seeds grow and grow.
Splash on the windows with fear.
Grey clouds are splashing down to Earth.

Smooth, crystal clear, going into the bath.
Shiny drips appear in your hands.
Sparkly drops come out of the taps.
The bubble bath is smooth when you get in it.

Tiffany-Jayne Bull (9)
Higham Ferrers Junior School, Higham Ferrers

The Stormy Sea

The horses were crashing onto the face of the rocks.
The water was crashing and banging like drums.
The houses were standing tall in the fierce, whining wind.
The waves were charging like a fierce, angry bull.

Sam Tebbutt (9)
Higham Ferrers Junior School, Higham Ferrers

Sea Meets The Wind

The huge waves being torched
The wind yelling like a baby
A mad elephant, charging onto the surface
The clouds shaped like angry dragons
Like blue whales smashing onto the sea
A claw came down from the sky
Like a giant shark eating its prey
Waves splashing like horses onto the sea
The mouth rowing onto the sea
Arms splashing the stones
Storm clouds like a great white shark
The hand comes down and splashes the rocks
The great storm cat.

Harry Underwood (9)
Higham Ferrers Junior School, Higham Ferrers

The Storm

The sea growled as the wind sang a terrible tune.
The sea sent his white sea horses.
The wind blew a raspberry
And looked up at the blackened sky.

The sea crashed on the rocks.
The grey, old clouds with their grey hair hugged and went hunting
And crashed the wind into the stone walls.

The wind grew old
And blew on the screaming sea.
The sea growled and stormed,
Wounded, it looked up and calmed down.

Danielle Coley (8)
Higham Ferrers Junior School, Higham Ferrers

The Storm

There I stood in the lighthouse
Watching the sea crash like a bull.
It was like a giant shark tearing up its prey.
Mad elephants charging in anger.
It's like the storm going over the sea.
The mouth rolling over the sea.
Arms splashed onto the stones.

Joel Hughes (8)
Higham Ferrers Junior School, Higham Ferrers

Storm At Sea

Ships sailed along the calm sea,
Suddenly an enormous wave
Punched through the heart of a spiky rock
Swallowing the ship,
The sea frowned at the pebbles of the beach,
Infested with seaweed.
But then the teeth of the sea
Chomped and gobbled the shiny, wet pebbles.
A huge wing of the sea
Crashed on the wooden pier, shaking it.
A clap of thunder hit the angry, wet sea.
The eye of the sea closed as the waves went down.
As that happened, the sun's eyes opened in the bright blue sky.
The sea was calm again, the storm had ended.

Ben Thomas (9)
Higham Ferrers Junior School, Higham Ferrers

The Storm

The hands of the sea were splashing on the rocks,
Then the eyes of the storm had nearly begun.
Then the wind was hitting at the town.
The storm galloped over the sea.
The body rose to the hard mountain,
The mouth roaring onto the sea.
Arms splashed onto the stones,
The chest lay on the surface.
The ugly sky opened his eyes,
The hand of the sea was splashing.
The giant hand was searching for his prey.

Liam Munt (9)
Higham Ferrers Junior School, Higham Ferrers

Stormy Seas

The dead sea glistened in the growing sun.
The sea suddenly became wild, like a human running.
The shark of the sea ran into a ton of rocks.
The old sea calmed down again.
It sighed at the face of death,
As the face of the water rose to the lanes.
As the water died it said,
'I will be gone forever at my fence of death.'

Laura Carey (9)
Higham Ferrers Junior School, Higham Ferrers

The Wave Controller

I stood on the pier looking down.
I saw the horses charging at the sand
And in the distance I saw a little town,
They had their own little band.

Then I saw a boat
And I saw the wave controller's face.
It kicked the boat, then it didn't float
And in the distance I saw a secret base.

In the distance I saw the wave controller's chest,
Then in the sea I saw a man.
I looked back at the wave controller,
He looked the best.
Then I saw a little boy with a suntan.

Henry Kelly (9)
Higham Ferrers Junior School, Higham Ferrers

The Storm War

As the storm dragon lay in wait
For the wind to push him over
As the wind bull charged out
The battle was already over.

As the storm dragon heard the battle was over
And opened its eyes with rage
As the wind bull said his prayers
The dragon flew off in dismay.

As the dragon came through his dismay
He was happy again
As he fell to the ground with happiness
And fell asleep forever in harmony.

Scott Lynes (9)
Higham Ferrers Junior School, Higham Ferrers

Storm At Sea

I stood by the shore
Watching the wild sea beast roar
Making wild pictures and crashing against the shore.
The grey, old sea waving her arms.
Great sea horses making a great show.
Water's face speaking a great cry, a great, fierce sigh.
The hands of the sea splashing.

Charlotte Freeman (9)
Higham Ferrers Junior School, Higham Ferrers

The Great Sea

The storm crowded round the houses.
The hands of the sea splashed
As the wave controller banged against the rocking boats.
The waves charged at the sand, hitting rocks on its way.

The sea was crashing madly at the rocks.
The sky yelled like a baby crying.
The sky was growing dark, like someone turning the light out.
The arms of the harbour curled round the bobbing boats.

Nicole Atter (9)
Higham Ferrers Junior School, Higham Ferrers

The Wind And The Sea

The howling, mad, freezing cold wind
Blew towards the wavy, stamping sea.
The wind noticed that the sea did not care
So the wind became lively and blew down.
Then he noticed what he was doing and said sorry.
The sea said, 'I guess it doesn't really matter.'
Then they fell in love!

Sophie Haigh (8)
Higham Ferrers Junior School, Higham Ferrers

The Great Sea Beast!

The great sea beast punched the rocks.
The horses raced towards the shore.
The waves were chasing each other.
The wind dragon fell from the heavens above,
Down into the fierce sea.
The sea was swallowing boats
As the storm leapt over the sea.

Ben Moir (9)
Higham Ferrers Junior School, Higham Ferrers

The Storm Cat

The sea was crashing and yelling
And the grey-haired clouds were glooming in the sky.
The sea looked like a giant shark swishing up and down.
The sea going in-between the rocks.
The sea went calm and quiet again.
The white horses came out of the sea.

Jodie Anderson (9)
Higham Ferrers Junior School, Higham Ferrers

Bullying
(Inspired by the song 'Trouble' by Coldplay)

Oh no, what's this?
They spun a spider's web for me
Some of the stupid things I've said.

Oh no, I never meant to do no harm
I lost my head
Mean actions they acted.

Oh Lord, what have I done?
Why would this happen to me?
Spider's web's tangled up with me.

Spider's web, I'm caught in the middle,
Bullying gets into trouble,
Mean words they said.

Alexia Mann (8)
Higham Ferrers Junior School, Higham Ferrers

Bullying

I'm stuck in a web of trouble.
I'm stuck in a maze of grief.
I'm fed up with being pushed around.
I'm fed up with bullies stealing from me.
I want someone to stop them kicking me.
I want someone to stop them calling me mean names.
Why won't they stop threatening me?
What have I done to them?
Why won't they stop bullying me?
They've dug a hole for me.

Tyler James (9)
Higham Ferrers Junior School, Higham Ferrers

Storm At Sea

I stood by the sea at the light of day,
With the storm galloping towards me.
The mouth rowing onto the water,
Going onto the surface loudly.
The storm's eyes opening.
Sounding like a jungle of elephants.
Arms stretching out to other waves,
Light shining through the monstrous wave.
The great storm beast.

Emma Garley (8)
Higham Ferrers Junior School, Higham Ferrers

The Great Storm

I heard the wailing wind crying out loud to the sea.
The brow and lip opened to the grey, old clouds.
The clouds put a black dress on as they danced in the sky.
The dancing clouds started to cry.
The raindrops touched the green, animated leaves.
The aching heart of the hard cloud of the clear, loving sky.
The fog got thicker and thicker as the soft wind cried louder
In the arched sea of the dead face and the whistling wind.

Frances Pegg (9)
Higham Ferrers Junior School, Higham Ferrers

The Storm

I stood by the shore and heard the wailing sea
As the wind cried loudly.
The sea's arms waved left and right with the wind.
The face of the sea played with the boats.
As I stood by the shore, the sea came crashing angrily onto the sand.
The cry of the wind.
The sea was grey and old.

Kia Barnett (9)
Higham Ferrers Junior School, Higham Ferrers

Fear

Fear is black.
It tastes like eating eyeballs and crunching spiders.
It smells like leaking oil.
It looks like a haunted house at midnight
And sounds like a headless ghost riding a horse.
Fear feels like I'm trapped in a spider's web.

Rachel Baker (8)
Higham Ferrers Junior School, Higham Ferrers

Dreamy

Dreamy is blue and light.
It tastes like a drink of hot cocoa.
It smells like a sweet-scented flower.
Dreamy looks like a warm, sunny day.
It sounds like the big, blue waves.
Dreamy is when I wake up in bed all cuddly and tired.

Emma Nolan (8)
Higham Ferrers Junior School, Higham Ferrers

Water

The water has come alive,
Into a dangerous lion
And is so angry, it started to fight,
The boat is terrified and wants to go.

His sharp, beating, cold heart,
Crushing the boat down,
The lion's feet swooshing in the sea
And making it dark and stormy.

The boat's tears going down his body,
The lion smashing the rocks down,
The lion pounces on the boat,
The boat is soon stuck under a rock.

The lion is now getting more angry
And the boat is getting more and more sad.
The sky starts to calm down,
So do the boat and lion.
So the game is over.

Rhiannon Jones (8)
Higham Ferrers Junior School, Higham Ferrers

Bullying

B ullying hurts inside and out
U sed and hurt people
L aughing at people when they are sad
L eaving people out
Y ou watch, they spin a web for me
I 'm so sad and upset
N ame-calling hurts
G o and help.

Sophie Coles (8)
Higham Ferrers Junior School, Higham Ferrers

Happiness

Happiness is blue.
It tastes like a chocolate bar.
It smells like a blue flower.
Happiness looks like a rabbit hopping.
It sounds like birds singing.
Happiness is a bedtime hug.

Bethany Wood (9)
Higham Ferrers Junior School, Higham Ferrers

Noidocky
(Based on 'Jabberwocky' by Lewis Carroll)

'Twas bloodthirsty and the yellow sand
Was kicked and blown in the desert
All limp were the cactuses
And the slimy, tough Quessert.

'Beware the Goodguys my noids
The rifles that shoot, the guns that fire
Beware the human race, and croid's
Fast singing choir.'

They, their evil blasters in claws
Long time the noid army sought -
So they rested by the armoured cyborg
And they stood awhile in thought.

And, as in deep thought they stood
The human race with guns of flame
Came marching through the sandy desert
And shouted as they came.

One, two! One, two! They injected through
The human bodies dropped like stone
They left them dead and with 15 billion heads
They went triumphing home.

'And have you destroyed the human race?
Come to my lair my invincible army,
We'll conquer the planet. Yahoo! Yahay!'
He went totally barmy.

'Twas bloodthirsty and the yellow sand
Was kicked and blown in the desert
All limp were the cactuses
And the slimy, tough Quessert.

Arthur Kelly (10) & Robbie Wilkins (11)
Higham Ferrers Junior School, Higham Ferrers

Happiness

Happiness is light blue.
It tastes like chocolate.
It smells like strawberries.
It looks like a flying kite.
It sounds like the wind blowing.
Happiness feels like the weekend.

Faraaz Moosavi (9)
Higham Ferrers Junior School, Higham Ferrers

Classwocky
(Based on 'Jabberwocky' by Lewis Carroll)

'Twas Andrew and the Dale danced
Did Sophie and Saffron in the Robbie.
All Ella were the Lauren
And the Layla Marilyn out Ryan.

'Beware the Sarbutts, my pupil!
The jaws that bite, the Charlotte that snatch.
Beware the Grindrod master, and shun
The staff's evil!'

She took her bright orange maths book
Long time she, the lesson boring Jamie.
So rested she by the Mrs Sears' tree
And Paige awhile in James.

And, as in Jack Florence she stood
The Sarbutts with SATs of flame
Came teaching through the Fred classroom
And Kieran as it kaddled.

Amy, Billy! Amy, Billy! And Charley and Jessica
The Dylan Indya went Kyler-Lucy!
She left the Sarbutts, and with the SATs
She went Arthuring back.

'And Nathan, thou slain the Sarbutts?
Come to my arms my Grindrod Jamie!
O classmates! Ward! Wallay!'
She blabbered in her joy.

'Twas Andrew, and the Dale danced
Did Sophie and Saffron in the Robbie.
All Ella were the Lauren
And the Layla Marilyn out Ryan.

Jessica Rymill (10) & Charley Fuller (11)
Higham Ferrers Junior School, Higham Ferrers

Romance

Romance is red.
It tastes like honey and jam.
It smells like bubble bath.
Romance looks like a hot heart.
It sounds like people kissing.
Romance is a hot room with a nice hot bath.

Shannon Bowyer (9)
Higham Ferrers Junior School, Higham Ferrers

Matcherwocky

'Twas wicked and the drizzly rain
Did slither and slithe in the wind
All dimsy were the Cobblers
And the Rushden and Diamonds outplayed.

Beware of the Andy Kirk my players
The feet that skill and head that scores
Beware the silky McGleish
And the furious Colin Calderwood.

He took his Vorpal boots in hand
And took a long while to reach the box
So rested by the goal post
And stood a while in thought.

Andy Kirk with feet of skill
Came running through the crowded box
And waited for the ball to whip in from the corner flag.

Kirk passed one-two, one-two and through the defence
The Vorpal Gulliver tackled hardly and left him injured
And with his body
The stretcher went striding off.

And has thou slain the Andy Kirk?
High five my wicked defence
O wonderful day, hallooh hallay,
He laughed in his joy.

'Twas wicked and the drizzly rain
Did slither and slithe in the wind
All dimsy were the Cobblers
And the Rushden outplayed.

Cody Parker & Billy Freame (11)
Higham Ferrers Junior School, Higham Ferrers

Bullying Poem

B ig spiderweb all around me
U sing someone to bully is against school rules
L arge spiderweb and I'm in the middle
L onely is what you'll be when you bully
Y ou can get suspended from school if you bully
I n this country we are trying to stop bullying
N o more bullying in Europe please
G reat Britain has had enough bullying thank you very much.

Thomas Fidler (9)
Higham Ferrers Junior School, Higham Ferrers

Glossorater
(Based on 'Jabberwocky' by Lewis Carroll)

'Twas smooth and shiny when the scissors chopped along the blonde hair
as the mascara dragged up the brown, gerloping eyes.

'Beware the Glossorater, my daughter, the lipsticker that smears across the cracked lips
Beware the blumping blusher and the pink, gloomy earrings!'

She took the white Angel perfume in her shiny, glittery hands
Long time the lipsticker saciplote foe her sought
So she rested by the hair tree and stood a while in thought.

And as the black dye covered her seemingly long blonde hair
The Glossorater with eyes covered in purple eyeshadow
Came swanking through the glittering, misty wood
And burbled as it came!

Spray, spray, spray, spray, the perfume covers the tail Glossorater
The perfume bottle was completely empty
And left it dead and with its head she went galloping back.

'And hast thou Glossorater slain?
Come to my glittery arms, my bemish girl
O fabulous day, aarrooh away!'
She chortled in her joy.

'Twas smooth and shiny when the scissors chopped along the blonde hair
as the mascara dragged up the brown, gerloping eyes.

Saffron Blissett (10) & Sophie Hill (11)
Higham Ferrers Junior School, Higham Ferrers

Water

The raging rhino's horn bashes little boats
Carrying people to the shore of the rhino's feet.
The boats are torn by the rhino's sharp horn.
He likes the big waves and stormy weather
That can damage a delicate feather.

Alasdair Berry (8)
Higham Ferrers Junior School, Higham Ferrers

Water

The sea cat slashing around in the saltwater.
The big claws reaching the boat as it was sailing.
There were big, big waves crashing on the big, hard rocks.
Clashing on the sea were glowing eyes.

Emma Rogers (8)
Higham Ferrers Junior School, Higham Ferrers

Doggerwocky
(Based on 'Jabberwocky' by Lewis Carroll)

'Twas grooming and the horses
Were eating all the hay,
All chirpy were the birds
And small kittens came out to play.

'Beware the Doggerwock, my girl,
The teeth that bite, the claws that scratch!
Beware the mockingbird
And shun the frumios lion.'

She took her vorpal muffles in hand,
Long time till she got there -
So rested she by the miaow-miaow tree
And so stood and thought.

And as she stood and thought,
The Doggerwock, with a wet, soggy nose,
Came panting towards Genie Wood
And barked as it came.

One, two! One, two! On and through
She fought to put the muffles on!
And with the muffles on its heads
She went riding back.

You've muffled the Doggerwock?
Come to my arms, my British girl!
Oh, glorious day, miaow marie!
She lathed in her joy.

'Twas grooming, and the horses
Were eating all the hay,
All chirpy were the birds
And small kittens came out to play.

Marilyn Coles (10) & Layla Allebone (11)
Higham Ferrers Junior School, Higham Ferrers

Water

The tiger smashes against the rocks, *crash, crash.*
The tiger's paws slashing and dashing.
The tiger's swaying the boat,
Jumping on the boat and slashing with his claws.
The tiger's jumping so high, like a wave diving deep down.

Kieran Prescod (9)
Higham Ferrers Junior School, Higham Ferrers

Candywock
(Based on 'Jabberwocky' by Lewis Carroll)

'Twas caramel and the candycanes
Did lick and stick in the mouth
All melty were the Maltesers
And the marshmallows got gooier

'Beware the Curly Wurly, my son!
The toffee that sticks, the chocolate that's rich,
Beware the gum-gum bird
And shun the frumios Starburster.'

He took his liquorice stick in hand
Long time the Munchie foe he sought
So he rested by the bubblegum tree
And ate awhile and thought.

And, uffish thought he stood
The Candywock with eyes of chocolate came rubbing his tummy
As he went through the Smartie Wood
And dribbled as he came.

Bite, munch! Bite, munch! Swallow and swallow
The liquorice stick went right in
And left it dead and with its head
He went munching back.

'And has thou ate the Candywock?
Come to my arms, my full-up boy
O, Cadbury day! Choco! Chocay!'
He chortled his joy.

'Twas caramel and the candycanes
Did lick and stick in the mouth
All melty were the Maltesers
And the marshmallows got gooier.

Charlotte Cumley & Amy Huckbody (10)
Higham Ferrers Junior School, Higham Ferrers

Dreamy

Dreamy is blue.
It tastes like ice cream soda and ice cream sundae.
It smells like fresh air on a Sunday morning.
Dreamy looks like a million clouds in the sky.
It sounds like a thousand birds flying by.
Dreamy is a line in the sky that lifts you every time.

Tyra-Jade Newman (8)
Higham Ferrers Junior School, Higham Ferrers

Smellysocky

'Twas smelly and the slimy clothes,
Did spread and reek in the bin,
All spinny was the washing machine,
Full with water to the brim.

'Beware the smelly sock, my son,
The smell that stinks, the toes that scratch,
Beware the boxer shorts, and shun
The T-shirts that match!'

He took the washing powder in hand,
Long time he washed and scrubbed -
So rested he by the tumble dry machine
And sat awhile in the tub.

And as in the uffish tub he sat,
The smellysock with eyes of flame,
Came snifferling through the reeking clothes
And got smellier as it came.

One, two! Three, four! He shut the door,
The washing powder went snicker-*crack!*
He left it dead and with its toes,
He went stumbling back.

'And hast thou washed the smellysock?
Come to my arms, my smelly boy, you need a wash,
A non-smelly day! Hip hip hooray!'
He smelt nothing in his joy.

'Twas smelly and the slimy clothes,
Did spread and reek in the bin,
All spinny was the washing machine,
Full with water to the brim.

Fred Devereaux & Andrew Ward (11)
Higham Ferrers Junior School, Higham Ferrers

Excitement

Excitement is gold.
It tastes like pick 'n' mix sweets.
It smells like cooking pancakes.
Excitement looks like fireworks in the night sky.
It sounds like kids laughing and shouting.
Excitement is a fairground ride that makes you happy.

Ashley Thorneycroft (9)
Higham Ferrers Junior School, Higham Ferrers

BMW Wock
(Based on 'Jabberwocky' by Lewis Carroll)

'Twas greacy as the filthy alloys
Did plyre and spanner in the garage
All gritty were the overalls
And the whooshing sponge did outspoud

'Beware the BMW wock, my son
The grills that snarl, the tyres that squish
Beware the Mini-min car and shun
The fantdoodle boy racer!'

He jumped into his fearbuff crane in search
Long time the aruxious foe he sought
So rested he by the breakers yard
And sat revving in thought.

Andyso in crazen thought he sat
The BMW wock with blinding headlights
Came screeching down the canatry lane.

Riv, rav, riv, rav and bang and clang
The cruishing claw went smash-attack
He left it crushed and with its alloys
He went flashing back.

'And hast thou squashed the BMW wock?
Come to my garage, you greasy boy
Oh, what a smashing day! Crushay! Crushar!'
He whistled with joy.

'Twas greacy as the filthy alloys
Did plyre and spanner in the garage
All gritty were the overalls
And the whooshing sponge did outspoud.

Joshua Cox, Ria Merifield & Indya Ramsay (11)
Higham Ferrers Junior School, Higham Ferrers

Bullying

B ullying hurts inside and out
U nder a spider's web
L ord, what have I done to deserve this?
L ord, why did you give me my web now?
Y ou are tangled in a web
I never meant to cause trouble
N ever spin me a web again
G iant spider's web tangled up with me.

Daniel Wiggins (9)
Higham Ferrers Junior School, Higham Ferrers

Chocowocky
(Based on 'Jabberwocky' by Lewis Carroll)

'Twas milky, and the shiny wrapper
Did crunch and cringle on the shelf:
All creamy were the yumminess
And the brown bar revealed.

'Beware the Bounty, my son!
The coconut taste, the rough brown top!
Beware the M&Ms, and fear
The honeycomb Crunchie!'

He took his caramel Twix in hand:
Long time the Mars melted in his pocket -
So rested he by the Smartie tube
And stood awhile in thought.

And as in the dreamy thought he stood,
The Bounty, with coconut smell,
Came waffling through the Milky Way
And melted as it came!

One, two! One, two! And munch and munch
The caramel Twix went Snickers-snack!
He left it melting and with its wrapper
He went galumphing back.

'And, has thou slain the Bounty?
Come to my arms, my Galaxy boy!
O, fudgy day! Truffle! Truffay!'
He chortled in his joy.

'Twas milky, and the shiny wrapper
Did crunch and cringle on the shelf:
All creamy were the yumminess
And the brown bar revealed.

Ella Averill (11) & Florence Ward (10)
Higham Ferrers Junior School, Higham Ferrers

Bullying

B ullying hurts inside and out
U pset, I wish I wasn't here
L aughing at people is horrible
L eaving people out
Y ou watch them spin a web for me
I thought of all the stupid things I've done
N ot letting people play
G oing into the spider's web.

Claire Eaton (9)
Higham Ferrers Junior School, Higham Ferrers

Jabberclothes
(Based on 'Jabberwocky' by Lewis Carroll)

'Twas lying on the lonely shelf
It did sparkle and shine
All short were the mini skirts
And the long coats were fine.

'Beware the spotty tops, my love!
The colours that clash, the straps that dig!
Beware the high-heeled shoes and shun
The slippers shaped like pigs.'

She took the underwear in hand
Long time it took to get them on
So rested she by the New Look sign
And stood awhile with Tom.

And as she bought her sparkly top
Her mum with eyes of flame
Came sniffling through the shop
And gagged as she came.

Atchoo! Atchoo! Atchoo! Atchoo!
The mother of two said, 'Come right back!'
And with her ear she shed a tear
And drove into a sack.

'And where have you been all this time?
Come to my arms, my foolish girl!
Oh horrid day! Shopping, you pay.'
She shouted to her pearl.

'Twas lying on the lonely shelf
It did sparkle and shine
All short were the mini skirts
And the long coats were fine.

Lauren Kirkpatrick (11) & Amy Gilson (10)
Higham Ferrers Junior School, Higham Ferrers

Water

The powerful seawater playing with the boat.
The water crashing into the rocks.
The shark crashing into the wonderful, big, white boat,
Filling the boat.
Powerful seawater.
Big, crashing waves.
Big, powerful, cold, blue hands.
A big, cold, blue, face.

Hollie Brown (9)
Higham Ferrers Junior School, Higham Ferrers

Andrewocky
(Based on 'Jabberwocky' by Lewis Carroll)

'Twas Fred with the Loz
Cody was there with Saffron
As the moonlight shone
The Robbie got mad

'Beware the Andrew, my Billy!
The Arthurs that bite
The Jacks that catch
Beware the Kieran, and shun
The frumious Sarbutts'

He took the Dale sword in hand
Long time the Andrew foe he fought
So rested he by the Jessica tree
And stood a while with Charley

And as in Sophie thought
The Andrew with eyes of Jamie
Came roaring out of the Kyler wood
With Nathan in the trees

Layla, Florence, Amy, Charlotte and Ella, Marilyn
The Dale blade went Dylan and Ryan
He left it dead, with its head
He rode Indya back

'And hast thou slayed the Andrew?
Come to my arms, you Paige boy
Oh, Ria day, Lucy, Lucy.'
He Jamesed in his joy

'Twas Fred with the Loz
Cody was there with Saffron
As the moonlight shone
The Robbie got mad.

Nathan Kirkbright & James Eaton (10)
Higham Ferrers Junior School, Higham Ferrers

The Death Of The Sea

The face of the water at death.
The wind blows as the sea horse bobs on the sea,
As the sea swirls boats,
As the sky is full of grey clouds that look like hair.
The sea is charging like a bull.
The sea as it is charging, is cutting through the rocks,
As the sea horses spread against the shore.

Emma Cumley (9)
Higham Ferrers Junior School, Higham Ferrers

Me, The Storm

I was crowding round the houses
The white horses came charging at the sand
My mouth opened
I was waving in the old, grey sky.

The sea charging like a bull
Cutting the rocks in half
I waved like a wild thing
My chest lay on the surface.

The sky yelling like a screaming lady
The hands of the sea splashing
My face looked like a rock.

Summer Hill (8)
Higham Ferrers Junior School, Higham Ferrers

Transfer List

On offer:
One snappy defender, ten years old
Has scored 2 goals and not had any red or yellow cards
Got tremendous skills
Knows how to be a good captain
Guaranteed to do a bad tackle
But he comes with filthy boots
A wrecked shirt
Needs chips three times a week
And a hard look
This offer opens at the January transfer
And ends the beginning of February
Any offers?

Sam Marshall (10)
Holy Redeemer Primary School, Pershore

Scary School
(Based on 'If' by Rudyard Kipling)

If you can go into assembly and sit on a cold, hard bench
If you can get to your peg without tripping over
If you can play outside and not get hit by the ball
If you can stand the teacher giving you test after test
If you can stay awake through the boredom of lessons
If you can read through the whole of the day
Then you've passed SATs with flying colours!
And you'll be on holiday, my girl!

Hannah Evans (10)
Holy Redeemer Primary School, Pershore

Alphabet Class

A is for Andrew, who is very, very shy
B is for Ben, who is ready to cry
C is for Claire, who screams *soooo* loud
D is for Danielle, who's always so proud
E if for Ellie, who loves meat
F is for Finlay, who's ready to beat
G is for Gurlinda, who is always sad
H is for Henry, who is always bad
I is for Isabelle, who's always carrying a plate
J is for Josie, who is my best mate
K is for Katie, who's always caring
L is for Lydia, who is always sharing
M is for Melissa, who likes to howl,
N is for Nadia, who likes to play with her owl
O is for Oliver, who is always in a pickle
P is for Petunia, who loves to play with a skittle
Q is for Queenie, who's always in charge
R is for Ryan, who is quite large
S is for Sam, who is stupid
T is for Tyler, who's Melissa's cupid
U is for Ursula, she's nice and kind
V is for Violet, she's almost blind
W is for Wendy, who's always nice
X is for Xander, who names his price
Y is for Yvonne, I love her pet bunny
Z is for Zac, he's got loads of money!

Jessica Tarran (10)
Holy Redeemer Primary School, Pershore

Dad On Offer

On offer:
    One nippy driver, in his 40s
    Has played rugby, but too old now
    Has a scary smile and black hair
    But not a lot!
    Likes to eat curries
    It makes the toilet stink
    Wears old grandad trousers
    But he comes with monkey arms
    And needs a big bed as has a farting problem
    This is a free transfer
    But I need him back on Tuesdays.

Danielle Burney (11)
Holy Redeemer Primary School, Pershore

Mothers

On offer: one nippy mother 45 years old,
Has done everything in our house,
Has a nifty smile and a cheeky voice,
Knows how to give attention,
Can spill food,
Guaranteed to tidy our house,
This is a tidy woman,
But she comes running to mess,
Weeks of washing, ironing, tumble-drying,
Pants, socks, T-shirts and even trousers!
You name it, she will wash it,
She scoffs food down like there is no tomorrow,
Chips, burgers, fish fingers, the lot!
This offer is open until Christmas Eve!
Any takers?

Katherine Danckert (10)
Holy Redeemer Primary School, Pershore

School

(Based on 'If' by Rudyard Kipling)

If you can bear the smell in the loo,
Or the stampede of children trying to get through,
If you can pretend you understand when you don't have a clue,
Or if test after test is what you'll get through,
If you can take the teachers' awful jokes,
Or in hymn practise the sound of cat chokes,
If you can stand in the cold,
Eat food covered in mould,
Then you can stand the tortures of school!

Alice Winters (11)
Holy Redeemer Primary School, Pershore

Bonfire

Spiky fire
Whistling about
Glowing in the dark
Surprised children
Screaming
Sparklers in their hands
Final explosions
Rainbow-coloured sky
Aaaah! Wow!

Kevin Jo Sung Tse (10)
Holy Redeemer Primary School, Pershore

My Brother On Offer

One nippy runner, 13 years of age,
Says please and thank you (often),
Nice smile, not very tall,
Doing handstands all the time,
Gets very frustrated with machinery when he cannot win.
I'll tell you, this is a free transfer,
But he comes with real sarcasm,
All day and night,
He puts sticky hair gel on my comb,
Then my straighteners are steaming hot.
Be careful,
He's very annoying.
So any offers?
I'll tell you, he's really great (not),
Even though he's my brother.
But who cares? I don't.
So please come and take him away,
You'll love him a lot.
Any takers?

Emily Taylor (10)
Holy Redeemer Primary School, Pershore

Teacher Transfer

On offer:
One good babbler,
Leaves you in the class alone,
Goes to lots of meetings,
Lets you talk, sometimes,
Lets you say cheeky things,
Again, sometimes,

But . . .

Sends you to sleep in seconds,
Can get strict,
Witters on about SATs,
Hates residents on table four,
Gets moody over tiny things.
£50,000 paid straight to table four,
Offer ends after tests.
Any takers?

Isobel Fallon (10)
Holy Redeemer Primary School, Pershore

Sister On Offer

One nippy six-year-old
Has tidied up her room
Does say please and thank you
Cheesy smile most of the time
Eats like mad
Loves to go swimming
Guaranteed to be annoying
This is a free transfer!
But she comes with wrecking everything
Copying everything you say
Being such a smelly child
Getting worse every day
Eating sweets all day long
Chips, pop and burgers too
Offer open! Quick, choose her!
Take her! Take her!
She is very good really
Any takers?

Jade McKillup (11)
Holy Redeemer Primary School, Pershore

Sister On Offer

One nippy chatter, 13 years old
Has smart mouth, so many questions
Spends loads of money and has a pretty smile
And all she thinks about is her family
Can get carried away by shoes and clothes
Guaranteed to want new clothes every week
This is a *free transfer*
Spending all her money
On rabbits, guinea pigs
Dogs and cats and more
Tries to be healthy, but eats junk food
Likes fruit and veg
But likes chocolate and sweets

This offer is until the end of the month,
Quick buyers, I want her back by my birthday
So she can get me a present!
Any buyers?

Hannah Grubb (10)
Holy Redeemer Primary School, Pershore

Cat Poem

C ats are fluffy and mad
A nd they can be very bad
T ails fluffy, fat or thin
S leeping anywhere!

K ittens are the cutest of the feline kind
I adore them, sweeter than a lollipop and ice cream
T ender and loving, so gentle and kind
T easing them isn't nice
E ncouraging them to make them smart
N aughty kittens are still cute
S leeping everywhere!

Lydia Stephens (8)
Holy Redeemer Primary School, Pershore

Teacher Transfer

On offer:
One nippy maths worker, late thirties,
Has successfully taught lots of children,
Always working on the whiteboard,
Knows how to spell, add and divide,
Guaranteed to finish before playtime,
This is a *free* transfer,
Can get a little moody,
Doesn't allow chatting,
Needs lots of peace and quiet
And a little more quiet.
This offer is on until tests are over.
Any takers?

Sean Kerr (11)
Holy Redeemer Primary School, Pershore

Harvest

Harvest is all about fruit, like a pear
For a charity to make the world fair
There's all different fruits, like a banana
We want people to have clothes or pyjamas
You could bring more than a pear
So people have lots of food to share
Soon after October month comes November
Another month to harvest crops
Let people grow their seeds today
Maybe they'll give their crops away.

Nyle Tomlinson (8)
Holy Redeemer Primary School, Pershore

Stupid School Reports

Isaac has not worked hard this year
In fact he's really been a trial
He's arrived late every morning
Dawdling with his brother, Kyle.

He talks in line
He doesn't try his best
He talks all the time
He walks around so much.

He is always finishing work late
He has had the cane twice this week
In the playground he's clumsy and fast
He's always idle in science.

He always distracts others
He could do better
I think
    Signed: Miss Strat.

David Pollard (8)
Holy Redeemer Primary School, Pershore

Mad Maths Test

Mad maths tests
I hate them
Mad maths tests
They make me rip my skirt hem

Silly maths tests
I'd rather go to the army
Silly maths tests
They make me really barmy

Rubbish maths tests
I'd chuck them in the bin
Rubbish maths tests
Will I ever win?

Stupid maths tests
I can never get it right
Stupid maths tests
I came top of the class!

Grace Oldfield (9)
Holy Redeemer Primary School, Pershore

Dog Kennings

Fast runner
Fetch lover
Twig searcher
Bone cruncher
Cat chaser
Great racer
Toy chewer
Deep drooler
Quick eater
Kennel sleeper.

Connor Thompson (10)
Holy Redeemer Primary School, Pershore

Kennings About Ellen McArthur

King fisher
Well wisher
Sea sailor
No failure
World record breaker
Good navigator
Off today
On my way
No mishap
Back ASAP.

Ruth Pollard (10)
Holy Redeemer Primary School, Pershore

Band

Great sounding
Electric pounding
Shock absorbing
New thing forming
Amazing playing
Goes on and on
Long-haired blokes
Playing notes
For the world to see them!

Harry Dowling-Bingel (11)
Holy Redeemer Primary School, Pershore

Stupid Spellings, Mad Maths

I hate spellings, I hate maths
Especially times tables, they drive me crazy
The spellings are hard, well to me
I just want to go outside and pick a daisy.

I want to fall asleep in the middle of spellings
I want to go to the shop and buy some earplugs to snore
Oh, two times two equals four, I want to have a day off school
Oh, times tables and spellings are a real bore.

Spellings are on a Thursday
Can't I have a day off school?
Times tables are hard
I want to make a new school rule.

Sian Sliwinska (8)
Holy Redeemer Primary School, Pershore

Harvest Time

Spiders' webs with crystal dewdrops,
With the last conkers on treetops,
Leaves are crunching and crisping at my feet,
Keep with the rhythm of the autumn beat,
Squirrels running to hide their nuts,
Hedgehogs hibernating in their huts,
Vegetables, nature, fruit and berries,
Cabbage leaves, apples and cherries,
Catherine Wheels spin and rockets scream,
As the sun pours down a tiny beam,
Leaves are crunching and crisping at my feet,
Keep with the rhythm of the autumn beat.

Josie Chapman (10)
Holy Redeemer Primary School, Pershore

Tiger, Tiger
(Based on 'The Tiger' by William Blake)

Tiger, tiger burning bright,
In the darkness of the night.
Tiger, tiger with black and orange stripes
Leering in the forest with your eyes glowing like lights

Tiger, tiger is very silent
Tiger, you can be violent
Watch your back in case he pounces
Tiger, tiger you can creep like a mouse.

Melissa Carroll (10)
Holy Redeemer Primary School, Pershore

School

I like lunchtime, I like break
I like the mural, it's a picture of a lake

I like friends, friends are fun
I like friends, we really love to run

I like teachers, when they're in a good mood
I like teachers, to a teacher you should never be rude

I like the bird area, the bird area is cool
I like the bird area, it's one of the best things at school

I like the pond, full of wildlife and nature
I like the pond, I wish there was a waterfall feature

I like the computers, it's much better than writing
I like the computers, over computers we end up fighting

I like school, school is great
I like school, especially with my mates.

Katie Lloyd (10)
Holy Redeemer Primary School, Pershore

Mad Maths Teacher

My teacher gives me lots of maths
Adding, taking away, times and dividing too!
I hate maths and teachers -
They don't have a clue!

Mad maths teacher, gives me lots of work
I get worse at maths every day
Why can't she just leave me alone?
If she doesn't shut up, I'll make her pay.

Mad maths teacher
I don't understand what she's on about
I can even hear
Uh oh, she's starting to shout!

Lucy Harrison (8)
Holy Redeemer Primary School, Pershore

Football Boots - Haiku

Tired and so battered
As Wayne Rooney's boots pass by
Season ends at last.

Zachary Brant (10)
Holy Redeemer Primary School, Pershore

Bats

B ats are flying high at night,
A nd even sometimes give you a fright
T urning and twisting round and round
M aking a type of squeaking sound
A erobic bats flying in the sky
N ever wake when the sun is nigh

B ruce Wayne is afraid of a bat
R unning and agile, like a cat
U nderstands justice and used to be in a league
C an run fast at a speed
E veryone knows he's been up above

W hen he's a bat he flies like a dove
A nd when it's night
Y amaha's screeching at the sight
N ever goes to sleep at night
E ven when it's time for a rhyme.

Xander Colombo (8)
Holy Redeemer Primary School, Pershore

Myself On Offer

On offer:
One strong midfielder, 11 years old
Scored 26 goals last season
Has excellent finishing and can score from anywhere
Left-footed and loves dribbling past people
Great at getting a tackle in
Soaked to the skin with mud after the game
Remember this is a free *transfer*
He needs to eat lots of fatty food to keep him happy
Washing needs to be done twice a day
Because he loves exploring
Very fussy about his trainers
Doesn't eat vegetables
Has lots of friends round
This offer ends at the end of January transfer window.
Any offers please?

Patrick Harrison (11)
Holy Redeemer Primary School, Pershore

The Door
(Based on 'The Door' by Miroslav Holub)

Go and open the door.
Maybe outside there's some crisp, white snow
Or Santa Claus in his big, red suit
Or a lovely seaside with two umbrellas
And one million beach balls.

Go and open the door.
Maybe outside there's a world made of sweets
Or a chocolate city
Or a rainbow.

Go and open the door.
If there's an elephant, it will soon pass.

Go and open the door.
Even if there's only the moon and stars gleaming in the dark night.

Go and open the door.
Even if there's only the darkness ticking in the night.

Toni Fletcher (9)
Lindridge CE Primary School, Tenbury Wells

The Door
(Based on 'The Door' by Miroslav Holub)

Go and open the door
Maybe there's a zebra with pink lines and a black head.

Go and open the door
Maybe there's a brown dog.

Go and open the door
The dog may be there to bite us!

Ricky Evans (8)
Lindridge CE Primary School, Tenbury Wells

Flowers

They can stand alone, or they can stand together,
They have the strength to stand tall or bend in the breeze,
Their colours are amazing.

They put a smile on everyone's face,
The birds and insects never leave them alone,
There is always colour and beauty all year round.

Leanne Potter (10)
Lindridge CE Primary School, Tenbury Wells

The Door
(Based on 'The Door' by Miroslav Holub)

Go and open the door
What will there be?
Maybe a snow garden
And a sea over the hedge
Or a beautiful rainbow
Or a big, scary ghost.

Go and open the door
I wonder what's there
Maybe thunder clouds
The pizza man all wet and soggy
Or a garden of colours.

Go and open the door
I wonder what there will be
A dancing ballerina
A bunch of flowers
A herd of elephants
Quick, shut the door!

Chloe Griffiths (9)
Lindridge CE Primary School, Tenbury Wells

A Poem To Be Spoken Silently

It was so quiet
That I heard a leaf drift gently across the floor
Which swayed softly.

It was so silent
That I heard the wind wander by
As it picked up sticks.

It was so quiet
That I heard a snail
Make his way across the floor.

It was so quiet
That I heard a butterfly
Step on a leaf.

It was so quiet
That I heard a bird
Sing softly.

Rosie Hall (8)
Lindridge CE Primary School, Tenbury Wells

The Door
(Based on 'The Door' by Miroslav Holub)

Go and open the door
Maybe outside there's an alien
With blue skin and pink eyes.

Go and open the door
Maybe outside there's a tiger
With pink and blue stripes.

Go and open the door
Maybe outside there's a witch
With a golden broom.

Go and open the door
Maybe outside there's a pizza man
With a sporty motorbike.

Go and open the door
Maybe outside there's a seaside
With lots of seagulls.

Go and open the door
Maybe outside there's a chocolate city
With pink candyfloss and red sticks of rock.

Go and open the door
Maybe outside there's a rainbow
With 20 or more colours.

Morwenna Vaughan (9)
Lindridge CE Primary School, Tenbury Wells

The Door
(Based on 'The Door' by Miroslav Holub)

Go and open the door
Maybe outside there's a room
That we don't know about.

Go and open the door
Maybe there's a spooky coffin
Or a large spider.

Go and open the door
Maybe there's a ghost
Or a mummy.

Go and open the door
Maybe there's a bloodsucking vampire.
Even if there's nothing
Go and open the door.

James Ward (7)
Lindridge CE Primary School, Tenbury Wells

A Poem To Be Spoken Silently

It was so silent
I heard a fly's wings flutter.

It was so quiet
I heard the trees blowing in the silent wind.

It was so calm
I heard a piece of grass blowing in the wind.

It was so calm
I heard the raindrops pattering on the pavement.

It was so silent
I heard my dog snoozing.

It was so quiet
I heard the leaves brushing on my window.

It was so quiet
I heard all the little insects walking in their homes.

Bethany Williams (8)
Lindridge CE Primary School, Tenbury Wells

A Poem To Be Spoken Silently

It was so quiet
That I heard my breath breathing in and out.

It was so quiet
I heard the book flicker the page.

It was so quiet
That I heard a rabbit making a big hole.

It was quiet
That I heard a pencil roll down the table.

It was so quiet
That I heard my dog dreaming about chasing a cat.

Isobel Farr (8)
Lindridge CE Primary School, Tenbury Wells

The Vampire Case On The Wall

Creepy is the ghost gliding in the air,
Creepy is the spider crawling on the chair.
Creepy is the rat crawling on the floor,
Creepy is the candle hanging on the door.
But the creepiest of all is the vampire case,
Hanging on the wall!

Freddie Hall (7)
Lindridge CE Primary School, Tenbury Wells

The Door
(Based on 'The Door' by Miroslav Holub)

Go and open the door
Maybe outside there's a pizza man or a lion,
A garden or a chocolate city.

Go and open the door
Maybe there's some fluffy white snow.
Maybe you'll see a world of sweets,
Or the sea,
Or colours of a rainbow.

Go and open the door
If there's a storm,
It will pass.

Go and open the door
Even if there's only the darkness ticking,
Even if there's only the hollow wind,
Even if nothing is there,
Go and open the door.

Isabelle Dix (7)
Lindridge CE Primary School, Tenbury Wells

The Door
(Based on 'The Door' by Miroslav Holub)

Go and open the door.
Maybe outside there's snow falling,
Or a hungry lion rummaging in our bins,
Or a stormy day,
Or a world of sweets.

Go and open the door.
Maybe there's a chocolate city,
A pizza man or a tiger,
A scary room or a herd of elephants.

Go and open the door.
If there's a frog jumping around
Then it will hop away.

Go and open the door.
Even if there's only the darkness ticking,
Even if there's only the hollow wind blowing,
Even if there's nothing there,
Just open the door.

Jordan Turrell (7)
Lindridge CE Primary School, Tenbury Wells

The Door
(Based on 'The Door' by Miroslav Holub)

Go and open the door.
Maybe outside there's a lion
Or snow
Or a ghost
Or pizza man.

Go and open the door.
If there's a snowstorm
It will pass.

Go and open the door.
Even if there's darkness all around you
Even if there's a storm at night
Even if there's nothing there
Go and open the door.

Ben Fillery (7)
Lindridge CE Primary School, Tenbury Wells

Flu

I am in bed with flu,
And don't know what to do.
It is really boring,
But it helps the curing.
Away for six days,
Now back to my normal ways.
School!
Yes, *football!*
School is better than lying in bed,
Now my cheeks aren't red
And I get to see my best friend, *Fred!*

Samantha Matravers (11)
Lindridge CE Primary School, Tenbury Wells

Speedily

Speedily as a Ferrari car
Speedily as a speedboat
Speedily as a jet plane
Speedily as a roadrunner
Speedily as a cheetah
Speedily as a dormouse
Speedily as a horse
Speedily as a hare
Speedily as a shark
Speedily as me.

Stuart Lewis (8)
Lindridge CE Primary School, Tenbury Wells

Tim And Flo

Tim and Flo from the science TV show,
Always had so much glow,
Even when times were low,
Or Tim was on the floor,
Their cheer would never run out,
The best episode by far
Was when Flo gave Tim an almighty clout,
Or perhaps it was 'forces' when Tim fell off his chair
At least five times,
The producer said it was great,
Much to Tim's disappointment,
But Flo went over the moon,
Now she has the enjoyment of pushing Tim off cliffs and chairs,
Or right into the middle of a pack of grizzly bears.

Victoria Harris (11)
Lindridge CE Primary School, Tenbury Wells

A Poem To Be Spoken Silently

It was so quiet that I heard my hamster snore.
It was so quiet that I heard a bird do his morning yawn.
It was so quiet that I heard the wind blow gently.
It was so quiet that I heard the waves crash onto the shore.
It was so quiet that I heard a ladybird having his lunch.

Tommy Farr (9)
Lindridge CE Primary School, Tenbury Wells

Limerick

There was a young man from Leeds
Who planted a garden of seeds
The seeds grew so tall
That they covered the wall
So the man could not get to the weeds.

Patrice Attias (9)
Manor House School, Ashby de la Zouch

Limerick

There was a young lady from Leeds
Who always wore long strings of beads
They broke on the floor
Rolled out of the door
So the lady now wears strings of seeds.

Zak White (10)
Manor House School, Ashby de la Zouch

Limericks

There once was an old man from China
Who had a huge meal in the diner
He ate lots of pork
With his very big fork
And travelled back home on a liner.

There once was an old man called Bill
Who met a young man called Phil
They went to have cake
Which was a mistake
As both of them felt very ill.

There once was a boy called Ben
Who met a young boy called Glenn
They went to school
Which was not very cool
So Glenn went home with Ben's hen.

Gabriella Neal (9)
Manor House School, Ashby de la Zouch

Limericks

There was a young man called Bill
Who swallowed a very big pill
His good friend from York
Who loved lots of pork
Said, 'Why are you so very ill?'

There was a young boy called Glenn
Who always hid in a den
But when he came out
He gave a great shout
And now he lives with a hen.

Riordan Knott (9)
Manor House School, Ashby de la Zouch

Limerick

There once was a young man called Tim
Who lived in a very long gym
He had a six pack
But then he got the sack
But at least he is now very slim.

Oscar Robinson (10)
Manor House School, Ashby de la Zouch

Limericks

There once was a girl called Molly
Who had an overgrown dolly
Her mother came in
Threw the doll in the bin
And Molly hid under her brolley.

There was a young man from China
Who had a enormous diner
He started to sing
That he was the king
So dressed up in clothes even finer.

Hannah Foster (10)
Manor House School, Ashby de la Zouch

Limericks

There once was an old man from York
Who tried to eat soup with a fork
He had a big fright
When it didn't work right
So he used his big fork to eat pork.

There once was an old man from Leeds
Who ate a big packet of seeds
He liked them a lot
But a tummy ache he got
And then through his skin grew some weeds.

Jonathan Rose (9)
Manor House School, Ashby de la Zouch

Limericks

There was an old man from Rye
Whose favourite food was pork pie
He ate such a lot
He fell over the pot
And then he just wanted to cry.

There once was a dog called Bertie
Who was constantly getting so dirty
He had a hot bath
And vented his wrath
On his patient owner called Gertie.

George Shattock (10)
Manor House School, Ashby de la Zouch

Limericks

A girl once sat on a chair
Suddenly she had a big scare
As people would say
It was there today
A huge spider was living right there.

There once was a boy with a snake
But of course it was a mistake
He fed it on rats
But it ate all his hats
So instead he fed it some cake.

Claudia Langley-Mills (9)
Manor House School, Ashby de la Zouch

Limerick

There once was a young man from Norway
Who ran straight into a doorway
He shouted his mum
Who was home drinking rum
So he's still lying there on the floorway.

There was an old lady from Rye
Who loved to look at the sky
When the sky fell
She jumped down a well
That poor old lady from Rye.

Glenn Charles (10)
Manor House School, Ashby de la Zouch

Limericks

There was a young man from China
Who was a really good miner
He fell down a hole
And saw a huge mole
But when he came out he felt finer.

There once was an old man from Wales
Who ate one hundred big snails
He soon felt so sick
He called his friend Rick
And then told him not to tell tales.

Joseph Andrews (9)
Manor House School, Ashby de la Zouch

Limerick

There was a young man called Bill
Who went for a walk up a hill
He fell down a hole
And sat on a mole
And found out his wife was called Jill.

Eleanor Bonser (9)
Manor House School, Ashby de la Zouch

My Family

My older brother is eleven,
He has the brain of a child of seven.
My younger sister, Isabel,
Makes more noise than Big Ben's bell.
To get some peace my dad goes out,
He runs for miles to avoid our shouts!
He runs and runs down country lanes,
In sun, snow or pouring rain.
Then there's Mum whose name is Celia,
In the kitchen she's better than Delia.
As for Duncan (that's me),
I'm as perfect as can be!

Duncan Morgan (9)
Mordiford CE Primary School, Nr Hereford

The Tiger

Tiger, tiger, in camouflage
Green eyes staring, ready to charge.
His body so still in a stance,
How large is his prey?
Does he have a chance?

Tiger, tiger, his skin so bright
His first chance to kill and fight.
His dad had taught him to this day
But then he had thought it was fun and play.
Now perfectly in his pounce position
Thinking if he'd made the right decision.

Adam Turner (9)
Mordiford CE Primary School, Nr Hereford

Fire

I am a fire flame that burns.
I move left and right, back and forwards.
Flames are red and yellow
And they twist and spread.
Fires come when most not needed
And they also burn lead.
Fireflies are so bright
They give the whole world light.
The fire leaps silently as it creeps upwards
And produces more flames and gives us light.
It is boiling with hotness and brightness
And makes everything hot.
But fire is a good thing when you cook
Because it booms and crackles and sparkles with light
And it is so bright, but be careful -
Fire is dangerous!

Rhiannon Pailing (10)
Mordiford CE Primary School, Nr Hereford

My Hand

My hand is bony,
And my nails are shiny,
The bones in my knuckle stick out when I make a fist,
My nails shine in the light,
My veins you can see in my hand
And my fingers are like sausages.

My hand feels all bumpy,
But smooth sometimes,
In the dark you can make puppets with a torch in the night,
My fingers when I get out of the bath are all wrinkly,
And my hands look like my feet.

Zoe Holmes (8)
Mordiford CE Primary School, Nr Hereford

Summertime

Summertime is nearly here
Goodbye winter for another year
Goodbye snow, goodbye cold
Hello sunflower, you're so bold
Your colours are light and you're bright
You're so high you can touch the sky
That's why I love summertime.

Sarah Scotford (10)
Mordiford CE Primary School, Nr Hereford

I Wish I Lived In A Sports Car

I wish I lived in a sports car,
We'll stop and eat a chocolate bar!
With an engine, lightning speed!
It will be a good thing indeed.

The sports car will have four wheels,
We'll look in a shop called Steels.
I bought a sports car today!
I drove the red sports car away!

Now I've bought it, we can run
And we can have lots of fun!
Now it's dirty, oh no, it's dirty!
Now the car can count to thirty!

I have taught the car new tricks,
It can pile up sticks!
I like my red sports car,
It's gleaming like a star.

Jacob Broadbridge (8)
Mordiford CE Primary School, Nr Hereford

Fire

Fire blazing, waving to the left and to the right,
Speeding through the forest and on,
Going through the night,
Twisting and turning through the blazing sight.

The sizzling flames come up from the blazing heat
Of the dangerous fire,
Spitting and flashing, the fire goes sizzle, sizzle, sizzle,
Then it goes *bang!*

The fire cooks food from its hot burning embers
And the crackling fire burns through everything.
As the blazing fire flickers around,
Then the water comes and the flames burn down.
Water is an enemy of fire,
So is mud and sand,
Fire is dangerous
And sometimes it is helpful.

Ashley Stanton (11)
Mordiford CE Primary School, Nr Hereford

Fire

I'm a fire flame, speedy and fast,
I spit fireballs and burn through meat.
I'm a hot, hot sonar,
I burn through everything in my path in a single second.
I'm quick and very strong.
My colours are bright like the sun
Or a torch in a dark black field.
My colours move quickly
And my flames blow around in the air.
I can cook food, kill and destroy a city with my mighty powers.
I'm always warm and hot, I never go cold.
I am a sizzling fire-burning monster
Who can kill and rip everything apart.
My flames start as a little flame
And then it starts to spread everywhere.
Then everything is on fire by me.
Everything is destroyed.
　　　I am fire!

James Clough (10)
Mordiford CE Primary School, Nr Hereford

The Zoom-By Nights

Up they go to the moon
Passing through darkness and gloom.

Up the rocket goes to the sky
Nearly hitting a comet passing by.

There they go past Orion
Then they come face to face with the glimmering lion.

Now they have to be leaving
It's half-past eight, so they'll need to go speeding.

Eliot Broadbridge (8)
Mordiford CE Primary School, Nr Hereford

The Zoom-By Nights

Up on their jets the rockets zoom
Up and away to the moon
One jet red and one jet blue
Zooming, crashing and shooting they flew
Under Orion they bang and crash
And away they sweep under the flash.

Ben Juckes (8)
Mordiford CE Primary School, Nr Hereford

Fire

I'm a fire spreading everywhere
Destroying everything in my path
I'm a fire growing in my secret lair
I like to kill, I like to spread
So fear my wrath.

I like to spark, I like to crackle
I make cookers and barbecues work
I can help you keep warm in your room
I can hide, you will never know where I lurk.

Don't ever mess with me
Or you might meet your doom
Watch out!
You'll end up on the hot end of the stick!

Sam Benjamin (11)
Mordiford CE Primary School, Nr Hereford

Tigers

See the wild beasts as they splash through the ocean,
Moving through the water with a fiery motion.
Dare you approach the powerful cats,
As they prance through the waves with their weapons of prey?
Are you that brave?

They are orange and black,
Their stripes disguise them.
They run as fast as the wind.
If there is a lonely cub in the woods,
He will crouch down low in the long grass
And pounce onto it
And eat it for its lunch.

Margaret Martinelli (9)
Mordiford CE Primary School, Nr Hereford

The Zoom-By Night

Up on their jets the rockets zoom,
Shooting and zooming on the moon.
One jet red and one jet blue,
Zooming, blasting and crashing they flew;
Under Orion with a bang and a crash
And away they flew under the planets.
With a dip and a dazzle they swoop and sway
And crash down to the Milky Way.

Mary Whitting (8)
Mordiford CE Primary School, Nr Hereford

Taking Out The Tigers

A gigantic roar,
At early morning,
Waking up the people,
As the sun's dawning.
This huge cat,
Running through the ocean spray,
Sliding about,
On Sandown bay.

When they're
Taking out the tigers
On Sandown beach.

These tough tigers,
Trudging through the sand,
Their feet sink in,
So they need a helping hand.
When the sun rises up,
It's time to go,
They want to go to India,
But it's impossible, they know.

When they're
Taking out the tigers
On Sandown beach.

James Moruzzi (9)
Mordiford CE Primary School, Nr Hereford

Fire

I am fire.
I move, twisting, turning, spitting,
Throwing myself everywhere.
I am fire.
I move, dodging every liquid I can.
I am fire.
I fear sand and water,
They are my enemy.
I am fire.
I conquer wood, paper, dead leaves best,
But I conquer many.
I am fire.
I cook food for humans
And burn nasty chemicals and objects.
I am fire.
I help rockets into the air.
I am fire.
I am a cousin to the sun.
I am fire!

Mikey Hollis (10)
Mordiford CE Primary School, Nr Hereford

Taking Out The Tigers

As he zooms by the sea
Dampening the sand,
Going too close to the man
Splashing the keeper on his hand.
He scares all the bathers
Out of their wits,
When they're eating their sandwiches
Dropping all of the bits.

When they're
Taking out the tigers
On Sandown beach.

As the cat moves
Further into the waves,
Watching the seals
In the caves.
Chasing it deep to the beach
So it can have a meal,
Pinning it down
And eating the seal.

Hannah Prestwich (10)
Mordiford CE Primary School, Nr Hereford

Teddy

There once was a teddy
With a hole on his side,
Nobody loved him,
He always cried.
Forgotten in a corner,
Where no one goes,
Under a pile
Of smelly clothes.
Then one day,
Along came Jess,
Started to tidy
Up the mess.
She found the teddy
And felt sad,
That he had been
Treated so bad.
She sewed him up
With a patch
And they both
Were a perfect match.

Sophie Fortey (10)
Mordiford CE Primary School, Nr Hereford

Fire

Fire is a heat which rips through meat,
Moves with the flow with its shiny glow.
No mercy, fire is evil.
With this fire it burns with desire,
Boom! bang! smash! With its shiny flash.

Fire helps us cook food like sizzling sausages,
Keeps us warm on a winter's day.
But fire can trouble us too,
Rescuing people's lives from kids playing with matches,
When food's been in a cooker too long that really pongs.
Fire is evil.

The orange light mixing between the red and yellow fire,
As bright as a rainbow.
Fire is evil.

Leo Bristow (10)
Mordiford CE Primary School, Nr Hereford

The Hairy Bikers

The hairy bikers ride like hell,
Zooming past old, cranky wells,
The speed of their bikes is like sixty jets,
Get ready for their amazing bet,
They'll beat you to Timbuktu,
And beat you back to London Zoo.
They are both very big
And they both like to wear a wig.
They both have a scary dog
And their dogs are called Hog and Frog.

Owen Rogers (9)
Mordiford CE Primary School, Nr Hereford

Tiger

Slinking across the sandy bay
With its strong, loud purr.
Slinking across the cold, sandy bay
With only its warm fur.
As the sun drowns
The children flee.
It runs wild,
It runs free.

Charlotte Hart (10)
Mordiford CE Primary School, Nr Hereford

Fire

The fire from the flame thrower
That burns inside the house.
The fire is so big that it can't be doused.
From the grenade,
A big explosion from the house.
Here comes the fire brigade from the fire station
And somehow calms the infestation.

There goes the fire alarm
From inside the house.
Here come the people with a fire extinguisher.
Here comes the water spreading
It is like a bonfire, the flames don't stop.
It is roaring from the fire
There goes off the gas cooker!

Bodhran Brito (10)
Mordiford CE Primary School, Nr Hereford

The Showboatin' Midfielder

I'm a shirt removin', crowd salutin',
Tough trainin', muscle strainin',
Dirty tacklin', just outstandin',
Forward flippin', shirt rippin',
Hard kickin', ball flickin',
Goal scorin', net breakin',
Great divin', dirty slidin',
Bone crunchin', air punchin',
Good curvin', great whirlin',
Bone breakin', free kick takin',
Cup winnin', glory singin',
       Midfielder!

Harry Bee (10)
Mordiford CE Primary School, Nr Hereford

My Foot

My foot is tough
My toes are bumpy
My sole is rough
And my nails are pointy

My nails are shiny
My sole is lumpy
My foot is liney
And my toes are tiny.

Emily Greenow (9)
Mordiford CE Primary School, Nr Hereford

The Witch's Brew

Hubble, bubble, at the double,
Cooking pot stir up some trouble.

Into my pot there now must go,
Yellow snake's blood and a squashed tomato.

Pink snail's slime, eye of a lion,
Mouldy cheese and a star from Orion.

Hubble, bubble, at the double,
Cooking pot stir up some trouble.

Stale bread, black monkey's brain,
Heart of a snake and a gold unicorn's mane.

Head of a bear, bluebird's feet,
Ear of a dragon, all of this you won't like to eat.

Hubble, bubble, at the double,
Cooking pot stir up some trouble.

Hubble, bubble, at the double,
Cooking pot stir up some trouble.
Hubble, bubble, at the double,
Cooking pot stir up some trouble.

Lauren Hart (8)
Mordiford CE Primary School, Nr Hereford

Fire

I am a fire flame.
I jig up and down as I dance.
I am gold, orange, yellow and red.
I can be small, big, wide and thin,
I can be all shapes and sizes.
I can speed over everything in my path.
I pop and jump.
I smoke all day and night,
I am a fire flame.
I am warm and soft,
I can cook with gas, paper, wood.
I can tell stories.
I have a warm feeling to people.
I bring happiness to families.
I can go to all places you can think of.

Jessica Hill (10)
Mordiford CE Primary School, Nr Hereford

The Witch's Brew

Hubble, bubble, at the double,
Cooking pot stir up some trouble.

Into my pot goes some long horse's mane,
Or a spotty dog's tail, or a green frog's brain.

Fluffy green buns, smelly burnt peas,
One rotten egg, or some mouldy cheese.

Hubble, bubble, at the double,
Cooking pot stir up some trouble.

Guts of cow, blood of king,
Liver of pig, a wasp that stings.

Some black cats' ears, heart of mouse,
Yucky man's socks, a little girl's doll house.

Hubble, bubble, at the double,
Cooking pot stir up some trouble.

Bit of snail's slime, feather of eagle,
Gross pig's trotter, one fat seagull.

Abbi-Jayne Rickson (8)
Mordiford CE Primary School, Nr Hereford

The Wizard's Brew

Hubble, bubble, at the double,
Cooking pot stir up some trouble.

Into my pot goes black slug and slimy toads,
Green toes and a jar of wine.

Into my pot there now must go,
Monkeys' brains, bats' wings and old men's canes.

Hubble, bubble, at the double,
Cooking pot stir up some trouble.

Into my pot goes a bear's great ears,
Crow's black beak and turtle's tears.

Into my pot goes leg of lamb,
Jar of malt and leg of man.

Hubble, bubble, at the double,
Cooking pot stir up some trouble.

Sam Stevens (7)
Mordiford CE Primary School, Nr Hereford

The Wizard's Brew

Humble, bumble,
Make people trip and stumble.

Into my pot there now must go
A wand of a fairy
And so it's all tickly
A leg that's so hairy.

Yucky monkey's brain
A hard bit of mud
To make it disgusting
A big jar of blood.

Humble, bumble,
Make people trip and stumble.

Next in my pot there must go
Lots of burnt toast
A bundle of paper
Raw meat from the coast.

Smelly socks
Grandad's nose
Old teddies
Cute baby's toes.

Humble, bumble,
Make people trip and stumble.

Next there must go
A ball of mist
Now we must say
Psst, psst, psst!

Kate Greenow (8)
Mordiford CE Primary School, Nr Hereford

The Wizard's Brew

Cooking pot stir up some trouble

Into my pot is going to go
Some snail slime and rotten sprouts
And smelly mushrooms

Heart of a king, head of a moose
Bird's beak, lion's claw

Cooking pot stir up some trouble

Eye of sheet, small dune
Dog's tail, heart of snake
And rotten egg.

Aron Williams (8)
Mordiford CE Primary School, Nr Hereford

The Witch's Brew

Hubble, bubble, at the double,
Cooking pot stir up some trouble.

Into my pot there now must go
A leg of lamb and green frog's toe.

Old men's socks and dirty jeans
Mouldy salt and mouldy cheese.

Hubble, bubble, at the double,
Cooking pot stir up some trouble.

Into my pot there must go
Cold tomatoes and a horn of a unicorn.

Hubble, bubble, at the double,
Cooking pot stir up some trouble.

Into my pot there now must go
Sour milk and lots of silk.

Into my pot there now must go
A dragon's tail and a whole big whale.

Emily Stanier (8)
Mordiford CE Primary School, Nr Hereford

The Wizard's Brew

Hubble, bubble, at the double,
Cooking pot stir up some trouble.

Into my pot there must go
A brown pig's trotter
And a green frog's toe.

One dead spider, mouldy cheese
A wild wasp's sting and rotten peas.

Hubble, bubble, at the double,
Cooking pot stir up some trouble.

Rotten carrots, mouldy buns,
Rotten apple, cow's tongue.

Mouldy bread, dirty jeans,
Sock of a baby and cold baked beans.

Hubble, bubble, at the double,
Cooking pot stir up some trouble.

Brain of monkey, tongue of snake
A policeman's hat and a prong from a rake.

Oliver Powell (8)
Mordiford CE Primary School, Nr Hereford

The Wizard's Brew

Hubble, bubble, at the double,
Cooking pot stir up some trouble.

Into my pot there now must go,
A monkey brain and a child's toe
And a large horse's mane.

Vampire's teeth and snail slime,
A snake's tongue, we haven't much time.

Hubble, bubble, at the double,
Cooking pot stir up some trouble.

Mouldy cheese, a rotten egg,
Take a man, but don't let him beg.

Beak of a bird, stale bread,
Take a rabbit, but make it dead.

Hubble, bubble, at the double,
Cooking pot stir up some trouble.

Now they're in, mix it up,
Have a smell, don't drink it up!

Michael Cunningham (9)
Mordiford CE Primary School, Nr Hereford

The Wizard's Brew

Hubble, bubble, at the double,
Cooking pot stir up some trouble.

Into my pot they all must go
Monkeys' brains and beak of crow.

Mouldy cheese and frozen bacon
Snail's slime and claw of raven.

Hubble, bubble, at the double,
Cooking pot stir up some trouble.

One mummy's bandage and arm of man
Tongue of snake and leg of lamb.

Some old bread and some mushy peas
Some wool of sheep and some big fleas.

Hubble, bubble, at the double,
Cooking pot stir up some trouble.

In my pot is a smelly sock
Now all I need is a hammer's knock.

Rhys Cooper (9)
Mordiford CE Primary School, Nr Hereford

The Wizard's Brew

Hubble, bubble, at the double,
Cooking pot stir up some trouble.

Into my pot there now must go,
Stale buns and a giant troll.

A horn of rhino, a flying bat,
A stolen book and a smelly cat.

Hubble, bubble, at the double,
Cooking pot stir up some trouble.

A monkey brain, a jug of blood,
Wool of sheep and a pot of mud.

And don't forget the mammoth knees,
Smelly sock and lost keys.

Hubble, bubble, at the double,
Cooking pot stir up some trouble.

Hubble, bubble, at the double,
Cooking pot stir up some trouble.
Get it cooking very fast,
Get it ready for the flask.

Sam Prestwich (8)
Mordiford CE Primary School, Nr Hereford

The Wizard's Brew

Hubble, bubble, at the double,
Cooking pot stir up some trouble.

Into my pot goes the scale of a louse,
A rotten egg and head of a mouse.

A slab of raw meat, a smelly monkey's brain,
A stale bun and a black horse's mane.

Hubble, bubble, at the double,
Cooking pot stir up some trouble.

Glistening snail slime, mouldy cheese,
Hoof of a cow and squishy peas.

Tongue of a snake, ear of a bat,
A dragon's spike and the tail of a cat.

Hubble, bubble, at the double,
Cooking pot stir up some trouble.

Smelly socks, feather of owl,
Vampire teeth and tail of fowl.

Rosie Cox (8)
Mordiford CE Primary School, Nr Hereford

The Witch's Brew

Hubble, bubble, at the double,
Cooking pot stir up some trouble.

Into my pot there now must go,
Green frog's toe and giant's woes.

Hubble, bubble, at the double,
Cooking pot stir up some trouble.

Dirt of pig and jug of blood,
Rotten honey and queen bees,
Paw of kitten, tail of dog,
Mouldy salt and old men's knees.

Hubble, bubble, at the double,
Cooking pot stir up some trouble.

Finger of human and cold chicken,
Dragon's tooth, hand of goat,
Wing of bird and slime of slug.

Hubble, bubble, at the double,
Cooking pot stir up some trouble.

You don't want to know, but I'll tell you if you're brave,
Ear of rotten shrimp, hair of bear,
Stolen jewels from Aladdin's cave.

Hubble, bubble, at the double,
Cooking pot stir up some trouble.

So do all these make you feel sick?
Go on, try it, it won't hurt - just take a lick.

Sophie Hollis (8)
Mordiford CE Primary School, Nr Hereford

The Wizard's Brew

Mixy, mixy, mixy, mixy
This very thing is quite a pixie
Now my pot has a rotten egg and tongue of snake,
A stale potato and now my potion will awake.

Rotten apple, gerbil's tail,
Ear of a rabbit, and in goes a kind of hail.

Mixy, mixy, mixy, mixy,
This very thing is quite a pixie.

Mouldy banana, blue dog's ear,
Mammoth's lungs.
Bubble, bubble, I can hear slippy stones,
Monkey's toe and some sticky glue.

Evan Cooper (7)
Mordiford CE Primary School, Nr Hereford

The Witch's Brew

Hubble, bubble, at the double,
Little pot stir up some trouble.

Into my pot goes the smelly cheese,
Hot and stripy with squashed peas.

Mouldy buns and liquorice sweets,
Rudolph's nose and lots and lots of lovely sweets.

Hubble, bubble, at the double,
Little pot stir up some trouble.

Smelly chicken and chocolate cakes,
Yucky socks and sharp snakes.

Lumpy mash and lots of cheese,
Lovely cups like coffee and tea.

Charlotte Oakley (8)
Mordiford CE Primary School, Nr Hereford

My Utter Zoo

The Bullofudge is small and round
Its feet are stuck to the ground.

The Dandaboo is blue and red
And half its life is spent in bed.

The Ecaroo is huge and white
And can only be seen in the night.

The Googlybob is small and pink
It eats its food out of a sink.

The Idiommpemonic is king of all the creatures
Although he has extremely ugly features.

Kedublefudge is big and green
It's not from Earth but planet Zeen.

The Mintaloo is like a cat
Although it wears a funny hat.

The Pankaroo looks like a tree
And has its nose stuck on its knee.

The Sherker is ten foot big
Its favourite food is chocolate fig.

The Wilamoo is orange and blue
It can jump higher than a kangaroo.

Richard Hart-Mould (10)
Our Lady & St Werburgh's RC School, Newcastle

My Utter Zoo

The Elagogle is very fast,
But they're dead at last.

The Hazawasul is very strong,
But they let out a great big pong.

The Prog is very cool
And he likes to play in school.

The Qweenabable is very poor,
But she likes Roger Moore.

The Slagalway likes to drink tonic,
But it always makes him vomit.

The Tanket is very small,
But they think they're very tall.

The Uounaligile goes into a trance,
In which he takes off his pants.

The Wsae has floppy ears,
With which he flies away to drink beer.

The Womble stands up at the dawn of day
And then it walks away.

The Zote squeaks and moans,
While eating bones.

Peter Baggley (10)
Our Lady & St Werburgh's RC School, Newcastle

My Utter Zoo

The Ampo likes to eat
But cannot always keep neat.

The Carlagonga is so fat
And goes to sleep on a mat.

The Earlybarto wants to fly
But only has one eye.

The Hofleclofle is pink
And always wants a drink.

The Jimparoo jumps around
And sometimes makes a funny sound.

The Kifadofle is good-looking
But is unsuitable for cooking.

The Milvarto is French
And wants to drench.

The Nirder is a flea
And his friend is a bee.

The Ondersia is a cat
And always wears his top hat.

The Slithertron has spiky hair
And is always making a dare.

Sam Thorley (9)
Our Lady & St Werburgh's RC School, Newcastle

My Utter Zoo

The Bongoth has a big nose
And sometimes he licks his toes.

The Congro has bad manners,
He also likes to make banners.

The Drondue gets extremely drunk
And he likes to be a wacky punk.

The Endabel eats a lot of cake
And his brother is called Jake.

The Flobaboba likes to clap,
I also like to do a little tap.

The Globab goes to town
And walks around in a gown.

The Januall has a pet
And knows he wants to be a vet.

The Manloop has long claws
And makes a lot of laws.

The Opglo likes to float
And also likes to eat goat.

The Panoo has a big head
And he always goes to bed.

The Roop likes to snoop
And he speaks to the roof.

The Starp looks at the sun
And puts up his gun.

Madison Regan (10)
Our Lady & St Werburgh's RC School, Newcastle

My Utter Zoo

The Baggalopycrag has many, many eyes
It feasts at night on week-old pies.

The Dungadooda is a star footballer
The strange thing is, it's always getting smaller.

The Eppyong is always ill,
That's why it's constantly sucking a pill.

The Fiddledodoo is blue and squelchy
It's always feeling a little belchy.

The Graggygrum is made of stone
It's so frightening, everyone leaves it alone.

The Inkabong is bright and pink
It annoys people by squirting ink.

The Numcig has a giant head
He can't fit his body in his bed.

The Lumbelang has amazing powers
It can knock over skyscrapers and towers.

The Plippyalong is covered in butter
It always speaks in a mutter.

The Qaugaphong is red and hairy
Its bloodstained teeth make it rather scary.

The Stetaro is made of steel
It lives off rotten orange peel.

Matthew Shirley (9)
Our Lady & St Werburgh's RC School, Newcastle

My Utter Zoo

The Babbasoon is always on the go
But when he eats he's very slow.

The Dankercrush sews and sews
And he picks his smelly little nose.

The Hulglum walks on the ground
And he makes a lot of sound.

The Jelbushu can fly very high
And when he's up he waves goodbye.

The Neapatweap is supersonic
And he lives all his life on tonic.

The Olbersour is fat and jolly
And he likes a big ice lolly.

The Satrasun cannot cook
And he's got a nasty look.

The Twibitie cannot plant a seed
And he can't write or read.

The Ulpergum is very tall
And he's good at kicking a ball.

The Xile, what can be said?
He really, really likes his bed.

Marcus Smith (9)
Our Lady & St Werburgh's RC School, Newcastle

My Utter Zoo

The Alp is a famous movie star,
He can travel very far.

The Burno is small and bare
And it is extremely rare.

The Cobble is big and fat
And he just sat on a rat.

The Dandle is as bright as a jewel,
He would challenge you to a duel.

The Eediot is very tough
And his skin is very rough.

The Fumble's skin is extremely green
And he is ever so mean.

The Gasher is extremely neat,
He eats with his grimy feet.

The Humble eats and eats and eats
And eats and eats and eats and eats.

The Igapocky is very small,
It cannot be seen at all.

The Jellyslurp is like a pig
When he does a dancing jig.

Andrew Pover (10)
Our Lady & St Werburgh's RC School, Newcastle

My Utter Zoo

The Antezoo has big feet
And it can't walk in the street.

The Boowoo is very small
It wishes it was tall.

The Crakmak is very shy
No one knows quite why.

The Deewee is very neat
It always is on its feet.

The Edes is very smelly
Because it hides inside a wellie.

The Idot has a mane
It always is a pain.

The Jumpo eats a lot of chips
Sadly it died with lots of fits.

The Keywee is dead
Lots of swords cut off his head.

The Tong is as slow as a slug
No one knows why it should.

The Van is really small
But its shape is a ball.

Siôn Thomas (9)
Our Lady & St Werburgh's RC School, Newcastle

My Utter Zoo

The Aponot has never been found
Because he is beneath the ground.

The Boshont is small and green
And extraordinarily mean.

The Crash has a scatch
And always scratches itself with a match.

The Digger is covered with slime
And makes bad jokes that do not rhyme.

The Bellyful is incredibly tiny
But very rhymy.

The Flip-Flop has got big feet
Because he eats too much meat.

The Granola is very scary
Because he is very hairy.

The Hoomer is very long
Because he swallowed his tongue.

The Jellybone licks its nose
Because he never blows.

The Lipino likes books
And also is a very good cook.

Charlotte Cooper (10)
Our Lady & St Werburgh's RC School, Newcastle

My Utter Zoo

The Flobbadob is fat and jolly,
He always eats a lovely ice lolly.

The Gagawaly is purple and spotty,
But he still needs to have a potty.

The Hagaboo is very fat,
And he loves to wear a pink hat.

The Jigaloo cannot read,
But it loves to eat a seed.

The Kalafrog loves to jump,
And his cheeks are very plump.

The Rumberdush is blue and thin,
But sometimes it eats out of the bin.

The Sumdog loves to eat meat,
And he has his favourite seat.

The Trunkaloo smells so sweet,
But when you smell him he smells of feet.

The Unkoo is tall and round,
And he loves to make a rock and roll sound.

The Zong is pink and dotty,
His nickname is Mr Spotty.

Katie Ratcliffe (9)
Our Lady & St Werburgh's RC School, Newcastle

My Utter Zoo

The Babblop is flat and round
He always slithers around the ground.

The Calop is very smart
But his wife and him are apart.

The Dingerdonger rings a bell
But when he does it he doesn't feel well.

The Eiplimpy is very small
But in a glass he is tall.

The Figgyus is made from glue
But when he comes out he is blue.

The Giggy is extremely boring
When you play with him he starts snoring.

The Inkylop loves ink
And he is always pink.

The Jelman is very nice
But sometimes he is like ice.

The Minkymonk likes the pool
So he doesn't get to school.

The Ompog is very ill
That's why he has to take a pill.

Afifa Oamar (9)
Our Lady & St Werburgh's RC School, Newcastle

My Utter Zoo

The Alligoater is very fat,
It eats goats and is a giant cat.

The Bingadail always tings,
And goes around shouting, 'Bing, bing.'

The Crushaflabber carries a mouse,
If you go near him he will pounce.

The Doorknob is not shy,
It locks out all the passers-by.

The Earflipper loves the mist,
If you go near he holds up his fists.

The Flykicker needs a ball,
Otherwise it goes very tall.

The Glubbedy-Globbedy-Glue is always stuck,
It's very tough when it's shook.

The Hobber-Nobber is very bold
And always has a bad cold.

The Imp is very small,
But doesn't think we're tall.

The Mumbling-Mum always mumbles,
Her food always crumbles.

Abigail Hughes (10)
Our Lady & St Werburgh's RC School, Newcastle

My Utter Zoo

The Axplis is very shy,
But no one knows why.

The Cicloo likes glue,
He will scream when you go *boo*.

The Elphy likes to boogie,
He's not very groovy.

The Fmoo is very fat,
That's why he squashed his cat.

The Googal is a punk,
And he's always drunk.

The Hoomie is funny,
And he looks like a bunny.

The Jmoo likes jam,
But he also likes ham.

The Nictap is very nasty,
But he loves pastry.

The Twilby likes to go to a disco,
On his Sunday dinner he likes Bisto.

The Ulpy is always asleep,
Because he counts sheep.

Jessica Barber (10)
Our Lady & St Werburgh's RC School, Newcastle

My Utter Zoo

The Dazinapop really stinks
And stinks and stinks and stinks and stinks.

The Epitwang is like a worm
It's in your hair and makes you squirm.

The Jish-Josh is cold as stone
All I hear it do is groan.

The Kwigablob is so small
And is always in a ball.

The Nipablob picks its nose
And then eats all the crows.

The Qdob likes to eat chips
And has greeny-blue lips.

The Radkip likes to play ball
And falls asleep all through fall.

The Twingflop is round and fat
And swallows things on a mat.

The Ump has never got far
Because it is in a jar.

The Womble has a long nose
Which it tickles with its toes.

Samuel Baines (9)
Our Lady & St Werburgh's RC School, Newcastle

My Utter Zoo

The Ampla is big and round
And weighs a couple of pound.

The Cuckaloo is as flat as a cake
And glides in the lake.

The Efloo is clever and bright
And shines like a light.

The Flicker picks his nose
Not just that, he flicks his crows.

The Kickler can sleep all day
Even if he has to pay.

The Miller is really scary
And makes jokes about becoming a fairy.

The Pop really smells like cheese
But only eats peas.

The Quarter is that thin
He can fit in the bin.

The Par is a hungry girl
She could even eat a pearl.

The Yoyo goes up and down
When he stops he gives a frown.

Harriet Lowe (9)
Our Lady & St Werburgh's RC School, Newcastle

My Utter Zoo

The Abedushdo picks his nose,
Not just that, he licks his toes.

The Cuchalucha is so, so small,
Compared to the one who is very tall.

The Dabbasa is kind of magic,
But when it comes to spells, he's really *tragic*.

The Expodi is extremely sad
And because of that you should know he's mad.

The Flubodoo is amazingly shy,
And all the time he just wants to cry.

The Jipsalips has lost his head,
So now he knows it's time for bed.

The Morsk is happy but never sad,
Even though he's lost his dad.

The Twisp is very, very funny
And wishes that he was Bugs Bunny.

The Yabboo is extremely strong,
And has been wrestling for oh, so long.

And now we finally meet the Zope,
Who likes pudding and dirty soap.

Craig Smith (9)
Our Lady & St Werburgh's RC School, Newcastle

My Utter Zoo

A Skalen is very big
He loves to eat and dig.

Diggerbogger is big and fat
He looks just like a mutant bat.

Flabadab is extremely strong
He lets off a really bad pong.

Jabbahed is big and round
He mutters loudly and roars extremely proudly.

Maddybadegg is very fat
He wears a woolly hat.

Rybena has a pet pig
And he is extremely big.

Trubyed is ours
He eats gold bars.

Wumpa ice creatures are very cold
And extremely bold.

Xamp has no pace
And in its home there is no space.

Zamped is in his bed
He is nearly dead.

Ryan O'Connor (9)
Our Lady & St Werburgh's RC School, Newcastle

My Utter Zoo

The Aison is very shy
And never says goodbye.

The Foolerhooler is a fool
And always jumps in the pool.

The Goolyolly is nasty
And likes pasties.

The Hooloo is a dude
And runs round nude.

The Jummle is thick
And throws bricks.

The Mork drives people crazy
And is lazy.

The Oaich goes woof
And is rough.

Runnyer is a loser
And is kind of a boozer.

The Wamble is rude
And is nude.

The Yoo points at you
And doesn't like the loo.

Jacque Wootton (9)
Our Lady & St Werburgh's RC School, Newcastle

My Utter Zoo

The Bogyboon wears a suit
He really looks cute.

The Ejo likes to dance
But he never wears pants.

The Hupalog lives in a cave
He often tends to visit the grave.

The Jilly likes to eat jelly
And he has a very big belly.

The Kwon is now dead
Because someone chopped off his head.

The Lig has been sick
Because he ate a stick.

The Oggy is really small
But he thinks he's incredibly tall.

Thintaloop likes to eat felt tips
But he hates it when he gets it on his lips.

The Xadin is not a lady
But still he has a baby.

TheYew is very scary
From the waist down he's a fairy.

Poppy O'Rourke (9)
Our Lady & St Werburgh's RC School, Newcastle

My Utter Zoo

The Ampooga is intensely neat
It wipes its marks from its feet.

The Booger has five arms and legs
It slurps and slides when cooking eggs.

The Eggy-Weggy is quite shy
It goes home without a bye!

The Flibber is very rude
It goes around in the nude!

The Ippag is a whirl
Of course, she is a girl.

The Kaliabha has four heads
Eight arms and legs made of lead.

The Nincompoop is very drunk
It likes to drink on a bunk.

The Oma cares and cares
And cares and cares and cares.

The Renchit is tall
So she lives in a wall.

Hannah Poole (10)
Our Lady & St Werburgh's RC School, Newcastle

My Utter Zoo

The Appabong is smelly and strong
His arms are very, very long.

The Bobbolong jumps up and down
He bounces along all over town.

The Cattafink is shiny and black
He goes around in Santa's sack.

The Dingledot is round and fat
It is because he sleeps on a mat.

The Elkey is scaly and green
And is very, very mean.

The Flabon wants to fly
But likes steak and kidney pie.

The Gucey is very thin
And looks like a giant fin.

The Hullce is very big
And he eats like a pig.

Harrison Heath (9)
Our Lady & St Werburgh's RC School, Newcastle

My Utter Zoo

The Hattingoo is very funny,
He likes to eat roast bunny.

The Jellyslosh smells like pear,
It doesn't have any hair.

The Krakodong eats plastic,
He never ever eats elastic.

The Loomeroompa was going to fly,
Instead he ate a chicken pie.

The Uck likes to wear vests,
It rings up people who kill pests.

The Vinny-Death-Defier slept,
It never ever paid its debt.

The Wettywing died yesterday,
He never ever got to pay.

The Zig is such a big freak,
He always plays hide-and-seek.

Sam Begley (9)
Our Lady & St Werburgh's RC School, Newcastle

The Utter Zoo

The Almppalla eats smelly food
He then gets in a mood.

The Beacho is big and strong
He has a big bum and he sings a song.

The Creacho is dirty and smelly
And he has a big belly.

The Dido is very tiny
He's also very whiny.

The Eippo is very fast
When he goes past.

The Fipoio is greedy
He can be very needy.

The Gumpies is very shy
My, I hope he doesn't die.

The Humpiogo is very sleepy
He sleeps very neatly.

Fayola Knebel (9)
Our Lady & St Werburgh's RC School, Newcastle

My Utter Zoo

The Bangaroo is a shade of green
He can be incredibly mean.

The Dandiloon loves to kip
He sleeps to the side on his hip.

The Iglooy is very strong
He normally gets everything wrong.

The Jolly-Polly is a girl
In her dress she loves to whirl.

The Oorany has a great big smile
You can see it from a mile.

The Parky-Narky loves to party
Now and then he likes a Smartie.

The Stabaloo writes in pen
He also owns a great big hen.

The uggerlogg is long and flat
He has a girlfriend who is named Pat.

The Vangerlong loves to spin
In everything he does he has to win.

The Xoye loves history
He can always solve the mystery.

Harriet Bradbury (10)
Our Lady & St Werburgh's RC School, Newcastle

My Utter Zoo

The Ballaloo is extremely hairy
And always acts like a fairy.

The Dadalo is very small
And always takes things from the mall.

The Hairspairer sleeps and sleeps and sleeps
And sleeps and sleeps and sleeps and sleeps.

The Ratter-Tatter is a snake
And he likes to bake a cake.

The Sellaplo is so big
And then he turns into a pig.

The Unner-Bunner likes to eat sockets
And then he turns into a rocket.

The Vanetsa is drastic
And then gets tied up in elastic.

The Wibble-Wobble is a star
And then turns everybody into tar.

The Xlaby has googly eyes
And then sighs to passers-by.

The Zelefly is large
And he likes to barge.

Danielle Whitehouse (9)
Our Lady & St Werburgh's RC School, Newcastle

My Utter Zoo

The Alahama is really mad
I think it's because he is very sad.

The Blinky-Winky has three eyes
Oh no! He's staring at my apple pies!

The Carrea is really big
No wonder he can snap twigs!

The Doed Does likes his food
Don't try a bit, he gets too rude.

The Ecclesmell is very tall
Although his friend is small.

The Flobberjog has an odd face
He likes to walk at his own pace.

The Gwadle is very poor
Because he never shuts the door.

The Hula is so nice
She likes to dance on ice.

The Icealula is so hip
When people walk by he takes a nip!

The Joby is so bleak
When anyone comes he goes to sleep!

Megan Burke (10)
Our Lady & St Werburgh's RC School, Newcastle

My Utter Zoo

Aoong is tall and scary
And he wants to be a fairy.

Babblisla is very strong
And his arms are very long.

Crunk is very funky
He loves the smell of monkeys.

Dunkerlunk loves to fly
And loves eating pie.

Exel loves to fly around
But sadly he weighs a pound.

Funges always sleeps
And drives around in a jeep.

Gangio is very fat
That's why once he stole an old man's hat.

Huffulpuf is very lazy
That's why things seem hazy.

Inerglo is very sick
He is a smelly Nick.

Jako is not strong
That's why he does so pong.

Eamon Maarabouni (9)
Our Lady & St Werburgh's RC School, Newcastle

My Utter Zoo

The Killermongle eats and eats
And likes tasting different meats.

The Limleged threw a stone
It missed so it threw a cone.

The Naughtiestavee kidnapped a man
Then he bought him a frying pan.

The Pickerlicker played on computer
Then he took up home tutor.

The Quitchia lies upon his belly
On which he tries to watch the telly.

The Trouble-Maker-Tom got killed by a shark
Then his cousin started to bark.

The Umpilumpi eats television cords
And likes removing floorboards.

The Viciousmyst went to church
Now he goes on Google Search.

The Yiman looks at the stars
But sadly he's behind bars.

Thomas Fearns (10)
Our Lady & St Werburgh's RC School, Newcastle

Football - Haiku

Super fast players
Running from top of their goals
Kicking the ball down.

Terry Folwell (11)
Rowlett Community Primary School, Corby

The Cold Winter - Haiku

Snow creeps in winter
The cold suffocates the ice
Bear thick coat of fur.

Billy Bodenham (10)
Rowlett Community Primary School, Corby

Spring - Haiku

The days get longer
Roses are starting to grow
Summer will run in.

Nathan Brand (10)
Rowlett Community Primary School, Corby

Football - Haiku

Football spins the air
Strong wind does blow the white net
Cheering fans go wild.

Ben Page (10)
Rowlett Community Primary School, Corby

Winter - Haiku

Thick snow all around
People wearing woolly clothes
Cold frost covers ground.

Jordan Jamieson (9)
Rowlett Community Primary School, Corby

The Blue Tit - Haiku

Sings like an angel
Wings fluttering in the breeze
Stalks around for food.

Natasha Keane (11)
Rowlett Community Primary School, Corby

Autumn - Haiku

Glowing trees on fire
Leaves weep as they gently fall
Waiting for summer.

Shannon McLelland (10)
Rowlett Community Primary School, Corby

Cats - Haiku

Moonlight eyes sparkle
He follows me everywhere
Purring as he sleeps.

Holly Bradley (10)
Rowlett Community Primary School, Corby

Rugby - Haiku

Forwards driving through
Getting ball out of the scrum
Opposition charge.

Sam Fury (10)
Rowlett Community Primary School, Corby

School - Haiku

Learning every day.
Can't wait to go out and play.
Sorry, cannot stay!

Casey Cook (10)
Rowlett Community Primary School, Corby

The Wild Horse!

Horse, horse, glittering white,
In the dark sky night,
Galloping through the damp woods,
People following wearing hoods.

Shall I run, shall I run?
And I'm not having much fun.
When I have finished running,
Will I still be as stunning?

Horse, horse, glittering white,
In the dark sky night,
Galloping through the damp woods,
People following wearing hoods.

Ellie Smith (10)
St Bartholomew's CE Primary School, Quorn

Tiger, Tiger

Tiger, tiger, I see his orange coat
As he jumps over the old, old moat
I hear his growl as it so loud
So he should be proud.

The hunters see him in the light
And they hold their swords tight
They step closer then
The tiger sees them and goes back into his den.

The hunters close around his den
It looks more like a dog's pen
Then the tiger jumps over them
And runs away from his den.

He sees his prey
And jumps on it and there it lays
He tears it apart
Like a jam tart.

Tiger, tiger, I see his orange coat
As he jumps over the old, old moat
I hear his growl as it is so loud
So he should be proud.

Robert Jefferies (9)
St Bartholomew's CE Primary School, Quorn

Tsunami Dragon

A beautiful village stood by the coast,
Where the sun shone down as warm as toast.
But the sea so blue,
Could surprise me and you . . .

The tsunami dragon came,
His army of waves over his rein.
With water-wings,
The sound he makes almost sings.

He had a crest of foam
And not a single body bone.
His flames of water,
Scared child, son and daughter.

This village it was so good,
All that's left is rubble and wood.
The site looks never started,
For everyone here is departed.

Eleanor White (10)
St Bartholomew's CE Primary School, Quorn

Bedd Gelert

Llewelyn heard the hunting sound
And set a task for his faithful hound.
'Look after my baby while I'm gone,
For he is my precious and only son.'

Then a wolf came in
And made an awful din,
He tried to eat the son,
But Gelert made him gone.

Gelert stood his ground,
Blood was all around,
Then Gelert, having the wolf slain,
Lay peacefully down again.

Prince Llewelyn then did return,
He saw blood, his eyes started to burn,
He plunged his sword in Gelert's heart,
Then his crying did start.

He saw the baby then the wolf for sure,
And felt the guilt for evermore.

Lucy Gilkes (9)
St Bartholomew's CE Primary School, Quorn

Hyena! Hyena!

Hyena, hyena, giggling about,
Spotty back and gleaming snout.
Hyena, hyena, running away,
Jumping into a stack of hay.

Hyena, hyena, leaping around,
Shouting like an angry hound.
Hyena, hyena, scared to death,
Using up valuable breath.

Hyena, hyena, eating its prey,
Ready for tomorrow's great day.
Hyena, hyena, shiny teeth,
Wishing it could eat some juicy beef.

Hyena, hyena, giggling about,
Spotty back and gleaming snout.
Hyena, hyena, running away,
Jumping into a bundle of hay.

Veeran Govan (9)
St Bartholomew's CE Primary School, Quorn

The Spotted Cheetah

Cheetah, cheetah, running so fast
The sand blows away as you go past
As it does not care if it kills a hare
As it goes past something stares.

Cheetah, cheetah, how can you see?
Make the stars' light lead me
Cheetah, cheetah, where are you going?
Up the tree to get some fruit.

Cheetah, cheetah, I can hear something
What should we do?
Run, run, it's a hunter coming to kill,
Run as fast as you can.

Thomas Hewitt (10)
St Bartholomew's CE Primary School, Quorn

Snow Leopard

Snow leopard, snow leopard, gleaming white,
Walking in the beautiful light
I can see you hunting for your prey,
But sometimes in the snow you play.

You may be cute, but you can bite,
You're a beautiful sight, but you can be a fright,
I can see you lying in your snowy lair,
When the moon comes out, I can see you glare.

Snow leopard, snow leopard, gleaming white,
Walking in the beautiful light,
I can see you hunting for your prey,
But sometimes in the snow you play.

Zoe-Mae Dalby (10)
St Bartholomew's CE Primary School, Quorn

A Boy At The Window

Seeing the snowman standing on its own
Brought a tear to the boy's eye
And was more than he could bear.
Outside, the snowman was staring up at the bedroom window,
Wondering why the boy was crying.
The snowman had a black hat and scarf.
The rain dropped down his face.
Rain! Death to a snowman!
Suddenly, the snowman understood.

Megan Morrison (7)
St Bartholomew's CE Primary School, Quorn

Bedd Gelert

Once upon a time
In medieval times
There was a man called Llewelyn
Who liked to go out hunting

One day he went out hunting
And left Gelert in charge of everything
Suddenly he heard a sound
He looked around and around

He saw the wolf in the corner of his eye
He let out a howl and a cry
The wolf tried to devour
But Gelert would not have this now

Gelert raised his paw
And ripped through the wolf's jaw
As blood spattered all over the wall

Llewelyn arrived home
And saw blood on his baby's clothes
Llewelyn let out a cry
As he plunged his sword into Gelert's heart

But soon after his baby awakened
He saw the wolf in the corner
And everything was clear
His faithful hound had saved his baby's life
From the wolf that was near.

Samantha Harrison (9)
St Bartholomew's CE Primary School, Quorn

Love Is . . .

Love is like butterflies in your stomach
Making you feel strange.

Love is hearts everywhere
When you first fall in love.

Love is like hugs squeezing you tightly
Because it cares for you.

Love is soft and gentle
When you come home upset and lonely.

Love is like a heartbreak when you have let someone go
It makes your heart break into a million pieces of pain.

And love is sometimes hard to get
When you are struggling on your own.

Lemeece Sargent (9)
St Bartholomew's CE Primary School, Quorn

Snow Leopard

Snow leopard, snow leopard
In the mountain snow
Where no other animal dares to go
Your glistening coat blends in with the ice
It makes you invisible to the human eye

You are a giant to your prey
You get stronger and stronger every day
As you travel to the mountain peak
You come across an icy creek

Your claws are like a row of daggers
Once you attack, your prey staggers
Your teeth are like a bullet point
To pierce any limb or joint

Snow leopard, snow leopard
In the mountain snow
Where no other animal dares to go
Your glistening coat blends in with the ice
It makes you invisible to the human eye.

Sean Lowe (10)
St Bartholomew's CE Primary School, Quorn

The Mouse

Mousey, mousey, come here mouse,
Scattering along each floor of the house,
Sneaking in the pantry for some food,
Then in a second everything was chewed.

I thought to myself, *what shall I do now?*
Then the mouse heard something go *miaow, miaow,*
He ran, ran, ran past the stairs,
Then he jumped into a big bowl of pears.

He heard a bang, could it be the cat?
Then he hid under the doorstep mat,
Soon the cat went out to have a stretch
And her best pal (dog) went out to play fetch.

The mouse ran out,
Then he heard a shout:
'Oh no, could it be me?'
He ran out the house, then he was free!

Danielle Fenner (10)
St Bartholomew's CE Primary School, Quorn

The Night Horse

Prancing around under the moon,
But the light will come soon,
The horse stands proudly, happy and free,
He is beautiful and graceful but will not let anyone see.

He comes out at night,
When the stars are bright,
When the day comes he is gone,
Darkness falls and he is switched on.

Graceful animal,
Why do you hide?
Come out and show off your beautiful stride,
Your coat gleams white,
It brightens up the night.

To some people you are a dream,
Why not join the horse riding team?
Your hazelnut eyes stare at the stars,
You would be best in a show jumping over the bars.

But when light comes, his head is down,
He is so elegant, he should be wearing a crown.
His friends are the birds and flowers,
He is gentle and brave and is not a coward.

Prancing around under the moon,
But the light will come soon,
He stands proudly, happy and free,
He is beautiful and graceful, but will not let anyone see.

Halle McCarthy (10)
St Bartholomew's CE Primary School, Quorn

A Boy At The Window

Seeing the snowman standing all alone
Is more than he can bear.
Outside the cold and frosty window
The wind is blowing nearby.
It is cold and snowy and the snow covers the fields
Like a soft, white blanket.
The round snowman with beady eyes looked lonely.
The snowman was ice-white,
It was very frosty.
The boy sat on the window sill and looked sad
Staring at the cold and frosty snowman.

Jade Callis-Capell (8)
St Bartholomew's CE Primary School, Quorn

Wild Horse

Horse, horse, oh brave horse,
How can you run with such fantastic force?
Your glistening coat shines like the moon,
If we need you, you will be there soon.

Where do you go in the pitch-black night?
Even a bird won't come near you, not even a lark!
Do you scare? Do you kill?
Racing across meadow, field and hill.

Are your eyes blue or are your eyes red?
Do you sleep softly in your bed?
How did you get an amazing tail?
You can do everything with no fail.

Is everyone your friend?
If you have a task, you will do it to the end,
Do you have friends or are you alone?
You are made of muscle, not skin and bone.

Where are your friends?
To get to them do you go round the bends?
Are you proud or are you scared?
Do people like you if they are dared?

Horse, horse, oh brave horse,
How can you run with such amazing force?
Your glistening coat shines like the moon,
If we need you, will you be there soon?

Niamh O'Mara (10)
St Bartholomew's CE Primary School, Quorn

A Boy At The Window

Seeing the snowman
Standing all alone
Is more than he can bear
Outside, the cold snowman stands
Upon the white and icy lands
Where the long carrot nose and buttoned chest
In the garden in which it rests
Grins with a coal mouth
Way down in the south (of the garden)
Where it is a cold and misty place
Which says goodbye to the snowman's face
The sun was prepared
So the boy was scared
He wept and wept and then said
'I'm so sorry you have to be dead.'

Sam French (8)
St Bartholomew's CE Primary School, Quorn

The Swan

Swan, swan, gleaming so bright,
How very graceful you are at night!
All the stars look down on you
And reflect on the lake of crystal-blue.

As you sit, the world passes you by,
You lift your wings ready to fly,
The big white moon glistens on the flash of a fish,
Making all life a beautiful wish.

You soar so high,
In the dark night sky,
The gentle breeze makes your wings flutter,
And your elegance makes our hearts melt like butter.

Your fire-red beak, how it is so sleek,
You are very innocent, fish is all you seek,
Your black beady eyes are always a surprise,
From the water like a lotus flower you rise.

Swan, swan, gleaming so bright,
How very graceful you are at night,
All the stars look down on you,
And reflect on the lake of crystal-blue.

Danielle Allford (10) & Tessa Boyd (9)
St Bartholomew's CE Primary School, Quorn

Beddgelert

As Llewellyn heard a horn
Of a passing hunting swarm
He left his only child's room
Leaving Gelert in the gloom
Soon a wolf came to the door
And Gelert had to protect his ward

His ward he had to protect
From a death he could predict
Using his fangs and claws and rage
He killed the wolf in an age
The unappeased prince returned and found
Blood bespattering his faithful hound

'Murderer,' shouted the fury-blind prince
He never has forgotten since
Just after he slew his hound
His baby he found
Next he found a wolf's body
All torn and ripped and very bloody.

Sam Cain (10)
St Bartholomew's CE Primary School, Quorn

Snake!

Snake, snake, big and bold,
In the forest all cold.
Slithering fast through the night,
His eyes glowing, sparkling bright.

In the morning eating his food,
Never in a bad mood.
Climbing up a tree,
Looking for something for his tea.

He starts off his journey,
He turns around and sees hunter Burney.
Snake, snake, what will you do
When he sees you?

When he sees the dreaded chain,
He feels like he is going to be slain.
Can he slip away
And survive another day?

Snake, snake, big and bold,
In the forest all cold.
Slithering fast through the night,
His eyes glowing, sparkling bright.

James Geary & Jacob Goddard (10)
St Bartholomew's CE Primary School, Quorn

Bison

Bison, bison, in the herd
With your only friend the bird
Eating grass on the plain
What goes through your bison brain?

Is it just you want to eat
Or do you like to stand on your feet?
Do you like to go to bed?
Why do you have that horned head?

Is it just to fight for a mate
Or is it for busting open a gate?
Do you like to have pride?
Why do you have such thick hide?

Bison, bison, in the herd
With your only friend the bird
Eating grass on the plain
What goes through your bison brain?

Luke Middleton (9)
St Bartholomew's CE Primary School, Quorn

Bedd Gelert

That very one morn,
Llewelyn challenged the hunt,
Left hound Gelert in charge,
Yet no warning of death.

Around the corner he spied,
A fierce black wolf reclined
For this day I've found my prey,
Not in a covered hide.

Hound Gelert in worry and fear,
Of losing little infant dear,
Belonging to someone very near.

So wolf and Gelert,
Struggle of life,
Blood splattering,
Gelert panting,
Down the wolf slowly died,
For Gelert his breath yet far behind.

Little Llewelyn not to know,
Sharply stuck his sword in fro,
Faithful hound Gelert fell sudden to the ground,
Trying to put up a fight,
But then for him, no more light.

Llewelyn felt his guilt,
Of killing his faithful hound,
Then the corner of his eye spied,
A dead wolf on the ground,
Paced up the little infant,
And no mark on his skin,
Memories for him as he obeyed Llewelyn like he was a king.

Elizabeth Norris (10)
St Bartholomew's CE Primary School, Quorn

Bedd Gelert

One day when Llewelyn went hunting hare,
He left Gelert to guard his son and heir.
When the wind was mild,
The wolf came in to eat the precious child.

Harry Baum (10)
St Bartholomew's CE Primary School, Quorn

Who?

Who saw the white glistening snow?
Who saw it fall gently onto tall leafless trees that blow?

Nobody
Not anyone
Not anyone at all.

Who saw the snowy owl flying quickly in the moonlight?
Who heard the wind whistling throughout the night?

Nobody
Not anyone
Not anyone at all.

Who saw the icy snowflakes slowly spinning?
Who heard the joyful people singing?

Nobody
Not anyone
Not anyone at all.

Asha Patel (7)
St Bartholomew's CE Primary School, Quorn

A Child At The Window

Seeing the snowman standing all alone was more than the child could bear.
Outside the wind was blowing the thin branches off the trees.
The snowman stood all alone in the cold, frosty morning.
The stormy weather was getting worse.
It was freezing cold outside.
The snowman was sad because the child didn't want this snowman to melt.
The snowman didn't like to see the child miserable
Because he was happy to be outside in the bitter cold,
The best place in the world for a snowman.

Annabelle Judge (7)
St Bartholomew's CE Primary School, Quorn

A Child At The Window

Seeing the snowman standing all alone,
Is more than the child can bear.
Outside, the wind was howling terribly
And the cold air whipped around the icy snowman
Who was snuggled under a red, woollen hat.
The child felt very upset looking out of his window at the carrot-nosed snowman,
All alone in the fading light, at the end of the winter's day.

Sophie Bujdoso (7)
St Bartholomew's CE Primary School, Quorn

Who?

Who saw the tiny robin poking around the frosty, white holly tree?
Who felt the cold, cold wind blowing hard and blowing free?

Nobody
Not anyone
Not anyone at all.

Who saw the snowman crying in the freezing cold garden?
Who watched the sparkling snow glisten and then harden?

Nobody
Not anyone
Not anyone at all.

Emma Furlong (8)
St Bartholomew's CE Primary School, Quorn

A Boy At The Window

Seeing the snowman standing all alone was more than he could bear.
He saw his snowman, cold, icy and fat.
He wore a woolly blue scarf and a pitch-black hat which had holly on the top.
He had button eyes and a carrot for a nose.
He was wrapped up in a big leather jacket
And a black pair of gloves on his stick arms.
He had black boots.
The weather was a blizzard.
The boy was scared he couldn't save the snowman.
It looked like it was about to snow.

Eleanor Mason (7)
St Bartholomew's CE Primary School, Quorn

A Boy At The Window

Seeing the snowman standing all alone is more than he can bear.
Outside the window was a poor little snowman,
Outside, all alone in the frosty, cold winter storm.
When the storm grew bigger, a tear dropped down his eye to his toe.
His small, woolly hat was icy and in a second some snow came down.
The snowman was saved by the snow.
The boy wasn't crying anymore.
He ran outside and gave the snowman a big hug,
Wrapping his arms around the snowman's cold body.

Sam Pollard (7)
St Bartholomew's CE Primary School, Quorn

Shark

A shark is like a scary monster,
Swimming through the sea.

It is like a speeding jet,
Shooting in the water.

A shark's fin is like a sign of death,
To all of its prey.

Its jaws are like a stack of deadly daggers,
Ready to stab anything.

Its scales are like a skin of knives,
Attached to its body.

The shark is waiting in the sea to come,
To attack, to get you!

Sam Tetlow (9)
St Bartholomew's CE Primary School, Quorn

Seaside Is Like . . .

The beach is warm and hot,
Like under your quilt.

The sea is wavy and fun,
Like a glass of water being shaken.

The sand is yellow and small,
Like crumpled up bits of bread.

The seaside is yellow and blue,
Like blonde hair with blue bobbles on the end.

Sophie O'Flynn (10)
St Bartholomew's CE Primary School, Quorn

Wind

I saw you blowing the trees back
And pushing someone back as they ran.

I saw you push someone's hair back
And push sweet wrappers along.

I saw you blowing leaves around
And making mini tornadoes.

You are everywhere but nowhere to be seen,
Except when you're blowing something.

Elizabeth Wood (10)
St Bartholomew's CE Primary School, Quorn

At The Shop

In the shops there are babies crying
Like a dog barking.

In the shops it's as packed as you
In a room the size of a door.

In the shops at 6am it's dead,
Then all of a sudden it's like an ants' nest.

In the shops it is as hot as a heater
And the sun put together.

In the shops the stock is the best,
Like a Cadbury's Cream Egg.

In the shops at 9pm the tills are overflowing,
Like beer being poured.

Benjamin Hall (10)
St Bartholomew's CE Primary School, Quorn

The Sun Is . . .

The sun is a ball of fire
Burning all day long.

It is a boiling football
Rolling round the Earth.

It is a scrunched up piece of gold paper,
Floating in the sky.

It is a golden penny
Sinking into the sea.

It is a dragon's breath
In a ball.

Caroline Andrew (9)
St Bartholomew's CE Primary School, Quorn

Gymnastics

Swing on the bar
Jump off the beam
And bounce on the trampoline

You're in such a rush
You have no time to drink
You have no time to even blink

You're having so much fun
Doing jumps and kicks
And even round off flick, flick.

Alice Cox (7)
St Bartholomew's CE Primary School, Quorn

Love Is Like . . .

Love is like a tummy bug,
Sometimes good and sometimes bad,
You always feel you need a hug,
When you feel sad.

Love is like the lottery,
You never know if you'll win,
Love is like pottery,
Delicate and fragile.

Will you end up heartbroken?
You will never know.
You can't buy a love token,
Because it's not a show.

When love has let you down,
Don't feel sad and blue,
Wear a smile and not a frown,
Because someone will always love *you!*

Lizzie Francis (10)
St Bartholomew's CE Primary School, Quorn

What Is The Moon?

The moon is a piece of cheese
Shining in the bright night.
It is like a shining star
Moving left to right.
The moon is a sphere
Trapping the world in.
It is a planet in the sky
Going around in a circle.
The moon is a doughnut
Coming to the end of the day.

Kirk Howells (9)
St Bartholomew's CE Primary School, Quorn

Night

The night is a scary shadow following you all around
It is evil, like being locked in a dark, cold cellar
The night is a place where evil and monsters lurk
It is a time of day when the bogeyman comes out
The night is a good time to be scared when you least expect it.

Sean Somers (9)
St Bartholomew's CE Primary School, Quorn

Dogs

A dog is like a shadow of love
Following you and protecting you wherever you go.

A dog is like a lump of friendship
Gleaming with love and companionship.

A dog is like a ball of knitting
Sitting there when you are feeling cold.

A dog is like a best friend, there when you need it
Gleaming with friendship.

A dog is like a brand new heart, always there
Pumping when you need it most.

Stephen Allen (9)
St Bartholomew's CE Primary School, Quorn

Fire

Fire is like a multicoloured ball of flames
Rolling down a hill.

Fire is like a big football getting passed to a person
With fiery football boots.

Fire is like a dragon's breath
Ferociously catching animals.

Fire is like an evil spirit burning furiously
In the shaded sky.

Fire is like a ghost
Coming to haunt you.

Michael Byard (10)
St Bartholomew's CE Primary School, Quorn

The Phoenix

The phoenix is like a red and gold figure draped in silk,
He glides through the sky at night showing off his grace.

He snaps his sharp beak at his prey to carry them to the bay,
Where his nest is lying.

The nest is decorated with big, colourful feathers
And coated with soft, damp wool.

At the end of its life, it flies gracefully back to its nest,
Only to be reborn from the ashes.

Poppy Gentleman (10)
St Bartholomew's CE Primary School, Quorn

Leaves

Leaves are like ladies dancing at a ball
When they are twirled around by the wind.

Leaves are like comets falling through the sky
When the trees drop them in autumn.

Leaves are like a window shining and gleaming
When the sun shines down on them.

Leaves are like a rainbow of autumn colours
In the morning.

Leaves are like a swan gracefully setting in for flight
When they are carried by the wind when they drop.

Leaves are like stars twinkling
As they hang in the night sky.

Bethany Simpson (10)
St Bartholomew's CE Primary School, Quorn

The Snow Is Like . . .

Snow is like a shimmering snowball
It glitters in the moonlight
Like a fairy's dress.

It is as cold as a freezer left open
Every day snowflakes hit your face
Like a dream coming true.

When a snowball smacks your cheek
Its icicles begin to melt.
It is as white as a snow bear's face.

Snow, snow, it's so much fun
It's best when you throw it
At people's faces.

Georgia Deakin (10)
St Bartholomew's CE Primary School, Quorn

What Is The Rain?

The rain is a leaking hosepipe that drips on my head.
It is water falling from Heaven's drain.
The rain is water coming out of a shower.
It is a flow of water that I can't stop.
The rain is water pouring from a watering can on flowers.

Poppy Brown (9)
St Bartholomew's CE Primary School, Quorn

Love Is . . .

Love is a hardship,
Full of heartbreak and devastation.
Love is an illness,
All fuzzy and weird.
Love is an atomic bomb
Which explodes so suddenly.
Love is a dark dungeon,
Packed with surprises.
Love is a disco,
Happy and energetic.
Love is a cloud
With a silver lining.
Love is sadness,
An everlasting sadness.
Love is a knot,
Never to be undone.
Love is a skill
That has to be mastered.
And love is difficult,
Oh, ever so difficult.

Beth O'Flynn (10)
St Bartholomew's CE Primary School, Quorn

Love Is Like Love

Love is like a world of happiness,
Just for you and me.
Love is like a sea of hearts,
Ready for you to jump in.
Love is like the colour red,
For you and me to see.
Love is like being set free,
When the feeling's trapped inside.
Love is like a cosy bed,
For you to snuggle down in.
Love is like a cloud of hugs,
For you to just walk into.
Love is like a wash of kindness,
Just waiting to pour down on you.
Love is like a cave of sadness,
Waiting to close you in.
Love is like a broken heart,
For you to overcome.
Love is like love,
That no one can change.

Harriet Oliver (10)
St Bartholomew's CE Primary School, Quorn

Kittens

Kittens are like soft balls of fluff
Rolling around by your feet.
They are like furry, soft rugs
Under your toes.
They purr like humming fans
Quietly in the distance.
They play happily
Like two excited children.
Their eyes are like glowing, green balls.
Their noses are bright pink.
They have rough tongues
Like pieces of sandpaper.
They feel like soft velvet
As you cuddle them tight.
They lie on your bed at night
Sleeping peacefully like baby cubs.

Alicia Biffen (9)
St Bartholomew's CE Primary School, Quorn

What Is The Earth?

The Earth is a sphere
Shining in space.
It is a flashing light
That guides me in the night.
The Earth is a jewel
In the crown of space.
It is a silver top
Of a pint of milk.
The Earth is a ball
Floating in the atmosphere of space.

Lewis Pywell (9)
St Bartholomew's CE Primary School, Quorn

Shark

A shark is like a slimy banana skin.
It is like a fearsome hound dog chasing after a cat.
A shark is like a shooting bullet going through the sea.
Its teeth are like gruesome knives.
A shark's fin is like a warning popping out of the water.
It's like a quiet monster ready to kill.
Its jaw is like a ring of death.
Its tail is like a wagging dog's tail.
Just remember it's ready to get you.

Oliver Blount (9)
St Bartholomew's CE Primary School, Quorn

The Solar System

Our solar system,
The Milky Way,
Nine planets all spinning in different ways,
You and I can remember there's nine
By this simple little rhyme.
Many volcanoes erupt,
Mouldy jam sandwiches,
Under normal pressure.
That was the rhyme,
Now here's the time and place,
Mercury, Venus, Earth,
Mars, Jupiter, Saturn,
Uranus, Neptune, Pluto,
That is our solar system -
The Milky Way.

Jacob Layfield (9)
St Bartholomew's CE Primary School, Quorn

The Sea Is Like A . . .

The sea is like a rubber duck,
Floating up and down.

The sea is a smooth piece of hair,
Being slowly brushed.

The sea is like a bath,
All ready to be splashed.

The sea is a wet puddle,
All calm and ready to be jumped in.

The sea is like a fish pond,
With shells and fish.

The sea is a swan,
So elegant and fine.

Evie Moxon (10)
St Bartholomew's CE Primary School, Quorn

That Man From Burton

There was a man from Burton
Who always slept in a curtain
He didn't have a bed
So sometimes he slept on his head
That weird old man from Burton.

Josh Andrews (10)
St Bartholomew's CE Primary School, Quorn

Witch's Brew

Wing of bat,
Eye of newt,
Mouldy cheese
And dead man's loot.

Squid's tentacle,
Poisonous snake venom,
Rabbit's toe
And the great
John Lennon.

Hubble, bubble, toil and trouble
Into the cauldron they must go.

Head of man,
Lion's jaw,
Whale's tail
And guinea pig's paw.

Tiger's tooth,
Shrivelled peas,
Leg of bear
And the bees' knees.

Hubble, bubble, toil and trouble,
Into the cauldron they must go.

Monkey's lung,
Dew of tree,
Sherbet dip
And beetle's wee.

Melting wax,
Sickly blood,
Ostrich egg
And watery mud.

For God's sake, I hope this spell works!
Phowh!

Jonah Stead (8)
St Bartholomew's CE Primary School, Quorn

Happiness

Happiness tastes like sweets
It smells like flowers
It feels like the cool breeze
It's like sharing your toys
It makes you want to dance
It sounds like people singing
People singing is a sign of love.

Edward Latham (9)
St Bartholomew's CE Primary School, Quorn

A Horse's Elegance

A horse's elegance and freedom
Will hit you in the face.

As brown as chocolate and as fast as a cheetah,
A horse gallops through a field.

Small as an ant, as big as an elephant,
All are the same, all are different.

Like an elastic band, a horse's heart will expand
To let in as many people as it needs.

Its mane and tail flow through the air like a kite cutting through the air,
Tossing and turning like a bird in the sky.

Uniqueness and love are all in a horse,
Their hearts are like suns over a rainbow, good and kind.

As bouncy as a jumping ball and as sweet as flowers,
Horses will always be in your heart.

Abbie McCormack (10)
St Bartholomew's CE Primary School, Quorn

Wild Horse

Horses gallop through fields of daisies,
While children sit and watch,
The horses are like beautiful lions.

Horses' hooves are like metal stars,
Shining when they're clean,
Their manes glisten in the moonlight,
Shining all the time.

Horses' tails are like pieces of silk,
Sparkling and slowly moving.

The daisies, some watching like a hawk,
This beautiful animal galloping through the fields.

Laura Andrews (10)
St Bartholomew's CE Primary School, Quorn

Water - Cinquain

White snow
Trees shake, leaves fall
Sun goes down, falling snow
Snowflakes floating like silver disks
White snow.

Charlie Lockhart (11)
St Bartholomew's CE Primary School, Quorn

Into The Cauldron

Hubble, bubble, at the double,
Cooking pot, stir up some trouble.

Into my pot
There now must go,
Leg of frog and mouldy lamb's toe,
Old men's socks and dried out guts,
A rotten egg, into the cauldron they now must go.

Hubble, bubble, at the double,
Cooking pot, stir up some trouble.

One dead fly and a dead pig,
Don't forget a wild wasp sting!

Phoebe Dunbar (8)
St Bartholomew's CE Primary School, Quorn

Into The Cauldron

(Inspired by 'Macbeth')

'Double, double, toil and trouble,
Fire burn and cauldron bubble.'
Into the pot there now must go,
Leg of lamb and green frog's toe.

Hairy spider's guts, cat's smelly heart,
Big, soggy chicken and a little small fart.
Slugs sticky and slimy, a cow's dirty calf,
Dinosaur's toe and a rotten old scarf.

Jake Samardzija (9)
St Bartholomew's CE Primary School, Quorn

Dog And Rabbit

There was a dog from York,
Who loved to eat pork,
He played with his ball,
Never left it at all,
That energetic dog from York.

There was a rabbit from Dublin,
Who wanted to play the violin,
He woke in the night,
Had a terrible fright,
That scared rabbit from Dublin.

Emma Stafford (11)
St Bartholomew's CE Primary School, Quorn

Future Town

Robots walking on the ground,
Laser radios with sonic sound.
NASA flying to Saturn's moons,
Cyborg bunnies for kids' Looney Tunes.

Machines sorting out the military's wars,
Microphone pencils and hovering stores.
Floating chairs and plasma guns,
Talking computers and chemical buns.

Robot teachers with laser canes,
Hover cars and flying lanes.
Aliens treating Earth as home,
Indoor gardens with walking gnomes.

Sensing cupboards and dazzling lights,
Global warming and no more cold nights.
Light speed engines and central heating boots,
Amazing jet packs and men in flying suits.

So in the future it could be good,
No more hiding, or maybe we should.

Andrew Russell (9)
St Bartholomew's CE Primary School, Quorn

Captain Scott

Scott once sailed across the Antarctic
With his two beloved mates
They had a fine journey there
And enjoyed the discovery
They'll start a new adventure
Across a frozen sea.

Scott's mates suddenly died
Such a sad thing
So Scott was all alone
He was such an unhappy fellow
So Scott cried and cried
Till his eyes turned red.

Scott wrote his last note
Cos he knew he was about to die
He got weaker and weaker
His writing got messier and messier
Till it was like a scribble
And . . .

Kirsty Allan (8)
St Bartholomew's CE Primary School, Quorn

Happiness

Happiness is falling in a pile of leaves,
It sounds like children laughing,
It looks like lots of smiles.
Happiness is the colour of red faces.
If happiness was a flower,
It would be a multicoloured flower.
If happiness was an animal,
It would be a happy lion.
Happiness smells like children's tears.
If you could touch happiness,
It would feel like a baby's cheek.
Happiness reminds me of all the happiness in the world.

Andrew Barrass (9)
St Bartholomew's CE Primary School, Quorn

Jack Frost

J ack Frost, the guy with all the might
A bove the snowdrift of the night
C overs the ground with soft, white snow
K icks it above him as he goes.

F rost is winning when he's near
R oasting night-time is not here
O verpowered he has become
S treaks of silver cover the sun
T ime to see if you can find Jack Frost.

Sebastian Applewhite (8)
St Bartholomew's CE Primary School, Quorn

Happiness

Happiness is something that makes you happy.
It sounds like people playing.
It looks like a smile.
Happiness is the colour blue.
If happiness was a flower it would be a bluebell.
If happiness was an animal it would be a human.
Happiness smells like chocolate.
If you could touch happiness it would feel like a ball.
Happiness reminds me of my family.

Alfie Moxon (8)
St Bartholomew's CE Primary School, Quorn

Darkness

Darkness is the swaying, swirling of the wind,
Rushing around my head.
It is the colour of blackness, but evil is around us.
It feels like a fierce panther growling at me with fear.
It tastes like a piece of dark chocolate and a crunch like bones.
If darkness was an animal, it would be a prowling panther spitting at me.
In the darkness you can imagine
There was a ghost inside me trying to get out.
Where can we find darkness?
The darkest place that I know is the woods
And in the middle, a graveyard with rustles
And a sway of wind going down my throat.
Darkness creeps over the world like a blanket
And blinking stars of light shine around me.
If we did not have darkness,
Owls would fly away and never come back.
I am fearful of the darkness
Because I think a ghost may be around here.

Holly Findley (9)
St Bartholomew's CE Primary School, Quorn

Happiness

Happiness is playing with your friends.
It sounds like a herd of giggles.
It looks like fun.
Happiness is the colour of gold.
If happiness was a flower it would be a water lily.
If happiness was an animal it would be a playful puppy.
Happiness smells like roses.
If you could touch happiness it would feel like a pillow.
Happiness reminds me of the world.

Sam Richardson (10)
St Bartholomew's CE Primary School, Quorn

Skateboard

Skateboard
Four-wheeled boarding
Bird house and element
An element with bumps is best
Skateboard.

Andy Sentance (11)
St Bartholomew's CE Primary School, Quorn

Friendship

Friendship is a roller coaster,
The ups and the downs,
Friendship is the colour of the sunset,
It feels like a warm fire on a winter's day,
If friendship was a flower it would be a bright yellow daffodil,
If friendship was an animal it would be a playful puppy,
If you could hear friendship it would sound like laughter,
If friendship was a food it would taste like chocolate,
Friendship is important because friends make you smile,
The worst friendship is when you lose your friends,
The greatest friendship is when you see your friends again,
Friendship is a link between people with different looks and different hobbies.

Megan Chanin (9)
St Bartholomew's CE Primary School, Quorn

Happiness

Happiness is when I am not bored.
It sounds like joy.
It looks like a big cake with a cherry on top.
Happiness is the colour of shiny yellow.
If happiness was a flower it would be a buttercup.
If happiness was an animal it would be a canary.
Happiness smells like sweets.
If you could touch happiness it would feel like a pillow.
Happiness reminds me of a rainbow.
The best of happiness is with your friends.
The worst of happiness is when you fall out with friends.

James Kent (9)
St Bartholomew's CE Primary School, Quorn

Happiness

Happiness is a birthday party
It sounds like people playing on a beach
It looks like some friends
Happiness is the colour of gold
If happiness was a flower it would be a rose
If happiness was an animal it would be a deer
Happiness smells like a pizza
If you could touch happiness it would feel like some kittens
Happiness reminds me of my two rabbits.

Ben Burgin (9)
St Bartholomew's CE Primary School, Quorn

Silence

Silence is quiet, without a single sound,
It's like the beach, the sound of the sea crawling up the sand,
Silence is the colour of snow, white and plain,
It feels like air, nothing,
If silence was a flower it would be a water lily,
If silence was an animal it would be a graceful swan,
Where can you find silence?
Silence is very special, it's hard to find,
When do we need silence?
When we want to get away from the world,
The most silent place I know is my bedroom.
In the silence of the night you can hear dogs barking in the garden next door
And clocks ticking in the midnight air.

Maia Harrison Bond (9)
St Bartholomew's CE Primary School, Quorn

Darkness

Darkness is the woods at night.
It is the colour of evil.
It is like nails screeching down a blackboard.
It feels like a bunch of porcupines.
It tastes like nothing.
If darkness was an animal it would be a crow.
Where can we find darkness?
In an echoing, dark alleyway.
Darkness creeps over the world like a big, black blanket.
I am not fearful of the darkness because I know I'm with someone.

Emma Lovett (9)
St Bartholomew's CE Primary School, Quorn

Happiness

Happiness is when you have a smile on your face and you feel happy inside.
It looks like a big, cheesy smile.
Happiness is the colour of pink, purple and green.
If happiness was a flower it would be a purple pansy.
If happiness was an animal it would be a playful kitten.
Happiness smells like fresh bread.
If you could touch happiness it would feel like a big balloon
With a smile stuck on with Superglue.
Happiness reminds me of my pets.

Maddie Sutton (9)
St Bartholomew's CE Primary School, Quorn

Silence

Silence is when I'm in bed asleep.
It is as if nothing is awake.
Silence is the colour of golden light.
It feels as if nobody is there.
If silence was a flower it would be a sweet and small snowdrop.
If silence was an animal it would be a tiny, timid mouse.
Where can we find silence?
We find it in our beds.
When do we need silence?
We need it when we go to sleep.
In the silence of the night you can sleep and dream,
You can dream and sleep.
The most silent place that I know is snuggled up in my bed.
I like silence because I love to read
And it is easier to concentrate on the pictures in my mind.

Amanda Stanton-Nelson (9)
St Bartholomew's CE Primary School, Quorn

Happiness

Happiness is when a dog is born.
It sounds like when there is a moon coming up.
It looks like an elephant.
Happiness is the colour green.
If happiness was a flower it would be a sunflower.
If happiness was an animal it would be a dog.
Happiness smells like food.
If you could touch happiness it would feel like a car.
Happiness reminds me of holidays.

Billy Addison (8)
St Bartholomew's CE Primary School, Quorn

Happiness

Happiness is being with my family.
It sounds like my cat purring wildly.
It looks like petals flowing off a flower.
Happiness is the colour blue.
If happiness was a flower it would be a rose.
If happiness was an animal it would be a bluebird.
Happiness smells like lavender.
If you could touch happiness it would feel like ten soft pillows.
Happiness reminds me of my cats.

Robert Simpson (8)
St Bartholomew's CE Primary School, Quorn

Noise

There's noise in the playground,
Noise in the street,
But the place that has the loudest noise
Is underneath my feet.
Underneath the pavement,
Underneath the ground,
The place that is most rowdy,
Is where the fairies are found.
There's good ones and naughty ones,
But all the noise is from,
Bad-tempered little fairies,
Foolishly exploding bombs.
They scream and holler and shout,
'Let us out! Let us out! Let us out!'
But nobody answers them,
Because nobody is about.
So if you ever hear a little squeak,
Do not answer it,
For it is almost certain to be,
Lots of little fairies,
Begging to be released.

Elizabeth Wells (9)
St Bartholomew's CE Primary School, Quorn

Happiness

Happiness is when I spend time with my parents and friends.
All of those friendships won't end.
Happiness sounds like fun and joy.
All you've got to do is be good and enjoy.
It looks like an aeroplane going today.
Wish you didn't have to pay.
Happiness smells of warm, wet, salty, blue water.
If happiness was a flower it would be a rose.
Happiness reminds me of love.

Joe Winstone (8)
St Bartholomew's CE Primary School, Quorn

Eleanor

There was a weird girl called Eleanor
Who went out with a rich fella
She thought he was dim

So she chucked him in the bin
That weird old girl called Eleanor.

Alex Cunningham (10)
St Bartholomew's CE Primary School, Quorn

Silence

Silence is a white blanket.
It is like a silver piece of paper.
Silence is the colour of whiteness and everything's blank.
It feels like silver air.
If silence were a flower it would be a water lily.
If silence was an animal it would be a penguin.
Where can we find silence?
When do we need silence?
The most silent place that I know is my frozen heart,
Stuck, but it cannot escape.
In the silence of the night you can hear
Clocks ticking and the wolves howling on the midnight mountains.

Megan Hunter (8)
St Bartholomew's CE Primary School, Quorn

Silence

Silence is an emptiness of sound.
It is like nothing else on Earth.
Silence is the colour of paper - white.
It feels like wind and air, but soft.
If silence was a flower it would be a snowdrop.
If silence was an animal it would be a timid mouse.
You can find silence in space.
In the silence of the night you can think of delicious things
Like owning a chocolate shop.
The most silent place I know is my bed.
You need silence when you are doing your A levels.

Euan Rae (8)
St Bartholomew's CE Primary School, Quorn

Limericks

There was a teacher from Sweden,
Whose favourite pupil was Eden,
She taught her all she knew,
Until her face went blue,
That silly teacher from Sweden.

There was a young girl called Blina,
Who went on a trip to China,
She went down a slide
And hurt her backside
And couldn't sit up in the diner.

Ashley Lincoln-Hollis (11)
St Bartholomew's CE Primary School, Quorn

The Wind

I am the squirming wind,
I bite around the trees,
I stomp all around the harbour,
Blowing over the boats with ease!

I am the thinking wind,
I hit vulnerable places,
And when I make a terrible mess,
I make sure I clean up my traces!

I am the calm wind,
I'm having a sit down,
But when I get a bit mad and lively,
I'll start heading for town!

I am the chilling wind,
I'll wrap around your ears,
I'll dominate your pinkish face,
Before the clouds break into tears!

George Allan (11)
St Bartholomew's CE Primary School, Quorn

The Wind

I am the wind, I am strong
But I am not long.
I am blowing the waves of the seas
And I am dancing through the trees.

I am pushing as the trees sway
But I am calm on May Day.
I am swirling with pride
As the people stand beside.

I blow people off balance
When they watch people dance.
Cloud carrier
A dustbin flipper.

I am the tree bender
And pollen sender.
I am the leaf pusher
The wave maker.

Sean Cato (10)
St Bartholomew's CE Primary School, Quorn

Stage Fright

I'm waiting in the dressing room;
Lights burning on my cheeks.
I try to think of lines I have
Been learning weeks and weeks.

I do not want to climb those stairs,
Those red stairs to backstage;
Show-caller's waiting patiently
With script and printed page.

I hide behind the scenery,
Beyond me lies stage right,
And even though it's hard and rough
I snuggle in it tight.

I enter with a gleaming smile
(Though it is very forced).
It's what the actors tell me, 'Say
It's pantomime of course!'

The audience just sit and stare
Intimidatingly.
My lines are zooming through my head
But I just think, *why me?*

My mouth opens to say a word
Yet no real words come out.
The spotlight flickers just a bit -
I'm speechless, without doubt.

I skip and dance across the stage
And off to my delight.
I'm always nervous on the stage -
I suffer from stage fright!

Dominic Applewhite (10)
St Bartholomew's CE Primary School, Quorn

Limericks

There was an old man of Kilkenny,
Who never had more than a penny.
He spent all that money,
On onions and honey,
That wayward man of Kilkenny.

There was a young lady whose chin,
Resembled the point of a tin.
So she made it sharp
And purchased a harp
And played several tunes with her chin.

Charlotte Schofield (10)
St Bartholomew's CE Primary School, Quorn

A Sword

Neck slasher
Brain basher

Blood spiller
Mass killer

Bone breaker
Life taker

Back splitter
Lung slitter

Heart ripper
Flesh stripper

War winner
Heavy sinner.

Ryan Kirk (10)
St Bartholomew's CE Primary School, Quorn

Kennings - What Am I?

Good thinker
Coffee drinker
Having fun
When work's done
Marking books
Giving looks
Classroom leader
Knowledge feeder
Bully beater
Can shout a metre.

Rachel Flatman (10)
St Bartholomew's CE Primary School, Quorn

Hamster

There is a monster,
I will tell you what it is like.
Its face is like meatballs,
Its feet are like flippers,
Its body is like a tennis ball,
Its teeth are like knives.
If you don't believe me,
It is coming closer.
Argh!

Shannon Taylor (10)
St Bartholomew's CE Primary School, Quorn

Cat

Curtain ripper
Milk sipper

Mouse catcher
Leg scratcher

Deep sleeper
Stealthy creeper

Soft fur
Gentle purr

Eats, eats
Yes, it's a cat.

Deanna Miles (11)
St Bartholomew's CE Primary School, Quorn

Wind

Face smacker
Leaf snatcher

Leave taker
Mess maker

Stick flinger
Excellent swinger

Light hucker
Brilliant looker.

What am I?

Kodi Andrews (10)
St Bartholomew's CE Primary School, Quorn

Cat

Mouse catcher
Food snatcher

Good sleeper
Great leaper

Sharp claws
Pink paws

Squeaky mouse
Cat will chase it round the house.

Benjamin Reeve (10)
St Bartholomew's CE Primary School, Quorn

A Boy At The Window

Seeing the snowman standing all alone
Is more than he can bear.
Outside the cold, frosty, windy, snowy,
Slippy, icy and blizzard coldness,
There is a snowman suffering from the weather,
It is breaking apart the boy's heart.
He is big and he has got a green woolly hat,
With black knitted scarf.
His eyes are made out of black coal
And he has a grey checked jacket.
The boy has his nose pressed against
The foggy and misty window.
Looking suddenly at the snowman, he looks very sad.
He has a tear dropping down his face.

Jake McCarthy (7)
St Bartholomew's CE Primary School, Quorn

A Child At The Window

Seeing the snowman standing all alone
Is more than the child can bear.
Outside, the wind was blowing the thin branches off the trees.
The snowman stood all alone in the cold, frosty morning.
The stormy weather was getting worse.
It was freezing cold outside.
The snowman was sad because the child didn't want his snowman to melt.
The child wondered what the snowman looked like.
The snowman didn't like to see the child miserable
Because he was happy to be outside in the bitter cold,
The best place in the world for a snowman.

Eleanor Cooper (8)
St Bartholomew's CE Primary School, Quorn

A Boy At The Window

Seeing the snowman standing all alone
Was more than he could bear.
He stared at the snowman with the orange nose.
He had a heavy cap
And what you would call one heck of a hole in his head!
It was foggy and the wind was howling,
Hurling the snow into great balls and dumping them next to the snowman,
Leaving him looking like a fat snowman bumped up against a big oak tree.
He felt like his dog had died in a car crash, only worse.
Now the sun was coming out more than ever - more dangerous than ever.

Alex Slater (8)
St Bartholomew's CE Primary School, Quorn

The Boy At The Window

Seeing the snowman standing all alone
Was more than he could bear.
Outside the house was a big blizzard
And it was lifting the snow and tearing it apart.
In the middle of all this stood a snowman
And he had a small, woolly hat and a different coloured scarf.
The child was feeling sad about the snowman being alone.
The snowman's eyes were small, pitch-black, beady eyes
That cried a tear as they started to melt.

Luke Sykes (8)
St Bartholomew's CE Primary School, Quorn

A Boy At The Window

Seeing the snowman standing all alone
Is more than he can bear.
Outside, the snowman was happy and he had a black hat,
Coal eyes, small arms and a buttoned chest.
The snowman happily stood in the night-time blizzard,
The ice-cold wind blowing the snow angrily off the trees.
The boy put his cold hands on the glass window and stared outside.

Oliver Bullock (7)
St Bartholomew's CE Primary School, Quorn

Wind

Rushing through the trees
With a slight and cooling breeze.

Blowing trees about
Freezing without a doubt.

Makes people shiver
Makes me quiver.

Elisa Glover (10)
St Bartholomew's CE Primary School, Quorn

My Wish - Cinquain

I wish
To have money
And masses of it too
Which will make me a millionaire
Kerching!

Rhys Ayres (10)
St Bartholomew's CE Primary School, Quorn

A Boy At The Window

Seeing the snowman standing all alone
Is more than he can bear.
Outside, the cold, frosty, windy, snowy,
Slipping, icy and blizzard coldness
There is a snowman suffering from the weather.
It is breaking apart the boy's heart.
He is big and he has got a green, woolly hat,
And black knitted scarf.
His eyes are made out of black coal
And he has a grey checked jacket.
The boy has his nose pressed against
The foggy and misty window,
Looking sadly at the snowman.
He is sitting on the window sill and he is still sad.

Michael Flatman (8)
St Bartholomew's CE Primary School, Quorn

A Girl At The Window

Seeing the snowman standing all alone
Was more than she could bear.
Outside, the weather was windy, cold and foggy.
The girl was sad.
She was sad because she didn't want the snowman to melt.
The snowman was wearing a blue hat and had a big tummy.
He had leaf eyes and wore a big, woolly scarf.
He had a carrot nose and was one metre high.
The girl wanted to protect the snowman
And take him away from the winter coldness.

Laura Smith (7)
St Bartholomew's CE Primary School, Quorn

A Boy At The Window

Seeing the snowman standing on its own
Brought a tear to his eye
And was more than he could bear.
Outside, the snowman was staring up into the little boy's window
Wondering why the boy was crying.
The snowman had a black hat and scarf.
The rain dropped down his face.
Rain! Death to a snowman!
Suddenly, the snowman understood.

Lucy Cramp (7)
St Bartholomew's CE Primary School, Quorn

A Boy At The Window

Seeing the snowman standing all alone
Is more than he can bear.
Outside, the snowman was happy.
He had a black hat, coal eyes,
Small arms and a buttoned chest.
The snowman happily stood in the night-time blizzard.
The ice-cold wind blew the snow angrily off the trees.
The boy put his cold hands on the glass window
And stared outside.

Robbie Andrews (7)
St Bartholomew's CE Primary School, Quorn

A Boy At The Window

Seeing a round, white snowman standing all alone
Was more than he could bear.
Outside the cosy house it was cold and icy.
The boy was crying as he watched the snowman
Standing on the snowy ground.
He was looking at the snowman as if he was his little child
Who needed looking after and keeping safe and warm,
Even though warmth would kill him.

Holly Millward (7)
St Bartholomew's CE Primary School, Quorn

A Child At The Window

Seeing the snowman all alone
Was more than the child could bear.
Outside, the wind was howling terribly
And the cold air whipped around the icy snowman
Who was snuggled under a red, woollen hat.
The child felt very upset looking out of the window
At the carrot-nosed snowman all alone in the fading light,
At the end of the winter's day.

Megan Jenkyn (7)
St Bartholomew's CE Primary School, Quorn

Snake

I can dance but I don't have legs.
You use my skin but not my body.
I have venom that could be deadly.
I can wind myself around your horrible, skinny neck.

Tessa Dunbar (10)
St Bartholomew's CE Primary School, Quorn

The Boy At The Window

Seeing the snowman standing all alone
Was more than he could bear.
He saw his snowman, cold, icy and fat.
He wore a blue, woolly scarf and hat
With holly on the hat.
He was wrapped up in a big, leather jacket
And black gloves.
He had stick arms and black boots.
The weather was a blizzard.
The boy was scared, he couldn't save the snowman.
It looked like it was about to snow!

Jessica Goddard (7)
St Bartholomew's CE Primary School, Quorn

A Boy At The Window

Seeing the snowman standing all alone
Was more than he could bear.
Outside, the wind howled and the snow drifted down
Onto icy ground.
The pale-bodied snowman stood alone in the dark.
The boy sat crying and could barely see his snowman.
The snowman had two coal eyes, two stick arms
And three coal buttons.
The snowman gazed upwards to see the tears
In the boy's eyes.

Henry Potter (7)
St Bartholomew's CE Primary School, Quorn

A Boy At The Window

Seeing the snowman standing all alone
Was more than he could bear.
Outside, the snowman was happy
And he had a black hat.
He had coal eyes, small arms and a button chest.
The snowman happily stood in the night-time blizzard,
The ice-cold wind blowing the snow angrily off the trees.
The boy put his cold hands on the glass window
And stared outside.

Matthew Astley (7)
St Bartholomew's CE Primary School, Quorn

The Secret Box
(Inspired by 'Magic Box' by Kit Wright)

I will put in the box . . .
A drop of rainbow glittering over the sea
The smell of lilies
A piece of gum that never loses its taste

I will put in the box . . .
A piece of chocolate that never melts
A rubber that knows when to rub out
A butterfly that grants wishes

I will put in the box . . .
The smell of cooked cake in the bakery
The tip of a mermaid's tail
A piece of hot steaming sun

I will put in the box . . .
A pen that does all the writing
The explosion of a firework
A supercalifragilisticexpialidocious horse

My box is made out of a gold and silver base and balls of fire like stars.

Leah Heath (9)
St Joseph's Catholic Primary School, Malvern

My Secret Box
(Inspired by 'Magic Box' by Kit Wright)

Into my box I will put . . .
A drop of rainbow after a storm
The sound of fireworks exploding in the night sky
The smell of red roses in the calm breeze

Into my box I will put . . .
A slice of the snowy white moon and the golden sun
A merry-go-round where the horses fly off
The tip top point of a star

Into my box I will put . . .
The tip of a mermaid's tail shimmering in the sea
The sweetness of hot melted chocolate
A butterfly that grants wishes

My box is fashioned from fish scales, gold and steel
With stars and hearts on the lid
Pictures of my friends and family on the corners
And the hinges are made of fairies' wings.

Emily Paine (9)
St Joseph's Catholic Primary School, Malvern

I Will Put In My Box
((Inspired by 'Magic Box' by Kit Wright)

I will put in the box . . .
The glitter of fish in a pond
The bang of a rifle, like a rhino stampede
The thunder of an elephant, like a clapping audience

I will put in the box . . .
The sound of the bomb, like the world falling apart
The sound of the bear, loud as a dinosaur
The look of a staring parrot

I will put in the box . . .
The look of an ogre as scary as a teacher shouting
The sound of music as boring as a teacher mumbling
The look of an antelope as weird as a dog running around in a circle

My box will be made out of ice, silver and gold
With freshly caught clams for hinges.

Mark Cappellina (9)
St Joseph's Catholic Primary School, Malvern

My Secret Box
(Inspired by 'Magic Box' by Kit Wright)

I will put in my secret box . . .
The sound of fireworks exploding
The smell of beautiful lilac lavender
And a drop of the rainbow sparkling like the sun

I will put in my secret box . . .
A puppy that never dies
An everlasting gobstopper
And a teddy that grants you three wishes a day

I will put in my secret box . . .
The tip of a mermaid's tail
A supercalifragilisticexpialidocious puppy
Some ice cream that never melts in the glittering hot sun

I will put in my secret box . . .
Some chocolate made by Willy Wonka himself
A slice of the moon
And a book that tells you what words say when you're stuck

My secret box is made out of gold and silver all over with glitter on the top to
keep the box safe.

Jasmine Broadbent (9)
St Joseph's Catholic Primary School, Malvern

If I Had Wings
(Based on 'If I had Wings' by Pie Corbett)

If I had wings
I would touch the elbows of trees as
I soar through the summer sky.

If I had wings
I would taste a slice of the moon as
Cold as the Arctic Ocean.

If I had wings
I would listen to a giraffe gently grazing
On the blue.

If I had wings
I would breathe delicately and smell the scent
Of all the colours of the rainbow.

If I had wings
I would gaze down on the trees that
Sway in the breeze.

If I had wings
I would dream of walking through forests
And riding on a shooting star.

Abigail Collins (8)
St Joseph's Catholic Primary School, Malvern

The Magic Box
(Inspired by 'Magic Box' by Kit Wright)

I will put in my box . . .
The taste of freshly cooked spaghetti
The smell of a pretty, lovely flower swaying in the breeze
The feelings of a cold freezing freezer

I will put in my box . . .
A spot of a dark cheetah leaping
A house so dark and old
Feeling of cars going past the houses

I will put in my box . . .
Shouts of children screaming in the playground
The sun so bright and yellow
The dream of a baby sleeping silently

My box is fashioned by the dark, blue sky
With clouds on the lock that flicks
And hangs on a star gold chain.

Tabitha Lewis (8)
St Joseph's Catholic Primary School, Malvern

The Magic Box
(Inspired by 'Magic Box' by Kit Wright)

I will put in the box . . .
The sound of smooth music
The salty scent of the sea
And the smell of puffy smoke

I will put in the box . . .
The touch of fizzy lemonade
The sparkle of fairy dust
And the sound of ice skating

I will put in the box . . .
The green of a wishing emerald
The wing of a fairy
And marble from a ring

I will put in the box . . .
The juice of a strawberry
My Christmas tree
And the feel of the summer sun

My box is old-fashioned, made
Of ice, light violet and purple
The hinges are made of a mermaid's scale

I shall surf in my box
On the wild, Welsh seas and I shall
Sink to the bottom
Where the rainbow coral reef lies.

Harriet Pascoe (8)
St Joseph's Catholic Primary School, Malvern

If I Had Wings
(Based on 'If I had Wings' by Pie Corbett)

If I had wings
I would touch the tiptoes of the clouds

If I had wings
I would listen to the whistling of the breeze in my ears

If I had wings
I would taste the sparkle of stars, like fizzy lemonade

If I had wings
I would sniff the fresh cheese from the moon

If I had wings
I would gaze at the fluffiest clouds as woolly as sheep

If I had wings
I would dream of flying to the sun and back.

Issy Heath (7)
St Joseph's Catholic Primary School, Malvern

My Magic Box
(Inspired by 'Magic Box' by Kit Wright)

I will put in the box . . .
A witch in a car and a man on a broom
A piece of paper that feels like glass

I will put in the box . . .
The taste of roast potatoes
A snowman with a bad bug
A Viking from the 3rd century

I will put in the box . . .
A ninth season and a yellow moon
The taste of oven fried chips
The last trip to the moon

I will put in the box . . .
The feeling of love
The taste of chocolate sponge

My box is decorated in ice cream and gold
I shall hunt in my box
It has secrets on the side
And I come where I stay.

Elliot McDonald (8)
St Joseph's Catholic Primary School, Malvern

If I Had Wings
(Based on 'If I had Wings' by Pie Corbett)

If I had wings
I would touch the head of the tallest mountain

If I had wings
I would taste a slice of the moon as cold as ice

If I had wings
I would listen to clouds of mothers singing lullabies

If I had wings
I would breathe the air and sniff the trees all covered in rosebuds

If I had wings
I would gaze at the dawn of new life being born

If I had wings
I would dream of cowboys cantering around Canada and sitting on a
                                        rainbow's sparkling colours.

Suzanna Sabin (8)
St Joseph's Catholic Primary School, Malvern

Whale Song

Hi, I'm a whale
Shining a pale, coolish grey
With a beautiful glistening tail
I'm chasing the food today

The pod and I
In the plummeting ocean below
We chase the little krill or die
We listen to their song like so:

We little krill
The key to the ocean
We give everyone a thrill!
We're the sea's magic potion
Everyone thinks we're brill;
Us with our slow cutting motion . . .

But what about the rest?
They don't usually stop at that
Have they quickly swum west?
And where is the pod and that?

I call and call
But no one comes for me
I sing the only song I know at all
Hoping it will comfort me:

We little krill
The key to the ocean
We give everyone a thrill!
We're the sea's magic potion
Everyone thinks we're brill;
Us with our slow cutting motion.

Oh, I've forgotten
And I've just remembered I'm hungry
But I lay down on the sand as soft as cotton
For I'm exhausted and sleepy.

A tiny voice I hear
I'm awoken by a familiar song
But I find it's nothing to fear
For there are the krill in a tiny throng.

We little krill
The key to the ocean
We give everyone a thrill!
We're the sea's magic potion
Everyone thinks we're brill;
Us with our slow cutting motion.

But they said this at the end
We've seen your mother down in the Channel
I'll follow them and for myself I'll fend
For Mother is in the Channel.

My hunger is getting worse
But they'll show me where Mum is
It could be just some evil curse
I know I'm in the Channel I feel that fizz

We little krill
The key to the ocean
We give everyone a thrill!
We're the sea's magic potion
Everyone thinks we're brill;
Us with our slow cutting motion.

It feels like days now
Only now I cannot fall
And little bit of hunger I can allow
Then I hear my mother's call:

'Are you alright?
When the water gets wider turn
I hope to see you soon my sprite
But you'll be alone one day, so learn.'

Alice Brankin (10)
St Joseph's Catholic Primary School, Malvern

The Magic Box
(Inspired by 'Magic Box' by Kit Wright)

I will put in my box . . .
A beautiful perfume that smells of rose
An everlasting fire to keep me warm
A crystal clear sea with gentle waves

I will put in my box . . .
A delicious chocolate with creamy strawberry
A lollipop with a pretty swirl
A midnight horse with a shiny tail

I will put in my box . . .
The sound of a dog jumping around
The sound of a bird singing all day
The sound of a lion roaring all night

I will put in my box . . .
A black midnight sky with glimmering stars
A bright yellow sun with a light blue sky
A magic palace with fairies flying around

My box is a quiet box; it has cotton wool on it and it is made of metal
It has sparkling stars on it and it has a red flashing star in the middle
It has a picture of sweets on it and smells like strawberry and raspberry
It has two drawers and inside has two sections.

Charlotte Rooney (8)
St Joseph's Catholic Primary School, Malvern

The Magic Box
(Inspired by 'Magic Box' by Kit Wright)

I will put in my box . . .
The sound of a football in the sky
The body of a rhino in a car
The herd of elephant feet

I will put in my box . . .
The bright light of a bomb
The sound of horses galloping
The sound of music playing through my speakers

I will put in my box . . .
The burn of a radiator
The squirt of perfume
The colour of gel pens

I will put in my box . . .
The scratch of an eagle
The colour of fireworks
A shake of a whiteboard

I will put in my box . . .
The colour of a coin
The whole class register
The howl of the wind

My box is made of fur, sponge and fabric
The hinges are made of ice and pencil sharpeners.

Shaun Pearcy (9)
St Joseph's Catholic Primary School, Malvern

I Will Put In The Box
(Inspired by 'Magic Box' by Kit Wright)

I will put in my box . . .
The smell of freshly baked chocolate cake
I will put in the sound of sizzling sausages in the pan
The sight of snow covering the fields like a fluffy white blanket
The feel of my warm blanket when I climb into bed
The sound of an elephant stamping in a jungle
The sound of a tiger roaring in a jungle

My box is made out of elephant skin, which feels rough
The hinges are made from a cat's spine, all twisted up.

Edward Lines (8)
St Joseph's Catholic Primary School, Malvern

The Magic Box
(Inspired by 'Magic Box' by Kit Wright)

I will put in my box . . .
The never-ending sunset
The Chinese symbol of a tattoo
The fire of an unexploded bomb

I will put in my box . . .
A witch on a crystal-white Pegasus
A pitch-black cat on a chocolate-brown horse
An evil, dark-spirited fairy

I will put in my box . . .
The sound of children grinding their teeth
The sound of my pot belly grumbling
The lovely smell of sweets and chocolate, mmm!

I will put in my box . . .
The groaning of an old, rusty van
The sound of a group of horses' hooves storming across the field
The crying of a dog in pain

My box is an old-fashioned box
It is made of glass and steel
It has a drawer at the bottom and inside it has two sections
One at the bottom, one at the top
The corners have a point like a dinosaur's tooth
It has thick glass at the top with a ruby inside
But no one can touch it!
The inside is the colour of blazing hot lava and it's as furry and as soft as a pillow!

Kia Gwyther (8)
St Joseph's Catholic Primary School, Malvern

The Magic Box
(Inspired by 'Magic Box' by Kit Wright)

I will put in my box . . .
A slash of a sword
A roar of a lion
A snap of a crocodile
A tweet of a bird in a summer's day sky
A smash of a plate on the ground

My box is made out of black panther skin
Like the midnight sky.

David Walton (8)
St Joseph's Catholic Primary School, Malvern

If I Had Wings
(Based on 'If I had Wings' by Pie Corbett)

If I had wings
I would touch the coat of clouds
And swoop through the air

If I had wings
I would taste a slice
Of the sun as hot as a microwave

If I had wings
I would listen to the trees
Swaying from side to side
Blowing the wind on my wings

If I had wings
I would sniff the stars
Smelling like cherries

If I had wings
I would stare at the rainbows

If I had wings
I would dream of lying on the cloud.

Sophy Sherwood (7)
St Joseph's Catholic Primary School, Malvern

If I Had Wings
(Based on 'If I had Wings' by Pie Corbett)

If I had wings
I would touch the sky and
Glide down below

If I had wings
I would taste a chunk of the moon
That was as cold as ice cream

If I had wings
I would listen to the people chatting below

If I had wings
I would smell Jupiter

If I had wings
I would gaze at the towns below

If I had wings
I would dream of riding on a shooting star.

Matthew Dooley (8)
St Joseph's Catholic Primary School, Malvern

If I Had Wings

(Based on 'If I had Wings' by Pie Corbett)

If I had wings
I would feel the tiptoes of trees
And glide through the air

If I had wings
I would race white clouds
As cold as ice

If I had wings
I would listen to the chocolate-flavoured birds
Eating their juicy worms

If I had wings
I would sniff deeply and smell the
Scent of the burning sun

If I had wings
I would stare at the cows
Munching on the lush green grass

If I had wings
I would dream of running in the meadow
And swimming in the deep blue sea.

Josephine Mooney (7)
St Joseph's Catholic Primary School, Malvern

If I Had Wings

(Based on 'If I had Wings' by Pie Corbett)

If I had wings
I would touch the tips of treetops
Above the clouds

If I had wings
I would taste a cloud as
Juicy as a watermelon

If I had wings
I would listen to the wind
Breeze through the air

If I had wings
I would sniff the raindrops pattering
Out of the clouds

If I had wings
I would gaze at the sun throwing
Light into every window

If I had wings
I would dream about swimming
Under the sea stroking the fish as they pass by.

Daniel Revell (8)
St Joseph's Catholic Primary School, Malvern

If I Had Wings
(Based on 'If I had Wings' by Pie Corbett)

If I had wings
I would touch the fingertips of the rainbow
And fly high over the trees

If I had wings
I would taste a chunk of an old oak
As hard as a gobstopper

If I had wings
I would listen to the stars playing
While jumping over the moon

If I had wings
I would sniff the slight smell of
Clouds breathing in and out over me

If I had wings
I would gaze at the birds flying over
My head would cling to the clouds

If I had wings
I would dream of
Flying over the tallest buildings
And exploring the jungles.

Joe Gwyther (7)
St Joseph's Catholic Primary School, Malvern

Whale

I heard my splashing rippling through the water
I was only eleven
Calling for my mother
All alone, I was vulnerable all by myself
What I didn't understand was why people were
Throwing heavy rocks and stones at me

I was covered in blood, which stained the water
I was very lonely
I felt very sensitive, unwell, tearful and sad
All alone in the middle of the Thames in London.

Rhianna Longstaff (10)
St Joseph's Catholic Primary School, Malvern

If I Had Wings
(Based on 'If I had Wings' by Pie Corbett)

If I had wings
I would feel the middle of the moon and
Touch the stars as I go by them

If I had wings
I would taste a chunk of the rainbow
As sweet as a packet of Skittles

If I had wings
I would listen to the music of angels

If I had wings
I would breathe deep and sniff the
Freshest falling raindrops

If I had wings
I would gaze at the people who
Are stuck on the Earth below

If I had wings
I would dream of swinging on stars and
Bouncing on clouds as if they were trampolines.

Robina Neupane (8)
St Joseph's Catholic Primary School, Malvern

My Fish Tank!

I sometimes wonder what my fish are thinking
Swimming round in their tank and not sinking

Some are colourful, some are fat, some are thin
Some the same like an identical twin

My big white fish steals most of the food
And he acts like he's the cool dude

The boss of the tank lives on the pebbles
Sucking at algae and hanging out with rebels

Every night at bedtime I turn off the light
I wonder if fish sleep, you never know, they might.

Joshua Philpott (10)
St Joseph's Catholic Primary School, Malvern

If I Had Wings
(Based on 'If I had Wings' by Pie Corbett)

If I had wings
I would touch the soft fur
Of the clouds

If I had wings
I would taste a chunk of clouds
As cold as ice cream

If I had wings
I would listen to the clouds shouting
At the sheep

If I had wings
I would breathe deep and sniff
The scent of moonlight

If I had wings
I would gaze at the people
Who cling onto the trees

If I had wings
I would dream of
Running through the wind
And jumping through waves.

Tori-May Owen (8)
St Joseph's Catholic Primary School, Malvern

Whale Song

I heard it, echoing
My voice kept desperately sounding
Like a steam train, I was dramatic
Tasting the water scared me now
I wait, sadly . . . no call

I can feel no goodness
Only pain, searing on and on
I'm bleeding, can't anyone help me?
Fading, slowly, oh I can't take it
If no one will help me, I guess I must go
Thank you.

Victoria Roskams (10)
St Joseph's Catholic Primary School, Malvern

The Thames Whale

The sound of my desperate mother calling from far away
But she'll never find me because I don't even know where I am myself
The echo of her cry rings around this unfamiliar place
I'm very confused at the moment
I just hope I can find some answers

The water is too shallow, it's not pure enough
Not enough food for me either, but the biggest
Problem of all is the humans
Some throw stones
Some shooting flashes, some even go into the water
Then they hoist me onto a boat

The last few minutes of my life are the worst
I am hurt, scared and alone, the worst a whale can be
Then a few minutes later I give up and die.

Daniel Mooney (10)
St Joseph's Catholic Primary School, Malvern

If I Had Wings
(Based on 'If I had Wings' by Pie Corbett)

If I had wings
I would touch the top of rain clouds

If I had wings
I would taste the coldest ice block
As cold as a frozen drink

If I had wings
I would listen to the beautiful birds sing

If I had wings
I would breathe the freshest air in the sky

If I had wings
I would gaze at the pretty butterflies

If I had wings
I would dream of
Skipping through a world of dreams.

Alice Bright (7)
St Joseph's Catholic Primary School, Malvern

If I Had Wings
(Based on 'If I had Wings' by Pie Corbett)

If I had wings
I would feel the fingers of fluffy clouds and
Stroke the face of the moon

If I had wings
I would lick a piece of the stars
As hot as fire

If I had wings
I would listen to the wind of air
That floats through the sky

If I had wings
I would sniff deep and breathe
The scent of snowflakes

If I had wings
I would look at the people who climb the Earth

If I had wings
I would dream of rampaging through
The desert and walking on seas.

William Gray (7)
St Joseph's Catholic Primary School, Malvern

If I Had Wings
(Based on 'If I had Wings' by Pie Corbett)

If I had wings
I would touch the top of the
Spiky mountain of the Caribbean

If I had wings
I would taste Mercury as sweet as macaroons

If I had wings
I would smell and sniff fresh bread out of the oven

If I had wings
I would gaze at the horses run
And see the sheep like clouds of cotton candy

If I had wings
I would listen to the cold clouds breaking

If I had wings
I would dream of swooping down to Rome and
Landing in a fountain of water.

Marie-Claire Alfonso (8)
St Joseph's Catholic Primary School, Malvern

If I Had Wings
(Based on 'If I had Wings' by Pie Corbett)

If I had wings
I would touch the waist of the wind

If I had wings
I would taste the first raindrop I see and carefully gulp my prey

If I had wings
I would listen to the sea swirling over the rocks down below

If I had wings
I would gaze at the school children playing down below my feet

If I had wings
I would dream of walking on the beach with water
Swishing and splashing between my toes

If I had wings
I would fly and sniff the smell of food cooking down below on the Earth.

Rebecca Maxwell (7)
St Joseph's Catholic Primary School, Malvern

If I Had Wings
(Based on 'If I had Wings' by Pie Corbett)

If I had wings
I would feel the breeze
Running through my hair
And glide on the air rushing
Here and there

If I had wings
I would taste a lump
Of cloud as cold as ice cream

If I had wings
I would listen to the trees shouting
And rustling in the breeze

If I had wings
I would breathe deeply and smell
The cool air

If I had wings
I would gaze down at children in the park
And adults walking and everyone having fun

If I had wings
I would dream of walking the globe
And running with the wind.

Martha Buckle (7)
St Joseph's Catholic Primary School, Malvern

If I Had A Unicorn
(Inspired by 'If I had Wings' by Pie Corbett)

If I had a unicorn
I would fly into
The air touching
The ends of clouds

If I had a unicorn
I would glide through
The wind tasting air

If I had a unicorn
I would swoop through the
Clouds listening to
The eagles flying
Closer and closer

If I had a unicorn
I would gaze at
The bright green
Fields below

If I had a unicorn
I would smell the
Shining clouds
And sniff the wind
And air brushing on my face

If I had a unicorn
I would dream of
Cantering out of
Space, jumping
Over stars.

Kathryn Bailey (7)
St Joseph's Catholic Primary School, Malvern

Sad Whale

S wimming slowly up river
A long way from the sea
D amaged liver and I hurt all over

W hales always mean a lot to me
H aving everybody staring at her
A ll alone in that shallow gloomy river
L onely as can be
E nd slowly coming so far from the sea.

Rosie Mead (9)
St Joseph's Catholic Primary School, Malvern

Fresh Water And Otters

The otters are friendly fellows
They are cool and they are mellow
They play beneath the summer sun
And all day long they enjoy having fun

They drink fresh water
They wash in it too
They think it's great
Cos they can't live without it, just like me and you

The otters eat fish
But they don't use a dish, or use a knife and fork
They use their paws to hold their food
And if I did that my mum would say I was rude!

Their fur keeps them warm and dry
Even if there is a frost in the sky
They stand upright to one metre high
So that they can see if their enemies are nearby

They have strong tails to prop them up
And to guide them when they are swimming
They enjoy sliding down muddy banks
And to swim they are always willing.

Thomas Gray (10)
St Joseph's Catholic Primary School, Malvern

Sugar And Spice And Not Very Nice

Sugar and spice and not very nice
Toes that are freezing cold from the ice

Dreaming of monsters in the middle of the night
That wakes me up and gives me a fright

Children on the playground calling me names
And won't let me play any of their games

A dinner plate full of Brussels sprouts
With no potatoes, meat or anything else

Feeling poorly all the day
When Mummy can't make the pain go away.

Lucy Wickett (9)
St Joseph's Catholic Primary School, Malvern

My Brother

My brother is a brother
That is like no other
One minute he is dreadful
Then he is helpful

Sometimes he is thoughtful
Then he is awful
Sometimes he is miserable
Then he is comical

He's got quite a temper
And gets very mad
This gets him into trouble
With Mum and Dad

My brother is a brother
That is like no other
But I still love my brother
Like no other.

Grace Crocker (9)
St Joseph's Catholic Primary School, Malvern

Some Brothers

Some brothers are big
While others are smaller

Some brothers are tiny
And others are taller

Some brothers are smart
And many are lazy

Some brothers are charming
Delightful and crazy!

Some brothers are proper
Still others pass gas

Some brothers are really
A pain in the . . . uh . . . never mind!

Some brothers are many things
These are few

And I'm really glad
That my brother is you!

Brogan Fedden (10)
St Joseph's Catholic Primary School, Malvern

Seasons

Spring is full of daffodils
Yellow all around
Dandelions in places
And daisies on the ground
The weather's getting warmer
Blossom on the trees
Have a look outside
Let's chase away the bees!

Summer brings the hot sun near
Shadows on the ground
Let's go fly a kite
Spinning round and round
Sun shining very bright
Laughter everywhere
Children playing in the pool
Happiness in the air!

Autumn leaves are falling
Twisting round and round
Slowly turning in the wind
And drifting to the ground
See the different colours
Orange, brown and red
Getting colder by the day
Let's snuggle up in bed!

Snow, melting very slowly
Icicles all around
Snowflakes twirling in the wind
Not a single sound
Leaves falling off the trees
Then frozen on the ground
Everyone wrap up warmly
A good time to be found!

Emily Shuttlewood (9)
St Joseph's Catholic Primary School, Malvern

Our Dog

Micca is our boxer dog
She wears a worried frown
Sometimes she sits just like a frog
And behaves just like a clown
We all call her our silly little mog
In her coat of black and white and brown
She likes to walk at quite a jog
And she plays with anyone in town.

Fiona Noble (10)
St Joseph's Catholic Primary School, Malvern

Zali Bing!

Zali Bing
Not a thing
Not a word
You're absurd!

Okay this is it,
You'll believe the next bit!

Zali Bing
Doesn't sing
Always smokes
Never jokes!

Sleeping on the sofa
Never had a lover
Never bathes
And never shaves!

Eating a chip
A piercing on his lip
He acts like a baboon
He's a bit like a tycoon!

His hair is tangled and knotty
His beard is curly and grotty
His face is fearsome and unclean
I don't know what to say but he's mean!

He has a piercing on his nose
A gold, shiny ring that he chose
He has another on his ear
Now are you shivering in fear?

Terrifying beast
Where does he feast?
Where does he live?
The town of Congtive?

He lives near me
Very near you see

Although he is a nasty thing
A bit like a sewing pin
One way or another
He still is my big brother.

Eleanor Clements (9)
St Joseph's Catholic Primary School, Malvern

The Seasons Of The Heart

I can see a flower in the summer sun,
I can tell my special one.
Colours, red, yellow and pink too,
But my favourite ones are purple and blue.
Summer brings a golden glow.
A smiling season, people will know.

Now it's time to cool things down
Through calm, calm country and very busy town.
Autumn's come, summer's flown by
So get out your school jumper and dig out your tie.
Teachers arming for the field of battle,
Preparing to hear the children prattle.

Winter's here with its freezing cold frost,
Find those hats and gloves that were lost.
Tobogganing down steep, snowy hills,
Lots of money in busy shop tills.
Extremely cold toes and frozen fingers,
Sleeping in while deep frost lingers.

Flowers blooming, spring is here
Hibernation's over, give a great cheer.
Good weather is here, get out the toys,
Celebrate all girls and boys.
Blooming flowers, dotted in the bright green grass,
Looking forward to the holidays, the end of class.

Seasons slowly come and go,
Each season you should know.
Through rain, sun, cloud and snow
The seasons round in a circle flow,
And each one may go flying by
But the memories will never die.

Genevieve Tyrrell (10)
St Joseph's Catholic Primary School, Malvern

Tree Clouds

I saw them on the hills, frosty birch trees
Their branches like spiders' legs, hanging from their bodies
I reached out to touch them and they were as cold as ice
Not hard, but soft like clouds in the sky
They gently shimmered soft grey, against the dull grey of the fog
That rolled around the hills
They stood proud on the ground
Waiting for the moon to dance with them
Moon beams ran across the branches to show their sparkly jewels
I stood and watched the tree clouds sway
As they gently faded away
But I will never forget the day the tree clouds came to stay.

Bryn Stubbings (9)
St Joseph's Catholic Primary School, Malvern

The Whale Of London

Scared, helpless. Help me, I'm lost!
I came here, now I'll pay the cost
I'm all alone, but there are people around me
Frightened, stressed. My mother, where is she?
Longing to get out, but it's fifty-fifty
I'm crying, waiting, screaming and yelping
Why isn't anybody helping?
Calming down now, lost my energy
I'm no longer waiting for a rescue team
I'm closing my eyes. Falling asleep
Will I ever wake up?

But death is such a big adventure
But such a little thing, it happens every day!
Although I'm dead my spirit will live on all the way
I know they did their best and I am thankful
It was scary, horrible and very frightful
But I know it doesn't feel like it
I am safe now, thank you
But other animals are in danger too
You didn't notice, but all the way we all knew.

Chloe Raynor (11)
St Joseph's Catholic Primary School, Malvern

My Great Gran

My great gran is ninety-two
She sits in her care home
With nothing to do
She sits in a big chair
Looking so frail
Her head hung low
Looking very pale
She smiles so sweet
As I kneel before her feet
I bring her flowers
And I bring her a sweet
But to her having me visit
Makes her day
I can cheer her up
In my own special
Way!

Chloe Jackson (9)
St Joseph's Catholic Primary School, Malvern

A Time To . . .

A time to hear the thrushes singing
A time to love the world
A time to know the daisies are coming
It must be spring

A time to get to know each other
A time to love the world
A time to see the roses blooming
It must be summer

A time to wear your boots, who bought 'em?
A time to love the world
A time to ask why birds fly south
It must be autumn

A time to hear the hamster pitter
A time to love the world
A time to stay indoors, it's snowing
It must be winter.

Eleri Normington (9)
St Joseph's Catholic Primary School, Malvern

Honey

I love honey
Especially when it's runny!

Winnie the Pooh
Loves it too!

It's sticky and sweet
And a real treat!

Have it on toast
That's how I like it most!

Come with me
We'll have it for tea!

Sophia Pelusi (10)
St Joseph's Catholic Primary School, Malvern

Flame

The flame glows with yellow light
Piercing the darkness.
The white wax
As it slides down the candle.
The light burning the darkness.
The flame flickering like a little
Drop of sunlight.
The dancing blue tinge
In the cold, dark room.
The hot yellow centre growing ever bigger.
The white ashes mark where it has been.
The smell of smoke in the air.
The flickering flame swinging round and round.
That is flame.

Ben Collins (10)
St Joseph's Catholic Primary School, Malvern

Whale Live

W ondrous that I got to this height
H elp, please help, they can't hear me
A lifeless thing they see, not knowing the real me
L ove I can't feel, something they can't heal
E choing my voice remains

L onging for this to end, quick I'm going round the bend
I mpossible that this is real
V ast, large I am
E ased, that life will soon stop . . . and it has . . .

Gemima Hull (11)
St Joseph's Catholic Primary School, Malvern

The Little Lost Whale

Scratch, scratch my tail whips
Bleeding badly like a battleship
I call, I call but my mum does not phone!
So confused, calling, crying
I'm alone!

Moaning, groaning, too stuffy and depressed
'Mum, oh Mum, I need you now
So startled!' *Kapow!*

I'm alerting
I'm hurting!
I'm dying
I'm afraid
I don't want to be dead;
You all lent me a hand, I'm grateful!
I was lost, and now I'm found.

Nicole Theakston (11)
St Joseph's Catholic Primary School, Malvern

Lost Whale

Come on Mum catch fish with me
Mum where are you?
Where are you Mum?
I'm not in the North Atlantic anymore
It's gloomy and green
Not like the Atlantic, clear and blue!
There's lot of people looking at me, taking
Pictures with their cameras flashing
Do they like me or hate me?
I hope they like me, I like them
They're trying to help me out of the Thames
They're lifting me out, I'm hurt!
I want to see my mum again!
I'm bleeding on my tail
I'm on the boat now I'm closing my eyes
Will I ever wake up?
Who knows?

Jessica Mead (11)
St Joseph's Catholic Primary School, Malvern

Autumn

Autumn is my favourite season
The leaves are gold, orange and brown
They crunch under my feet
They glide gently onto the ground
Without a sound they land, all over the garden
You wake up to see a beautiful sight of red and gold
It won't last long so make the most of it.

Mary Thornber (10)
SS Mary & John CE (VA) Primary School, North Luffenham

The Teacher Told Us To Write A Poem Today

The teacher told us to write a poem today
She didn't give me time to say how much I hated it
And here I sit
In silent thoughts
And wonder how I ought
To be writing something interesting
About winter or spring or
Ice skating
How should I start, will it come from my heart?
Or my imagination?
Or a nightmare?
I'm afraid I really don't care!

Megan Lamb (10)
SS Mary & John CE (VA) Primary School, North Luffenham

Killer Carrot

I saw a killer carrot running down our street
Seven feet tall, orange with very hairy feet!
It smashed down the fence into the cabbage patch
Leapt onto a cabbage and began a wrestling match
The cabbage leapt and kicked
The carrot dodged to the right
The parsnip saw this happening and joined in the fight
Now this was it, the moment of truth
Parsnip did a backflip and landed on the roof
Pulled out a bucket of acid, held it up high
And evilly cackled, 'You're both going to die!'
He threw up the bucket and acid came down like rain
The cabbage and the carrot were never seen
Again!

George Nichols (10)
SS Mary & John CE (VA) Primary School, North Luffenham

My Friend Amy

My friend Amy is really cool
She comes to school, and
Plays football
She is in a team!

My friend Amy really likes
Animals, horses, dogs and
Jumping frogs.

Me and my friend Amy
Sometimes fall out
But that's what friendship is
All about.

Chloe Barrow (9)
SS Mary & John CE (VA) Primary School, North Luffenham

My Rabbit

My rabbit is fluffy
Fluffier than a dog
He even jumps like a frog!
He scratches, he bites
He punches and fights
But
He's still my rabbit called
Guinness!

Megan Clephane (10)
SS Mary & John CE (VA) Primary School, North Luffenham

Tests

Today a test, a test today!
Screaming and running - a test today!
The teacher said, with a smirk on his face,
'It'll be all right,' tying his lace
We don't believe him, his face is white
He always gives us a really bad fright
So we sat down doing the test
And watching the teacher with a smirk on his face!

Deborah Allen (10)
SS Mary & John CE (VA) Primary School, North Luffenham

The Bogeyman

I saw the bogeyman, I swear it Mum
He came out of bed banging a great big drum
I thought I was dreaming, then I heard screaming
It was my teddy fighting in 'beddy'
It was his minion trying to grab him!
I jumped out of bed and fought like 'Aladdin'
There was bonking and bashing!
But I finally won!
I noticed just once that the monstrous face
Was actually my sister, dear old Grace!

Pascal Risi (11)
SS Mary & John CE (VA) Primary School, North Luffenham

The Irreplaceable Mum

A racing car
A casino bar
A barking dog
A talking log
A million pounds
A racing hound
A 20-ball shotgun
A trip to the sun
But none of these can
Replace my mum!

Sam Coupland (11)
SS Mary & John CE (VA) Primary School, North Luffenham

School Dinners

Those dinners, they're poisoned, spiked maybe
The schools probably made them in 1833

I heard the governor died without a crunch
At the sight of the kids going munch, munch

But just then I had a *brill* idea
It was what the dinner ladies feared

You won't guess it, you don't have a hunch
Okay, I'll tell you, I switched to packed lunch!

Hamish Reid (10)
SS Mary & John CE (VA) Primary School, North Luffenham

The Mystery

I saw something last night
Dark . . . still . . . gloomy
It swooped above my head
My hair flew and swished
It felt like a cold air in the wind
It seemed like silk on my skin
I stayed still . . . I froze like ice
It seemed to move through the curtains
And it seemed to go under the quilt
It went through the books
I started to move
I saw a shadow
It was coming over my head
I took small steps
One by one I moved closer to my bed
It must have gone
No! No! It was there
Going through my legs
I tried to move, it was like wire
It went through my pillow
It made me cold, chilly
I froze . . . it clung round my legs . . .
I couldn't see it
It was too dark
And then it went
I don't know where, I don't know how
Just gone.

Katie Frearson (9)
SS Mary & John CE (VA) Primary School, North Luffenham

Silver Bird

One morning
I saw something
Bright, glowing
It sat on the fence
And looked at me, I said,
'I wish this thing would go away.'
I approached it
Wanting to give it some food
It flew away
I think it heard
It was a shiny, glowing silver bird.

Kirsty Pridding (11)
SS Mary & John CE (VA) Primary School, North Luffenham

Words Spoken With Haste

You can cool the word hot
You can move the word still
You can colour the word blank
You can stop the word go
You can sink the word float
You can correct the word wrong
You can give the word take
You can half the word whole
You can soften the word hard.

Liam Cowzer (10)
SS Mary & John CE (VA) Primary School, North Luffenham

Not So Fluffy

Last night I was certain
That there was something creeping up my curtain
It was something evil, which had nasty habits
Of scaring children in their beds
And horribly ripping off their heads
I saw it clearly in the night
It gave me such an awful fright
With huge fangs and glowing eyes
And a body at least twice the size of mine
So I wasn't going to fight and I hid
With my pillow over my head
I closed my eyes tight and reached for
The light and that's when I felt
The bite of the . . . *killer rabbit!*

Jeffrey Lamb (10)
SS Mary & John CE (VA) Primary School, North Luffenham

Hamish

A climbing creeper
A cool keeper
Amazing reader
Disco diva
A doggy nibbler
A wormy wriggler
He's a top man
Always has a plan
That's my best friend
Hamish.

Charlie Binley (10)
SS Mary & John CE (VA) Primary School, North Luffenham

The War Of The Worlds

The war of the worlds has started, what are we going to do?
The infants versus the juniors
Our army needs you!

The juniors with the lunch boxes pelted us with bread
We replied with water,
'That'll dampen their spirits,' I said

They brought out man traps
Bin bags from the shed, then took 7 of our men
'What have you done with them?' I said
They'd taken their lunch money, made them eat
Worms and locked them in the classroom to their doom
Fought off the rebels with a very spiky broom
We'd had enough and we thought of this . . .
'Run inside tell the head we're being bullied,' I said

The war of the worlds has started, what are we going to do?

Callum Dickinson (10)
SS Mary & John CE (VA) Primary School, North Luffenham

Monstrous Maths Lesson

One hundred pages a day
That's all I have to say
Terrifying
Petrifying
Wondering what to do
To escape, I have to resort to saying,
'I really need the loo!'
The numbers are running
Through my brain
It's driving me insane
This is what our days are like
Maths, maths
Day and night
That's our monstrous maths
Lesson.

Amy Binley (10)
SS Mary & John CE (VA) Primary School, North Luffenham

My Cat

My cat is so soft
When I stroke her fur
My cat is so loud
When she starts to purr
My cat huddles up
Like a furry ball
My cat cuddles up
Against the wall
She beats me to my bed
Every night
At 10pm . . .
She starts a fight
As I grab her tail
She leaps up high
I didn't know
That cats could fly
When I feed her in the morning
She gobbles it all up
Then she drinks the orange
Out of my cup
She bites my foot
As I run off to school
Even though she's a minx
I still think she's cool!

Evie Doherty (10)
SS Mary & John CE (VA) Primary School, North Luffenham

The Cookie Monster

I lie in bed
With thoughts in my head
Thinking, thinking, thinking
Of the biscuit tin
Those poor little cookies
Lying inside
Having to abide
By their leader -
A custard cream
Then I hear it,
I have to stop it,
'No
Please no
No
Please no
Mr Cookie Monster. . . !'

 Evie Smith (11)
SS Mary & John CE (VA) Primary School, North Luffenham

Disco Diva

Disco Diva parties every night
She comes past my house and gives me a fright!
No one has ever seen her, but I know
She's a diva
You can see her bushy hair
Bobbing to the sound of the music
Her arms jigging from side to side
To the rhythm of the beat!
Disco Diva
In a fever
Tapping, tapping her feet into the night.

Victoria Pilgrim (11)
SS Mary & John CE (VA) Primary School, North Luffenham

Seasons

Spring, where trees have newborn leaves
Where new plants enter lush gorgeous gardens
Where glorious green grass grows
Where farmers harvest their crops

Summer, where the scorching sun shines down
On the lively earth
Rivers flow
Crystals grow
Birds tweet, laughter loudens

Autumn, where leaves fall off trees
Leaving them bare
The ground is hard as a skull
And everything is dull

Winter, where the frost comes in
Where a soft blanket falls from the sky
Snowmen are built
Snowball fights across the land

Seasons are great
There are four
But I wish there were more.

Callum Haskew (10)
SS Peter & Paul's Catholic Primary School, Newport

Darkness

Darkness, it's a box covering the world
Stuck inside, no way out
Banging, trying to get out, shouting for daylight

It reminds me of a baby crying for help
From the start of evening, till the morning that never seems to come
It's like a deadly song that never ends

It sounds like a lion roaring in your ear
Trying to get away, but it just keeps coming back

It tastes like rotten eggs rolling on your taste buds
The taste just staying there forever and ever.

Alex Mayer (10)
SS Peter & Paul's Catholic Primary School, Newport

Bang Boom

'Bang, boom,'
The wind whispered
As the thunder clapped
And as the lightning danced

'Bang, boom,'
The night is a black canvas
With the gods splashing
White and yellow paint

'Bang, boom,'
Yellow as the sun
White like the moon
Scared, scared

Scared in the night
Run as fast as you can
Jump as high as you can
Thunder and lightning
Have arrived.

Nancy O'Brien (11)
SS Peter & Paul's Catholic Primary School, Newport

Sea

Sea as calm as the midnight sky
Sea silently shuffling
Shining in the cold winter night

Trickling through your fingertips
As you touch the sea
Shining in the cold winter night

Waves singing as they whistle
Through your feet
Waves as blue as the midnight sky
Shining in the cold winter night.

Lauren O'Hanlon (10)
SS Peter & Paul's Catholic Primary School, Newport

Fear

Fear smells like the
Remains of a dead
Body locked in
Your neighbour's shed

It feels like a
Throbbing toothache
In your mind muddling
Up all your thoughts

Fear tastes like deadly
Poison and acid
Scarring your mouth forever

It reminds you of a
Terrifying horror movie
Where many people die.

Daniel Cattle (9)
SS Peter & Paul's Catholic Primary School, Newport

My Teacher

She is a red, soft, bouncy cushion
She is a window letting in the moonlight
She is a caring, cuddly cat
She is a swan floating in the water
The smell of a sunflower
The sound of a bird in a tropical forest
A refreshing glass of orange
A silver sunny spring
A piece of art.

Melodie Bowering (10)
SS Peter & Paul's Catholic Primary School, Newport

Through The Magic Window

Through the magic window I saw . . .
Ten ticking trees tugging for time
Nine naughty noses numbering newts
Eight enormous elephants eating emus
Seven silly swans singing solos
Six slimy slugs slithering solemnly
Five funny flamingos fooling frogs
Four fuzzy flies flipping food
Three thoroughbreds travel through thunder
Two tired toucans travel through the tropical treetops
Only one orang-utan eating oranges.

Lily Ramsden (9)
SS Peter & Paul's Catholic Primary School, Newport

Summer

When I think of summer
I think of
The scorching sun blasting
On my face

I think of the
Soothing homemade orange
Juice with extra ice

I see nothing but
Blue skies and clear
Blue waters

I dream of
Dancing with dolphins
In the depths of the
Ocean

I hear the squawk
Of a seagull
Gliding through the
Air

I feel the silky
Sand fleeing away
From my hand

But when summer ends
It closes its eyes
And sleeps until next
Year.

Katie Ann Mythen (11)
SS Peter & Paul's Catholic Primary School, Newport

Spring

I love to see
New baby lambs
Just being born
And about to grow wool

I love to feel
A warm and fresh feeling
As the spring breeze
Relaxes me

I love to see
The spring flowers
Stand to attention
Showing off their
Petals

I love to hear
The sounds of Easter
Everyone is chatting about
Can't wait!

It's great to have the sun again!

Hannah Hadebe (10)
SS Peter & Paul's Catholic Primary School, Newport

Nervous

Nervous smells like the very
Sweat that creeps up your crooked spine

It tastes like acid burning your wet
Slimy tongue

It sounds like the stiff iron
Walls are creeping in on you

It feels as if the world is coming
To a dark and gloomy end

It reminds me of my worst nightmare
When the nightmare never ended

Just remember it's nervous . . .
And it's bad.

Kieron Tregidga (9)
SS Peter & Paul's Catholic Primary School, Newport

Sun, Sun, Sun

Sun, sun, sun
Sweeping and eating
The dark night sky
Making it bright

Sun, sun, sun
Making the plants strong
Grow lighter
Getting bigger in the sunlight
Smashing through the gentle breeze

Sun, sun, sun
Making all the animals play
All around me is happiness
Eating like a horse.

Becca Hill (9)
SS Peter & Paul's Catholic Primary School, Newport

Through The Magic Window I Saw

Through the magic window I saw;
The glorious glittering sea,
Like a child playing excitedly
And the superb castles of sand,
Waterlogged, shimmering but amazingly grand.

Through the magic window I saw;
Dark and gloomy places.
Full of ghouls and terrifying trolls
With horribly strange faces.
They definitely do not struggle
To cause lots and lots of trouble.

Through the magic window I saw;
An underground cavern full of fish,
Some as red as a child's face
Holding their breath,
Whilst making a wish.
Water the colour of an emerald-green,
Lapping and splashing, a wonderful scene

But within a shark waits,
Preparing to bite,
Teeth like stalagmites,
Eyes like rubies, gleaming bright.

The window shows beauty
And horror too.

I had a look, so can you.

Ben Taylor (10)
SS Peter & Paul's Catholic Primary School, Newport

Tiger Tracks

Black coal eyes has the tiger
With lovely fiery fur
Quick as lightning
Dashing through trees
Trying to outsmart the hunters

Black coal eyes has the tiger
With lovely fiery fur
Quick as lightning
Keeping down low
Not wanting to be spotted
Playing 'tig' with the antelopes

Black coal eyes has the tiger
With lovely fiery fur
Trekking through the jungle
Animals bow heads down
For the tiger has returned.

Hannah Bishop (11)
SS Peter & Paul's Catholic Primary School, Newport

Things We Love

Don't you love love?
Don't you love life
The way it twists and turns?
Don't you just love football
When your team scores a goal?
Don't you love motor cars
When you hear them roar?
Don't you just love fireworks
The way the colour spills?
But the thing I love
The most, go on, take a guess
Well the thing I love the best
Is my family and my friends
They're something that
I would not swap
For the world
I know that, don't you?

Joshua Scoins (10)
St Mary's CE Primary School, Colton

Like

I like the colour blue . . .
It reminds me of the lake
With the beautiful silent
Shoals of fish
Swimming beneath me

I love the colour indigo . . .
It reminds me of a rainbow
With the crisp smell of fresh grass
After it has been raining

I like the colour red . . .
It reminds me of love
I like the thought of romance
Starry-eyed and exotic

I love the colour ruby . . .
It reminds me of expensive jewellery
Flashing like fire in the sunlight.

Victoria Densley (10)
St Mary's CE Primary School, Colton

Ghostly Dread

Late at night it gave me a fright
Something was shaking, slamming and creaking
What was that?
Screaming, coming out of the window

Swooping in the chimney
Howling at the locks
Cackling in the kitchen
Whistling wind through the door
The clock chimes for midnight . . .

Aaron Houseman (9)
St Mary's CE Primary School, Colton

My Spooky Poem

Late at night I lock the doors
The sound of creeping over the floor
In the dark the nightmare begins
Suddenly I'm *screaming!*
There is a shadow swooping by
And then it's gone into the night.

Luke Doherty (9)
St Mary's CE Primary School, Colton

A Hot Place

This hot, burning, terrifying land
Is made up mainly of sand
To cross it you would need a camel
It would be no use for any other mammal
In this place you have to stay alert
Take plenty of water my friend
If not it could mean the end
Because you, Sir, are in the desert.

Jack Brine (10)
St Mary's CE Primary School, Colton

Horse

I saw a horse in a field
Black as the night-time sky
He neighed and reared
Bucked and snorted
But then a girl appeared

She calmed him down
Stopped his sweat
Sponged him down till he was wet
Then drying him down with a towel
Until he gleamed and gleamed.

Laura Wykes (9)
St Mary's CE Primary School, Colton

White Witch

The white witch is grand and elegant
Her skin as white as snow
Her lips of rose-pink
Her voice roars like howling wolves
A twisting swirl of crystallised snow
A clatter of the sleigh as she glides across the snow
Her breath formed a thick circle in the air
Her coat warm and prickly
Boxes full of Turkish Delight to tempt the unwary
But you don't know the white witch
She is evil head to toe.

Abigail Edwards (9)
St Mary's CE Primary School, Colton

I Don't Like Being Alone

Don't leave me
Don't go away
Please let me come
I don't like being alone

How long are you going to be?
What can I do?
It is dark without you
I don't like being alone

Where are you going?
Who are you with?
Please hurry up
I don't like being alone

Don't worry
Dad will be here
I'll come back when you're in bed
You won't be alone.

Jennifer Bayliss (9)
St Mary's CE Primary School, Colton

Blue

I love blue, it floats in the sky
I love navy, rippling and wavy
I love cobalt, shimmering with light
I love marine, it's a glimmering pool
I love azure, it's a crystal clear ocean
I love turquoise, it's radiance on a jewel
I love indigo, well it's just plain indigo
I love sapphire, because I love my dog.

William Fender (10)
St Mary's CE Primary School, Colton

Fairies

F luttering in the sky
A round her is sparkly dust
I n her hand she has got a wand
R eally kind person she is
I n her heart she is helpful
E verlasting she is and always at your
S ervice.

Aman Kaur (8)
St Mary's CE Primary School, Colton

What Is Loud?

What is loud?
A drum is loud
What is quiet?
A whisper is quiet
Like the breeze on a summer's night
What is high-pitched?
An opera singer's voice is high-pitched
Like all the birds singing in the sky
What is low-pitched?
A dog's growl is low-pitched
Lower than a wolf's howl
What is soft?
Waves gently lapping on the shore are soft
Like a bird chirping a beautiful song
What is harsh?
A scream is harsh like the scream of somebody
          who has seen a dead body in a marsh.

Grace Pearson (10)
St Mary's CE Primary School, Colton

The Poem Of Narnia

The white world of Narnia
Was covered in shimmering snow
It was like a blanket of crystals
Over the ground, and frozen was your toe

The land of Narnia was as cold as ice
The wind shipped, spun and swirled
Across the sparkling, glittering land
In Narnia there were no animals there like mice

In the white land of Narnia
It was an unhappy, depressing and sad place to be
No flowers, no sun, no summer, no spring
No hot sweet drinks like tea

Narnia looked and felt like a
Big, fluffy, soft, smooth cloud
With no other colours, but white
The snow sprinkled down from the air
And it all was silent at night.

Mankeert Kaur (10)
St Mary's CE Primary School, Colton

What I Wish For

I wish I was a dragon
Who could fly really high
I wish I was a dragon
To breathe fire on everyone
I wish I was a dragon
In red, green or yellow
I wish I was a dragon
Who is fast as you can see

I wish I was a fairy
So I could be really small
I wish I was a fairy
Who casts spells on people
I wish I was a fairy
To do things I want to do
I wish I was a fairy
So I could do magic on myself.

Erica Bayliss (7)
St Mary's CE Primary School, Colton

Ghost

G ooey slime all around the house
H aunting children's beds
O ozy goo on your pillow
S limy stuff all over you
T errible feeling that someone's there!

Louise Cowcill (8)
St Mary's CE Primary School, Colton

I Wish I Was A Fairy

I wish I was a fairy, pretty as can be
I wish I was a fairy, that had a pet bee
I wish I was a fairy, that could fly high
I wish I was a fairy, that could eat pie

I wish I was a fairy, messy as can be
I wish I was a fairy who could have a fairy tea
I wish there was a fairy just like me.

Emily Fenney (7)
St Mary's CE Primary School, Colton

Creature Alphabet

A is for angels flying all night
B is for beautiful princesses in their castles
C is for creatures scurrying across the floor
D is for dragons breathing fire
E is for elves working hard
F is for fairies granting wishes
G is for giants scaring people
H is for hope that helped Pandora
I   is for invisible clothes
J is for jewels in a treasure chest
K is for King Midas in the story
L is for leprechaun carrying gold
M is for magical magicians by their pots
N is for nights alone in the dark
O is for ogres in their swamp
P is for pixies in the bottom of the garden
Q is for queens in the palace
R is for rude goblins being horrible
S is for smelly creatures in their homes
T is for trolls in their caves
U is for useless magic trees in the woods
V is for voices in your mind
W is for wooden boxes like Pandora's
X is for X-rays of bones, scary
Y is for yucky monster in your den
Z is for Zell the alien.

Maisie Scoins (7)
St Mary's CE Primary School, Colton

Unicorn

Twilight, twilight
Will you grant my wish tonight?
For long let my little pony
Be a unicorn
I will fly with my little unicorn
Through the midnight sky
The horn glowing
And leading the way
Pink, purple, red, yellow
He leads me to
The magic land of unicorns
It is time to go home now
Boy, come on, let's fly
Let's fly home.

Danielle Davies (9)
St Mary's CE Primary School, Colton

Light-Hearted

Think of a giant
Then think of a mouse
Think of a castle
Then think of a house
Think of a kettle
Then think of some ice
Think of a hot day
Then think of the winter
Think of a flash
Then think of a snail
Think of a horrible spider
Then think of a lovely horse.

Kayleigh Wallace (11)
St Mary's CE Primary School, Colton

Princesses

P rincesses are beautiful
R iding on their horses
I n their castles they admire their hair
N ow it is time for a feast
C astles so, so high
E agles flying high around the castle
S laves for princesses, here and there
S ilver tiaras sparkling on their heads
E legant princes looking for princesses
S o many princesses wandering around the castle.

Georgie Fender (7)
St Mary's CE Primary School, Colton

Beneath The Slime And Grime

Lurking and clinging to the earth beneath us
Lies a load of stagnant smells
Who would desire, inspire such dirt?
Who know what bacteria will lurk?
If we sniff or sample this rotten lot
We will come to a sticky, icky end
Who knows? I don't
Ooh, just think about the smell, the smell!

Lauren Banks (10)
Shevington Community Primary School, Shevington

Baby Owls

The dark has closed
Its big silver eye
No gleam, no moonbeam
You ask why we sigh?

Darkness is safe
You've always said so
But the moon was our first friend
Why did it go?

Do not fear, my baby owls
The moon will return
Of its moods you two
Have much to learn
Tomorrow or soon
There'll be a rebirth
The moon will brighten
Re-silver the Earth
So put away mourning
No need to sigh
The night will soon
Reopen its eye.

Kelly Staunton (10)
Shevington Community Primary School, Shevington

War In Sparta

Nothing is good
Nothing is bad
All it does
Is make you sad
Lots of people
Dying and crying
Nobody's happy
Even though they won the war
All their lives are no good
Everybody hates war
All friends dead
Nobody likes war
Nothing is good
About war in Sparta.

Bradley McGuire (9)
Shevington Community Primary School, Shevington

Millions

There are hundreds, even thousands, even millions of things in the world
Millions of animals
Cats, dogs, fish
Birds, rats, bats
Crocodiles and alligators
Millions more
Millions of pounds
To spend and spend and spend
Millions of sweets and chocolate
To eat and share mmmmmmm!
Millions of clothes
To wear and wear and wear
Millions of myths and legends
To read and write
Millions of food to eat
Like pasta, pizza and millions more
Millions of movies
Like horror, drama, fantasy and millions more
So why is there so much unhappiness in the world?

Jordan Kenney (9)
Shevington Community Primary School, Shevington

The Lion

The lion is as strong as an eagle
He runs as fast as a blasting rocket

He hides behind the plants
Walking slowly, getting ready

Then jumps like a flying bird
Hunting his food

He is as yellow as a duckling
With golden coloured cheeks

Every day running, running, running
Like a racer in a race

He is hiding as if he is playing hide-and-seek
He is clever-minded

In catching animals
But I don't think he can catch me!

Mohamed Ismail (9)
Shevington Community Primary School, Shevington

Tutsy, My Hamster

She rolls in her ball
And crashes into the wall
She sleeps in her house
And has teeth as sharp as a mouse
She scurries for food
And never bites when she's in a mood
She is brown and white
And never bites
She comes out at night
And sleeps when it's light
She spins in her wheel
And has a big meal
We feed her Mini Cheddars and Hula Hoops
Then she goes for big long poops
She bites her cage
With lots of rage
When we're not there she often breaks free
Then she shouts out with lots of glee
She goes up her tube
And hides her food
There she lies still and quiet in her bed
Is she alive? No, sadly she's dead.

Eleanor Campbell (9)
Shevington Community Primary School, Shevington

The Crocodile

There is a crocodile who lives on a sandbank
It goes hunting every day, shoots through the water
A big long tail swinging from side to side
Swinging faster than a lion's pounce
Mostly for catching prey and escaping predators

Teeth as sharp as a ninja's sword
Its long, powerful jaw contains 10,000 gleaming white teeth
Armoured better than a super star destroyer
Lived since the dinosaurs' age 65,000,000 years ago.

Jack Sixsmith (9)
Shevington Community Primary School, Shevington

The Shark

He lives on the seabed
At the bottom of the sea

No fear in him and pounces
When he needs to attack the wicked dolphin

His skin is wooden like trees
He bites like dinosaurs

He swerves through the rough seas
Back to his home where he rests
And goes to sleep.

Jake Shorrocks (10)
Shevington Community Primary School, Shevington

Nana

My nana made me laugh
My nana made me cry
But one day she floated up into the sky
My nana was a good cook
My nana always told my mum off when she had a nasty look
My nana loves me lots
I know my nana is looking down on me from afar
Thinking what a wonderful star.

Katie Holgate (10)
Shevington Community Primary School, Shevington

Cindy The Dolphin

Cindy the dolphin is my friend
If you've a broken heart Cindy's sure to mend
Fish is her favourite food
This is a fact, Cindy's never in a mood
Cindy can do a backflip, high up in the air
If you come to see her Cindy's sure to care
Cindy gives me rides on her back
Until I have to go back for a snack
Cindy swims back into the deep blue sea
But every day she comes back to me.

Charlotte Godwin (9)
Shevington Community Primary School, Shevington

My Sis

My sis really loves me
But sometimes she's not so nice
Like that time when she shook my hand
And her hands were as cold as ice
She can be good sometimes
When she bought me a PS2
But I know her hobby, it's to hog the loo!
I love her and she loves me
Me, Sis, Mum, Dad, we're a big happy family.

Liam Davies (9)
Shevington Community Primary School, Shevington

The Lion

Deep inside the jungle that's where it lives
Like a roaring racing car
Red, yellow and orange around the neck
Slowly but calmly he moves
Dangerous to be near

Hunting for tea
Beware
Don't be unlucky like some people
That's the lion, be afraid.

Molly Benfold (9)
Shevington Community Primary School, Shevington

Cakes

Big cakes
Little cakes
So many to choose
I would have one
How about you?
Little muffins
Big muffins
They're all tasty to me
Birthday cakes
Chocolate cakes
Crunchy munchy cakes
Just for my tea.

James Hancock (9)
Shevington Community Primary School, Shevington

Dolphin, Dolphin

Dolphin, dolphin
In and out of the sea
Jump, jump nice blue dolphin
Soft and shiny blue skin
Glistening blue eyes
It must be wonderful
To swim under the sea
What beautiful creatures
Dolphins are
Jump, jump
Beautiful blue dolphin.

Emily Wright (9)
Shevington Community Primary School, Shevington

My Hamster

My hamster climbs up her cage
And back down again
She sleeps in daylight
And is awake at night-time
She sometimes sets the alarm off
And wakes everyone up
Her name is Sparky
She likes crunchy nuts and lettuce best
And hiding in her hut!

Sam Wilde (10)
Shevington Community Primary School, Shevington

Football

Teams, teams, teams galore
Football, football more and more
Scoring goals and tracking back
Defensive midfield and defensive attack
Players get injuries, some in so much pain
And they think to themselves, *never again*
But players return old and new
And maybe one day it could be you.

Anthony Connolly (11)
Shevington Community Primary School, Shevington

In My Sacred Safe
(Inspired by 'Magic Box' by Kit Wright)

In my sacred safe I will put . . .

Five flipping frogs fighting
The reflex of a super fast king cobra
The lovely aroma of a red rose

A drop of gleaming, golden honey
A slice of the glorious sun
The laughter of young school children

My box is made of . . .

Hot steel to stop anyone from opening it
The ice from the coldest iceberg
With dreams in the corners
In this wonderful box there is no war or suffering

I will rule in this box
I will swim in this box
I will learn in this magnificent place
Everything will live in this box.

Luke Butler (10)
Shevington Community Primary School, Shevington

Christmas

Merry Christmas to us all
We open our presents with glee
We get beautiful things from our relatives
Mum, Dad and me

It's here every year
With Santa Claus as well
We hear the choir singing
And the ringing of the bell

We celebrate in our houses
And give a mighty cheer
It only lasts for twenty-four hours
So we have to wait another year.

Jake Wardle (10)
Shevington Community Primary School, Shevington

The Horrible Hurricane

Crash! The wind blew
Trees fell down
It was a *hurricane*
Lightning struck like whips
Roofs came off houses
Thud came the kings of *thunder*
The houses tumbled down
Children screaming
Babies crying
Adults climbing to safety
It's like the sky came crashing down on me
Although I thought a tidal wave
A tidal wave of thoughts I fear
I look outside and peer
The ripping of the lightning
I thought it was my imagination
But obviously it wasn't
This isn't where my journey ends
Because death is a big, big, big
Adventure!

Hannah Wilkinson (10)
Shevington Community Primary School, Shevington

Panda

Black and white hair
Sprouting from skin
Like a fur ball
Jumping on its prey
Pouncing and scratching
Like a dinosaur
Staring at me
With its beady eyes
A cheeky grin
And a grizzly character
Wet nose
Very, very damp!

Chantal Ormesher (10)
Shevington Community Primary School, Shevington

Parent's Evening

I dread the day when parent's evening comes
My mum and dad munching on the apples and juicy plums

The parents before leave the teacher's room with a smirk on their faces
The teacher shuts the door so it's firmly in place

My mum and dad walk in with a smile on their face, but me with a smirk on mine
I look at the clock, it struck half-past nine

I was worried that they had fainted
Then they ran out with a design I had painted

They congratulated me even though it was tainted
In the end it was me that had fainted!

Daniel Kelly (10)
Shevington Community Primary School, Shevington

People In School

People in school young and old
Standing in the playground freezing cold
Playing football, got kicked in the leg
Clean it up, put my coat on my peg
I'm running late, I think *oh no!*
I walk in the classroom awaiting my sorrow
Teacher tells me off, I'm always late
Look at my hair, it's such a state
I look at the pet hamster, it does another poo
If it does that again I'll throw it down the loo
Actually I'm quite a naughty boy
All I do is annoy, annoy
At dinnertime I have my lunch
Bite at everything, *crunch, crunch, crunch*
Lessons now and it's boring history next
I'd prefer to go home and play with K'nex
I look at the time, it's quarter-past three
I can't wait, I run out with glee.

Jack Woods (10)
Shevington Community Primary School, Shevington

Spooky Night

In the dark, my brother looks like a monster
At night the floorboards creak like a witch's laugh
The wind blows the door, *bang, bang*
Alex is mumbling to himself in his sleep
All of my teddies are moving in the moonlight
The curtains are blow open and a cat purrs like a werewolf howls
Trucks are like Big Foots crunching cars
My poster of a bike looks like a monster in the background
Street lights flicker on and off, dogs barking, it sounds like cups smashing.

Connah Farley (10)
Shevington Community Primary School, Shevington

The Jungle

The birds are squawking in the trees
Baboons laughing at the chimpanzees
Meanwhile on the grassy ground
The monkeys hear a familiar sound
The mighty tiger roars and growls
He is hunting as he prowls
He finds a deer that is his prey
But it sees the tiger and runs away.

Joseph Brennan (10)
Shevington Community Primary School, Shevington

West Ham United

Bobby Moore, Geoff Hurst, we have had them all
West Ham are always on the ball
With three FA Cups and hundreds of legends
We hope our club never ends

The famous Upton Park is our home
We've got strength down to the bone
The Hammers in claret and blue
Come on Chelsea we'll beat you!

Joel Webster (11)
Shevington Community Primary School, Shevington

The Google Blob

The google blob is a very scary monster
A very scary monster indeed
He flies through the air
Without any hair
He even wrestled a grizzly bear
He doesn't care about anywhere
He'll give you an awful fright
So you better watch out . . .
Tonight!

Decklan Yates (10)
Shevington Community Primary School, Shevington

Supply Teachers

During the register you mustn't say,
'I'm Bill Miss,
But I was Bob yesterday.'
Just stay cool
And make it look true
So she'll take the blame
For everything you do.

When the bell rings
Don't rush out
Stay inside and shout:
'Our supply Miss
Wipes her nose on that and this
And all over her clothes
Her false teeth are in my jar
And not in the boot of her toy car.'

Amal Abufares (11)
Shevington Community Primary School, Shevington

Alien

The alien has big melon eyes
It stares at people and makes them cry
It has 6 fingers and 50 toes
As people run, the alien goes
It has scrawny arms and wobbly legs
Its back bones are just like pegs
The alien has gone back to space
While people are trembling with a very pale face.

Vanessa Willetts (10)
Shevington Community Primary School, Shevington

Animals

Funny animals live in zoos
Funny animals always say boo

Then you get the other sort, cuddly animals

Cuddly animals act so nice
Cuddly animals include mice

After that there are just, well, serious animals:

Serious animals act so boring
Serious animals don't act mischievous.

Samantha Thompson (10)
Shevington Community Primary School, Shevington

Christmas Treats

Red paper, green paper
Wrapped around our presents
Bells on our trees
For everyone to see

Baubles hanging on the tree
Ribbons tied by you and me
Christmas pudding for all to eat
Isn't that a wonderful treat.

Elizabeth Clementson (12)
Shevington Community Primary School, Shevington

The Final: Wigan Vs Man Utd

F ootball is my favourite game, no one ever thinks it's lame!
O ut come the players hoping to win their game
O f course the player who scores will be the big name
T he referee blows for half-time
B alls roll out onto the pitch, the ref shouts, 'Mine!'
A goal goes in which makes it 1-1
L ots of men shouting, 'Come on my son!'
L ast minutes of the game, who will win?

Jack Trafford (11)
Shevington Community Primary School, Shevington

Groovy Granny

Groovy Granny
Likes to cook
Taking fantastic recipes from her book
Yum-yum what do you want to eat?
She will make you a great big treat

Groovy Granny
You will find in some sort of shop
Buying us some sort of pop
Fizzy drinks, sweeties too
She will let you eat more than a few

Groovy Granny
Is the best
Better than all the rest
She is so fun
And her smile is beaming like the sun

That's my
Groovy granny.

Alice Crawshaw (10)
Shevington Community Primary School, Shevington

Oh Hello

I hate meeting someone new
I cringe and yelp, it's really true
I never get my words out
In fact I speak blah, blah, blah, blah
My mum says, 'Stop it, you're twenty-two
Stop it dear you are twenty-two!'

We sat down for dinner when my old teacher came
She looked at me and said,
'Golly you haven't changed.'
I looked at her and cringed and cringed
She said once again,
'Golly you haven't changed.'
I've really got to change my ways
But I like annoying people
I'll stay this way!

Rachel Hancock (11)
Shevington Community Primary School, Shevington

My 11th Birthday

Today it is my birthday,
Can't wait to have some fun,
I've just got out of my bed,
I see Kai, my dad and mum.

'Happy Birthday!' shouts my little bruv,
Happy Birthday just for me,
Lots of food,
And lots of pop,
Bring everyone for tea.

A great big massive birthday cake,
With pretty icing on for me,
Invite all my friends round,
Can't wait for them to see.

My presents off my mum and dad,
My presents off my bruv,
My presents off my family and friends,
Who always give me love.

Today it is a special day,
I feel like I'm in Heaven,
Cos all my family and friends are here,
And now I am *eleven!*

Siobhan Gardner (10)
Shevington Community Primary School, Shevington

My Cat Felix

My cat loves me a lot
And I love him a lot too
Felix is really special to me
His black, silky fur is really soft
His eyes are like sparks in the night.

Laura Baggaley (9)
Shevington Community Primary School, Shevington

Totem Pole

'What is that gigantic pole for?
All those people worshipping it.'
He asked, 'What is that colourful pole?
What is so special about it?'
A sudden answer came so quickly
''Tis the totem pole of greatness
Mellow, plain and graceful colours
Sending messages every day
Laughing, cheering, shouting, singing
Whilst round the totem pole they dance
Worshipping their god of Heaven.'

Thomas Powell (9)
Shobdon Primary School, Leominster

Taste Chocolate

I love chocolate
It wafts through the air
As it comes closer to me
Chocolate swirls around my mouth
Twisting, turning, twirling
Like it's dancing
It waters down my chin, I sadly wipe it off
I wish I had chocolate every day!

Rebekah Norton (10)
Shobdon Primary School, Leominster

Snowflakes

Shining white, sparkling silver
Silky, twisting, violet-blue
Frost, cold snowflakes
Rippling downward
Rippling, twirling, falling downward
Snowflakes, snowflakes
Ice-cold snowflakes
Glistening, spinning as they fly
Beautiful snowflakes in the sky.

Natasha Marsh (10)
Shobdon Primary School, Leominster

The Forest Walk

Walking through the forest
Touching all the trees
Hearing all the birds and noises
Tasting all the rain
Seeing all the animals
Smelling the fresh air
Running through the trees
Kicking through the leaves
Crunching on the twigs
Looking at the rainbows
Hearing rabbits dig
Seeing the molehills rise
Climbing up the hills
Getting a good view
I can see a deer
And I can see you.

Lewis Dykes (9)
Shobdon Primary School, Leominster

The Summer's Sun

See the summer's sun you glimpse there
Warm, hasty Indian summer days
Crops and flowers growing in the blazing sun
Giving life and light and heat and growth

Holidaying in the sun giving a golden glow
The sun is like an enemy
Melting my milky ice cream
I will have to eat it quickly
To enjoy the sun again.

Daniel Griffiths (11)
Shobdon Primary School, Leominster

Stars

Stars that twinkle so bright
Glistening in the moonlight
Like a ball of glory
Like a shooting star
Falling from the sky
They sparkle in the starlight
They brighten up the sky
Shimmering as the night dies down.

Sarah Scatcherd (9)
Shobdon Primary School, Leominster

Flowers And Roses

Some flowers are green
And some are very mean!
They give us food to eat
And some are very sweet

You put them in the sun
Now they are very dumb
You give them lots of soil
You'll find they're very loyal

Give them as a winning prize
Give them when someone dies
Give them to someone sad
Or for being a good lad!

Matthew Beaumont-Pike (9)
Shobdon Primary School, Leominster

My Life

My life is good; marriage, celebrations
My life is bad; death, disaster
My life is tiring; school, work
My life is lazy; half-term holidays
My life is successful; graduation, achievements
My life is unsuccessful; failure, neglect
My life is many; many jobs, many tasks
My life is less; less jobs, less tasks

My life is my life
I can't change it whatever I do.

Craig Lawrence (11)
Shobdon Primary School, Leominster

Lights

Lights are amazing, twinkling, sparkling
Sun power fills the sky, shining all around us
Except at night, when the sun goes down the lights go on
Flashes of lightning whizzing through the moonlit sky
Out come the candles
Until the sunlight rises once again.

Lauren Dykes (11)
Shobdon Primary School, Leominster

Snow

Snow, white like a dove
Snow, white like a cloud
Snow, white, falling gently down
Snow is like a spinning, twirling, gliding feather

Snowmen are round like boulders
Snowmen are fat like spacehoppers
Snowmen like to stare through button eyes
Snowmen melt in the winter's sun

Snow, white like a dove
Snow, white like a cloud
Snow falling gently down on the ground
Snow is like a spinning, twirling, gliding feather.

Conor Price (9)
Shobdon Primary School, Leominster

Saw The Flowers

Saw the bright, colourful flowers
Saw their lovely petals shining
And of course he asked Komisno
And again Komisno answered,
''Tis the season of the blooming
'Tis the season everyone smiles
Their scented, sweet, beautiful faces
Is the best you'll ever see here.'

Kerri-Jane Greenhalgh (11)
Shobdon Primary School, Leominster

Yummy Chocolate

Chocolate is tasty
I love it so much
It makes me feel so happy
It's delicious when it melts
Velvety rivers down my chin
Chocolate will always win
Chocolate is like brown building blocks
You eat whenever you want
No one can beat a bit of chocolate
Now and again, and again, and again . . .

Natalie Jeakings (10)
Shobdon Primary School, Leominster

My Dog

Saw the flapping ears come running
Is the wet nose you see there
Touch the fluffy fur so stunning
Listen to the brown tail wagging
Eyes so pleading for a banquet
Paws so floppy pound the ground
'Tis the mongrel dog that loves me
Always a friend and companion.

Millie Hicks (9)
Shobdon Primary School, Leominster

Jaguar

J is for jaws
A is for ability
G is for glare
U is for unusual
A is for amazing
R is for ravenous!

Jack Hollins (10)
The Grove Primary School, Melton Mowbray

Love

Love is pink like a newly opened rose
It tastes like melted chocolate
It smells like a chicken roasting
It looks like a glittering diamond
It sounds like romantic music .
It feels like a brand new blanket.

Ellie Wilford (10)
The Grove Primary School, Melton Mowbray

Happiness

Happiness is bright yellow like the sun
It tastes like a birthday cake
It smells like strawberry air freshener
It looks like a bunch of children playing
It sounds like the ice cream van in the summer
It feels like fluffy white sheep.

Daniel Moorhouse (10)
The Grove Primary School, Melton Mowbray

Excitement

Excitement is like a multicoloured pair of trousers
It tastes like spongy meringue
It smells like a bag of strawberry sweets
It looks like lots of colourful patterns
It sounds like people screaming with excitement
It feels like you need to jump up and down.

Emma Bradley (11)
The Grove Primary School, Melton Mowbray

Tiger

T earing through the jungle
I gnoring other animals
G azing at his prey
E ating for a long time
R esting night and day.

Shane Curtis (11)
The Grove Primary School, Melton Mowbray

Anger

Anger is red like a demon's eyes
It tastes like slimy wriggly maggots
It smells like thick grey choking smoke
It looks like a whirling tornado
It sounds like bombs dropping all around
It feels like a sharp claw stabbing into your back.

Matthew Brown (11)
The Grove Primary School, Melton Mowbray

Love

Love is red like a newly opened rose
It tastes like a sweet cherry
It smells like freshly baked bread
It looks like a strawberry
It sounds like church bells ringing
It feels like a dream come true.

Sarah Culley (11)
The Grove Primary School, Melton Mowbray

Healthy Eating

Don't eat too much chocolate and sweets
Fruit and vegetables are very good treats
Eat apples, salad and broccoli too
And feel your weight escape from you

Eat fat, dairy, fruit and meat
Then you will start to look very neat
Pack a lunch with a crunch
And add some colour to your lunch

If you're getting overweight
Put less fat on your plate
Eat two types of vegetable with your meal
And a lot healthier you will feel.

Daniel Patterson (10)
The Richard Crosse CE Primary School, Kings Bromley

Flowers

A beautiful
Meadow of
Shimmering flowers
Shining in
The daylight
Golden flowers
Swaying
Gently
In the breeze
Sparkling
At nightfall.

Abigail Upton (9)
The Richard Crosse CE Primary School, Kings Bromley

Waterfalls

Powerful
Falling water
Shimmering gentle river
Beautiful fish
Glowing in the lake
Shining, sparkling water
Crystal clear stream
Running through the forest
Gentle breeze
Swaying trees.

Christopher Salt (10)
The Richard Crosse CE Primary School, Kings Bromley

Healthy Food

Fruit and vegetables are healthy foods
They make you feel in a healthy mood
All the colours are bright and shiny
Even the tomatoes that are so tiny

Five a day is good to eat
But it's also good to eat some meat
Fruits are all different sizes and shapes
Melons, apples and all the green grapes

Chocolate and sweets are a nice treat
But there are only a few you can eat
Too much sugar can be bad
So I'll listen to my mum and dad.

Annabel Shotter (11)
The Richard Crosse CE Primary School, Kings Bromley

Amazing Beach

Gentle breeze along
White pale sand
Far away palm trees swaying
In the breeze
Pale blue sea gliding
Along the golden sand
Pale blue sky glistens
In the glowing sun

People come
Footprints in the sand
Sandcastles built
Sea gets rough
Smashing against
The pale sound.

Jordan Shaw (9)
The Richard Crosse CE Primary School, Kings Bromley

Healthy Eating

Ditch the junk
Cakes and double cream
Eat your fruit and vegetables
Swallow all that green

If you eat healthily
You won't get overweight
Eat those healthy vegetables
Load them on your plate

Fruit is really good for you
Like oranges and pears
The fast food may be tempting
But you really shouldn't care

Look at all those vegetables!
The oranges, the greens
Eat up all your fruit and veg
That's what this poem means!

Mollie-Rose Dooley (11)
The Richard Crosse CE Primary School, Kings Bromley

People I Have Met

I met a boy called Ted
Who goes to sleep without a bed!

I met a man called Dave
Who was commanded by a slave

I met a girl called Tom
Who really wanted to be a mom

I met a person called Eddie
Who had a sister called 'Dee Dee'!

Daniel Pritchard (9)
The Richard Crosse CE Primary School, Kings Bromley

A Poem For Healthy Eating

Five a day is what you should eat
If it's the weight you want to beat

Eat it now, eat it fast
Before the weight gives you a blast

Pack your dinner with a crunch
Add some colour to your lunch

Oranges and lemons from overseas
Brought to England for you and me

Sweet and sour, juicy and round
Vegetables grow under the ground

So the moral is for you and me
To eat five a day to keep healthy.

Jack Watson (10)
The Richard Crosse CE Primary School, Kings Bromley

5 A Day

Apples, bananas, oranges and grapes
Different sizes, different shapes
In your diet include fish and meat
Sweets can be eaten as a treat

If you eat healthy food
It will put you in a healthy mood
In the supermarket check the label
Before you decide to lay it on your table

5 a day, the easy way
Gives you energy for work and play!

Beatrice Shotter (9)
The Richard Crosse CE Primary School, Kings Bromley

Waterfall Heaven

Shimmering water
Glowing bright
I see the
Sun shining
Light

Shining fish
In the
Sea
They are pink
And smiling
With glee.

Alice Read (9)
The Richard Crosse CE Primary School, Kings Bromley

My Favourite Fruit And Veg

You should eat fruit and vegetables every day
Oranges and apples will be okay
Eat as much fruit and vegetables as you can
Cook them all up in a pan

Fruit and vegetables are good for you
In a couple of days you'll look brand new
Try not to eat too many sweets
One or two will be your treat.

Ffion Trent & Katie Stanley (10)
The Richard Crosse CE Primary School, Kings Bromley

Rushing Water

Rushing water
Powerful streams
River flowing into
Shimmering, lapping lake
Glowing fish
In the golden sun

Beautiful view
Splashing waterfall
Swaying trees
Gentle breeze
Crystal clear
Bright blue sky.

Daniel Rich (9)
The Richard Crosse CE Primary School, Kings Bromley

Waterfalls

Dashing water
Hot blazing sun
Bursting waterfall
In the spring air

Water starts
Calming, shimmering
Rocks shine
In the red-hot sun

Waving palm trees nearby
Dancing to the beat
Of the splashing water.

Kimrun Basra (9)
The Richard Crosse CE Primary School, Kings Bromley

The Beach

Scorching hot
Crystal clear water
Clear blue skies
Wonderful sunset
On glowing sand
Beautiful, colourful trees
Luxury.

Austin Sullivan (9)
The Richard Crosse CE Primary School, Kings Bromley

The Desert

Heat waves
Float madly
In the hot
Scorching air

On the dry land
Silent swirling
Mists of sand

Vast dunes
Flash in the
Blazing sun.

Thomas Devey (9)
The Richard Crosse CE Primary School, Kings Bromley

5 A Day

Fruit and vegetables are good for you
Juicy oranges and apples too

Don't eat too much bread
Have vegetables instead

Chocolate and crisps are too much fat
Lower your fat and you'll be thin as a cat

If you eat sweetcorn you'll be the
Healthiest person ever born

Have a healthy portion every day
In the end you'll be OK

One last thing I would like to say
'5 a day - the easy way!'

Jack Ford & Matthew Pearce (11)
The Richard Crosse CE Primary School, Kings Bromley

5 A Day

Pure fruit and vegetables are refreshing
Always eat salad with low calorie dressing
All the colours give you a choice
Listen to your heart and your voice

Look at the peppers, red and yellow
Taste the spice, don't be mellow
Orange is the colour of the crispy, raw carrots
All the different colours look like parrots

Squeeze the orange for the blood-red colour
Add some grapes to make your fuller
Take a handful of strawberries and cherries
If you want add some raspberries
A handful of vegetable sticks
A medium pear
Share it with your friends
Make it fair.

Sarah Berriman (11) & Lucy Holland
The Richard Crosse CE Primary School, Kings Bromley

Camping In The Rainforest

Dancing fire
In the breeze
Chirping toucans
Golden beaks

Camping out
On a midsummer night
Brown huts
Yellow light

Golden-brown sun
Shimmering through leaves
Bright purple flowers
Shining on trees

Sleeping soundly
Waking up
Having breakfast
In a warm mud hut.

Hannah Coyle (8)
The Richard Crosse CE Primary School, Kings Bromley

The Wondrous Beach

Busy people
Rushing round
Distant cottages
Golden sand

Boiling bright sun
Glorious palm trees
Swaying calmly
In the gentle breeze

Waves crashing
Against ragged rocks
Smooth, round pebbles
Slimy green seaweed.

Hannah Watson (8)
The Richard Crosse CE Primary School, Kings Bromley

Healthy Eating

Don't eat too many chocolates and sweets
Fruit and vegetables are good treats
Eat some stir-fry, not too sugary or sweet
You'll start to look much more neat

Pack a lunch with a crunch
And you'll become a healthier bunch
Put in some carrots, celery, peppers and cherries

If you're getting overweight
Put less fatty foods on your plate
Eat two different vegetables with your meal
And a lot healthier you will feel.

Justin Allerton (11)
The Richard Crosse CE Primary School, Kings Bromley

Healthy Eating

Don't have too many strawberries and cream
Fruit and vegetables are like a dream
Broccoli, raisins and sweetcorn too
Altogether are good for you

Tender, juicy peaches and bright green beans
Do you know what all this means?
5 a day of fruit and vegetables
Take the fat off the tables

Don't eat too much sugary food
Only be the healthy dude
Crunchy bits of pear and beans
Take the pressure off your jeans.

Daniel Pettingale (9)
The Richard Crosse CE Primary School, Kings Bromley

I Saw

I saw a monkey eating bread
I saw some knitting without a thread
I saw my friend, his name is Jed
I saw him sleeping without his ted
I saw a teacher in a zoo
I saw my sister in some goo
I saw a watch that went tick-tock
I saw an elephant make a knock
I saw a lion make a roar
I saw a rabbit blow up the door
I saw an ogre who ate a shoe
I saw a cow who didn't moo
I saw an ant that made a click
I saw a tiger do a trick
I saw a pixie make a jug
I saw a train that went chug, chug.

Alex Bedford (9)
The Richard Crosse CE Primary School, Kings Bromley

The Burning Sunset

Golden, burning, orange
Fire glowing
Shining in the distance

High in the dark sky
Shimmering light
The sunset scorching
The sandy beach
And gazing at
The salty ocean

The sparkling water
Down below
The sunset reflection
Makes a glow.

Francesca Moreland (9)
The Richard Crosse CE Primary School, Kings Bromley

Winter World

Winter enters as it gets cold
Things are very hard to hold
People's fingers become frostbitten
Children are having snowball fights
Rivers and lakes start to freeze
There is a cold winter breeze
Hands and feet get really numb
The children's snowman is nearly done
Rocks and a carrot for the nose and eyes
The beautiful plants start to die
The children are having so much fun
That they can't see the rising sun
People are shivering in their sleep
As the snow crashes down in a massive heap
The houses change from brown to white
The children have stopped their snowball fight
There's the truck with loads of grit
Some people are having shivering fits
The people fall as they slip and slide
The cars skid off the bridge's side
The old people are having fun inside
As the young children are having fun outside
The radiators in houses are turned on full
As the weather outside turns very dull
The snow glistens in the light
As winter is a very beautiful sight.

Ajay Mohan (9)
The Willows Primary School, Penkhull

My Journey To School

I walk to school each morning
With my group of friends
We walk up some straight roads
And around a few bends

In the summer it's warm
And in the winter it's cold
But I must walk this journey
Until I'm sixteen years old

It takes me up to 15 minutes
To reach the school gates
Most days I'm on time
But the odd day I'm late

I usually walk to school with friends
But sometimes walk alone
And I also walk this journey
When I'm on my way home.

Jordan Halliday (10)
Thorpe Acre Junior School, Loughborough

Birds

Birds, birds
They fly up high
Up in the big, ginormous sky!
Up there everywhere
Where do they go?
I think and I'm sure
That they don't even know!

They might fly up to the seaside
Or maybe their nests
They always make sure that they have all
The rest!

Because they're tired all day
And they're out every day
They're always hunting, looking for prey
They share it and eat it together on a bench
Tweeting along as if they are on a fence!

They tweet early in the morning
And poo in the air
You should see the
Statues of Trafalgar Square!

Shannon Barker (10)
Thorpe Acre Junior School, Loughborough

My Sister Ate An Orange

My sister ate an orange
I'm astonished that she died
She swallowed it completely
She's a disconcerting kid

My sister ate an orange
First she chewed it for a while
Then digested it entirely
With a silly sort of smile

My sister ate an orange
It's a novel thing to do
Then she also ate a yellow
And a purple and a blue.

Insiyah Bharmal (9)
Thorpe Acre Junior School, Loughborough

The Butterfly

The butterfly's symmetrical
Wings flap and
Lead her through the air

She approaches the warm blue sky
When the golden sun
Strikes daylight

She flutters gracefully through the
Shiny blue sky
Without a trace of evidence.

Daisy Glover & Bethaney Wright (10)
Thorpe Acre Junior School, Loughborough

About Me

The name is Vic
I'm seven years old
Good at gymnastics
Or so I've been told
My legs are long
Like a couple of sticks
Which is very handy
When doing the splits!

Victoria Price (7)
Thorpe Acre Junior School, Loughborough

Ghostly Nights

The creaking floorboards
What's that noise I hear?
I am frightened to move
Rigid with fear

It feels so eerie
And it's dark outside
I'm under the bedclothes
Attempting to hide

Is it a burglar
Or is it a ghost?
I don't know which
Would scare me most

So am I being invaded?
Not really, I'm okay
I'm just alone in the house
Letting my imagination run away.

Katie Farmer (7)
Thorpe Acre Junior School, Loughborough

The Snail

The little snail is moving slowly
See him slide across the grass
He leaves a silver path behind him
We all knew when he has passed

Little snail is never worried
Though he wanders far and wide
For on his back his house
He carries and when he's
Tired he pops inside.

Nur Syafiqah Nor Azman (8)
Thorpe Acre Junior School, Loughborough

Winter Poem

Winter is cold, you can get a chill
When you go outside it's a thrill
It's too icy, you can fall over
And it will give you a fright
And the frost might get on your skin
And give you a bite
So wrap up warm and wait for dawn!

Sophie Vallance (9)
Thorpe Acre Junior School, Loughborough

Hot Chocolate

I drink it all the time with my mate
We drink a lot of hot chocolate!

We drink it in the morning
It keeps us from yawning

It keeps us awake
Until the school break

We drink it at night
So we don't get a fright

In our beds
When resting our heads.

Kathryn Wood (10)
Thorpe Acre Junior School, Loughborough

Goodnight

Tuck yourself in your cosy bed and dream about
Anything you like the most
As the sun goes down into the darkness, the misty moon
Puts on his nightcap
Stars come out to play and say, 'Goodnight, see you
Another day.'

Heather Onions (10)
Thorpe Acre Junior School, Loughborough

Fishy Tales

Zooming round and round my house
I have a friend, but not a mouse

He never wants to go for walks
And in his corner he never squawks

He has a tail, but not of a cat
But I sometimes wish he was that

In his little hiding place
He has such fun, I've seen his face

Up and down he always goes
With his big black eyes, they're never closed

His coat of scales glints in the light
At feeding time which is once a night

Could you guess? Well here he is
My best friend is Flopper the fish.

Eleanor Barnes (9)
Whittington CE Primary School, Whittington

A Football Poem

Here's an interesting football poem
With all the players, including Owen
Rooney, Ronaldo plus all the rest
Man United are the best

In this poem we focus on Man U
Sat in Old Trafford with a great view
Man U are winning 4-1
Watching them play is so much fun

Sat behind the goal, Rooney takes a shot
What a volley from the penalty spot!
Fergie jumps high into the air
Punching his fists, the other team just stare

And as the final whistle blows
The applause from the Man U fans grows
Man United are simply the best
Without a doubt they are better than the rest!

James Fletcher (9)
Whittington CE Primary School, Whittington

Why?

Why am I white and why is he black?
Why are there earthquakes and tornadoes?
Why are there fires and volcanoes?
Why did this happen and why did that happen?
Why is there pollution and poverty?
Why is there child labour?
Why are there starving mouths?
Why do I get most things I want
Whilst some people are begging for life?

Why do I care?
Why don't I just stare?
Because they need our help!

Esme Dyson (10)
Witton Middle School, Droitwich

Alone

Alone all day, alone all night
I wish I had a friend in sight
Along he came, a blue-eyed man
Offering me a Chinese fan

Swishing and swirling in my face
He had style, he had grace
With the fan he came
He is now my mate

Days went on with love and grace
I'm due to wed my new mate
On September the 8th
The wedding day has come and gone
And suddenly things have moved on

One by one the children came
Matt and Tom, they both have fame

Alone no more
We sit together
My husband and I, forever and ever.

Jade Ann Hewlett (10)
Witton Middle School, Droitwich

Today At Midnight

When it's night people will bark
When it's day it will be dark
The sky will turn rosy red
And I will jump happily out of bed

The moon will become a star
A ball will turn into a car
The sun will wilt and die
All the people in the world will cry

The hovering bees will turn to blue
All the actors will be on cue
All the cats and dogs will have fleas
And the moon will turn into cheese.

Megan Thomas (9)
Witton Middle School, Droitwich

A School Morning

I woke up in the morning not ready for the day
Early in May
I got my uniform on
And then suddenly I shone
I went to have some toast
And Mum thought she'd seen a ghost
I went and brushed my teeth
And met my brother, 'the beast'
Then I had a wash and . . .
Then, Oh my gosh!
Five minutes to leave the door
But then I've got more
Got to drink my tea
And then be
On the drive
Waiting for five
Or more kids to come out
And about
I saw my dad whilst I was walking to school
In his little car which is cool.

Dexter Williamson (10)
Witton Middle School, Droitwich

My Older Sister

My older sister annoys my mum
My older sister sucks her thumb
My older sister eats baby food
My older sister gets into a very childish mood

My older sister always gets cold
My older sister is 14 years old
My older sister likes her milk warm
My older sister thinks one bee is a swarm!

My older sister gets taught to be a teen at home
And to stop kicking the garden gnome
My older sister likes to trash my room
But most of all I make her fume.

Jay Akred (9)
Witton Middle School, Droitwich

The Writer Of This Poem

(Based on 'The Writer of this Poem' by Roger McGough)

The writer of this poem is green and comes from Mars
The writer of this poem is locked behind bars
The writer of this poem loves cottage cheese
The writer of this poem has never said please
The writer of this poem loves gooey gum
The writer of this poem really annoys his mum
The writer of this poem is as clever as can be
The writer of this poem is actually . . .
Me!

Robert Brewer (10)
Witton Middle School, Droitwich

Guess Who?

Loud screamer
Not cleaner

Strong walker
Annoying talker

Little tinker
Big stinker

Potty trainer
Bad blamer

Noisy sleeper
Babyish weeper

Peek-a-boo I see you!

It is a toddler.

Lauren Purser (10)
Witton Middle School, Droitwich

Teacher, Teacher!

'Teacher, Teacher what is the time?'
'Joseph, it's half-past nine.'

'Teacher, Teacher, what does this say?'
'Look at me,' said May

'Teacher, Teacher when is it break?'
'Joseph, shut up for goodness sake!'
'Teacher, Teacher you're about to explode.'
'Because you've put me in that mode!'

Georgina Bayliss (10)
Witton Middle School, Droitwich

Home Alone!

Am I home alone?
Mum and Dad aren't there
Am I home alone?
I can't see my brothers and sisters
I'm home alone
Argh! God, help me!

Mum and Dad aren't upstairs
They aren't in the garden
They're nowhere to be seen
I'm home alone
Argh! God, help me!

My brothers and sisters aren't upstairs
They aren't in the garden
They're nowhere to be seen
I'm home alone
Argh! God, help me!

Am I home alone?
Mum and Dad aren't there
I can't see my brothers and sisters
I'm home alone
Argh! God, save me!

They've just come through the door
I'm no longer home alone
Thank you God!

Aileen Baker (9)
Witton Middle School, Droitwich

That's My Body

This is my body
That's my hand that pats the dog
The legs that win the sprint
They're my teeth that chomp, chomp, chomp
The nose that smells the dinner
That's my ear that listens to the teacher
The voice that sings in the choir
They're the eyes that read the book
The feet that score the goals
They're my fingers that play the piano
That's my body!

James Spearing-Brown (9)
Witton Middle School, Droitwich

Alphabetical Names

A my's cycle was lovely and blue
B ethany's sister is only two
C laire's teacher is thirty-four
D iana's picture was glued to the door
E mily's clock stopped on the wall
F iona's nan likes to walk up the hall
G eorgina's uncle does a jig
H arriet's brother acts like a pig
I ndia's room is quite neat
J amie's dad is called Pete
K athryn's brother is called Jake
'L ucy . . . how long does this go on for, for goodness sake?'
M elissa's dictionary is rather old
N atasha's clock has been sold
O livia's kids were particularly fun
P enelope's sister likes a bun
Q ueeney's cousin likes to be keen
R ebekah's dad is nineteen
S amantha's teacher had a laugh
T roy's got a purple scarf
U rsula's mum is very thin
V ictoria's bought a needle including a pin
W alter's injection won't hurt him
X anthe's going to the gym
Y ukina's got a cousin called Jim
Z oe's now at the end of this poem.

Victoria Lake (9)
Witton Middle School, Droitwich

The Sea

The sea, the sea is as pretty as me
It's too big for mini me
It sways side to side and goes far, far behind
So the fish hide under the deep blue
People swim all over me
It's no wonder people can't see it's the fish not me.

Jack Fellows (10)
Witton Middle School, Droitwich

The Magic Box
(Based on 'Magic Box' by Kit Wright)

I will put in the box . . .
A warthog with a runny nose
A tail from a horse touching a tiger
And a liquorice sweet dancing to music

I will put in the box . . .
A smiling sun looking down on us
A taste of an ice cream that never melts
And a flip of a mermaid's tail

I will put in the box . . .
The day I was born
The first dream I ever had
And a dinosaur playing a piano

I will put in the box . . .
A human that looks like a clock
A dog that miaows
And a cat that woofs

My box is styled with memories and dreams
With rainbows on the lid and magic in the corners

I shall fly in the box
Way above the clouds
And then come down again
And land on a deserted field.

Annabelle Banner (10)
Witton Middle School, Droitwich

Swimming Race

S ix swimmers ready to race
W ater splashing all over the place
I mmediately everyone is quiet
M any people have a riot
M edals waiting to be won
I f you don't win, you've still gone
N ever ever give up
G etting swimmers their cups

R acing is a challenging thing
A nyone can just bring
C ostumes and goggles and everything else
E veryone can be good at swimming.

Katherine Kirkham (9)
Witton Middle School, Droitwich

My Favourite Colour Is . . .

'My favourite colour is . . .
Orange,' Ann said
'It's funny and fruity and reminds me of bed!'

'My favourite colour is . . .
blue,' George exclaimed
'But when Birmingham lose it's a down right pain!'

'My favourite colour is . . .
pink,' Ruby pointed out
'It's shy and it's pretty, the best with no doubt!'

But when the teacher declared
Who's so clever and wise
'Why not like the *rainbow,* it deserves a prize.'
Then the children thought
'That's a good idea
when a *rainbow* comes out
loads of colours appear!'

Emily May (9)
Witton Middle School, Droitwich

My Dad's A Dog

A wet, black nose
Three claws for five toes
One waggy tail
Dad drinks out of a pail
He sniffs at signs and lamp posts
He bites men in caps the most

He runs around in the yard
He makes a fantastic, brilliant guard
He eats cold leftovers from my plate
He embarrasses me in front of my mate

Well that's my dad, he's quite cool
The only problem is he has to drool!

Aidan Petrie (9)
Witton Middle School, Droitwich

My Pets!

Mittens my kitten is lovely and sweet
Mittens my kitten is careful and neat
Mittens my kitten makes no sound
Mittens my kitten likes running around

Jake my dog is brown and white
Jake my dog is scared of the night
Jake my dog likes eating my hat
Jake my dog likes chasing Sam's cat

Todd my fish is one of a kind
Todd my fish has a very dumb mind
Todd my fish just goes, *bob, bob, bob,*
Todd my fish makes the noise, *ob, ob, ob.*

Lily my hamster is a golden brown
Lily my hamster came from down town
Lily my hamster has sharp claws
Lily my hamster has dainty paws.

Sophie Vick (10)
Witton Middle School, Droitwich

The Spider

The spider is an awesome creature
Having eight legs is its feature
Did you know that spiders can't fly?
But some can leap very high
They do this by pulling back a strand of thread
Then go soaring through the sky overhead
The male is the smaller of the pair
And although this may not sound very fair
The female may kill the male
Because these spiders do sometimes fail
To get the food their families need
And their babies will be waiting for their feed.

Scarlet Roberts (9)
Witton Middle School, Droitwich

Painting

Thick brush, thin brush
Paint on the page
Lots of paint on the palette

The brush strokes across the page
Lots of different colours
Yellow, blue and red

I'm now painting stripes
I really don't know why
Thick stripes, thin stripes all across the page

I need to wash my brush
I dip it in the water
I dry it off with the paper towel

Back to my painting
Just finishing it off

Now it's time to tidy up
1, 2, 3
I hang my painting up to dry
And go to watch TV.

Amy Carter (10)
Witton Middle School, Droitwich

Football

Football, football kickin' around
In the net, out of the ground
In the final, havin' a laugh
See you later in the bath
Muddy as ever, skin never seen
On the way to the green
To play away
To Swansea
Playing our rivals
Maybe a win, maybe a loss, maybe a draw
But not with the player Ross
Stevie G havin' tea, bangers and mash will suit me.

Matthew Scott (11)
Witton Middle School, Droitwich

My Pets

Horses gallop and prance
Horses canter and jump
Horses turn left and right
Horses neigh with pride
Hamsters run in their wheel
Hamsters run around in the day
Hamsters wait for an owner
Hamsters have cute beady eyes
Cats scratch a pole
Cats run away from dogs
Cats have long tails
Cats have whiskers that tickle
Dogs have tails that wag
Dogs fetch bones
Dogs eat bones
Dogs sleep in their baskets.

Abbie Holliday (10)
Witton Middle School, Droitwich

Lovely Horse

Horses, horses, lovely horses
Lots of colours
Lots of breeds . . .

In their stables
They kick about
Trying to find their way out
But in their fields
They love it so much
Running free
Playing with their friends
And having so much fun

Riding, riding
It's so fun
Trotting
Cantering
Even jumping
It's so much fun
Why don't you come and have a go?

Emma Pingstone (11)
Witton Middle School, Droitwich

Brat

He runs around the school like a dizzy fool
His sister gets straight As, he just plays and plays
He's cheating test scores to get the best scores
Dropping banana peel all over the floors
It wasn't long ago, just a couple of weeks
He got in trouble, yeah pretty deep
Father was yellin', Mum was too
Because he put mothballs in the beef stew
Punishment time lurked in the room so cruel
Sitting by himself in his room
But he escaped out the window with a rubber band
A bus came round the corner and *bang!* like the hinges falling off
an old battered door . . .

Steven Rawlings (10)
Witton Middle School, Droitwich

Come To Witton Middle School

School, school, joyful school
Heads up high
On come the lights
Pens on the go all day long
At this joyful school

On the playground children play
On the desk the pencil case is placed
When down on the ground shoes are unlaced
In and out this happy school

In the hall lunch is served
Smiles on the field
And paint in the art and DT room
At this smiling school

Come to the school for some fun
Put on a frown and so will we
And then we won't be the
Joyful, happy, smiling school that we are.

Karine Price (11)
Witton Middle School, Droitwich

The Mystical Box
(Based on 'Magic Box' by Kit Wright)

I will put in my box . . .
A flickering flame from a fire bolt
The deadly sting from a bumblebee
And the non-existing monkey that never lived

I will put in my box . . .
An ice cube with a catapult
A gallon of the cleanest water from Lake Garda
And the tuna fish's funny bone

I will put in my box . . .
Five wishing trees from ancient Mars
The first joke from a fire cracker
And the tail from a hissing snake

I will put in my box . . .
A thirteenth season and a glass sun
A monkey in a Ferrari
And racing driver swinging on tall treetops

My box is mystical with gold and stain glass windows
With seven moons on the secret lid of Madagascar
Its hinges are four fairies bent by a T-rex

I shall skate in the box
On the tip of the Himalayas on Jupiter
Then be snowstormed away onto a volcano
Which is as red as roses.

Christopher Stanley (9)
Witton Middle School, Droitwich

Surfing

I hear the sails billow
As I skim across the water
Catching the wind and walking the waves

Salty flavours enter my mouth
The spray drenches my suit

The sun tans my neck and my face
As I speed towards the shore
Surfing wakes up my senses!

Clodagh Lodge (10)
Witton Middle School, Droitwich

I Went To Sea In A Raft

I went to sea in a raft
I screamed and I shouted and laughed
I fell in the sea, as cold as can be
I went to sea in a raft

I went to sea in a ferry
With my nasty big sister called Jerry
She pushed me off, I spluttered and coughed
I went to sea in a ferry

I went to sea in a boat
We went all around the old moat
I ate a cake by the lake
I went to sea in a boat

I went to sea in a raft
I screamed and I shouted and laughed
I fell in the sea, as cold as can be
I went to sea in a raft.

Ashleigh Jade Hinton (9)
Witton Middle School, Droitwich

Tonight At The Noon

Flying cars in the sky
Surfer world champion makes a tie
Horses galloping on the clouds
Rhinos rampaging through the towns

This is what happens tonight at the noon

Oranges falling from the heavens
Kings and queens arresting peasants
A little money the Prime Minister owns
All the dogs turn into little cones

This is what happens tonight at the noon

McDonald's in the middle of the sea
Suddenly we all catch a flea
Jupiter will come to get us
Then it suddenly lands in a bus

This is what happens tonight at the noon.

Abigail Thompson (9)
Witton Middle School, Droitwich

The Magic Box
(Based on 'Magic Box' by Kit Wright)

I will place in my box . . .
A scarf of palest green
A cat that squeaks
And a mouse that goes miaow!

I will place in my box . . .
A rosy red rabbit
And green, gungy goo
A small, smelly sock
And an extraordinary electric, everlasting wish

I will place in my box . . .
An enchanted harp with a broken string
A tooth of a great white shark
A pearl necklace
And a shell bracelet

I will place in my box . . .
A picture of my family
A pretty flower fairy
A precious magic spell
And a present from a long-gone aunt

My box is fashioned from silver and gold
With stars that sparkle in the sun
It has magic on the sides
Lace upon the lid
And flowers for the bottom

I shall sing in my box
A song of happiness and joy
A song of cries from sad people
Then dance with my fairy
Till I'm all tired out!

Hannah King (10)
Witton Middle School, Droitwich

A Poem About The Horrid Teacher

She is nasty and horrid to the kids
She takes all their pen lids
She makes them do forfeits
While she finishes her little bits

She gives them piles of homework
And she just sits and relaxes
They don't get any playtime
And the other kids do

She tells them their work is wrong
She starts to sing a song
She goes out of the room
And you can hear *boom, boom*

She dismisses the whole class
To have some time alone
But she's still the horrid teacher
With her horrid and nasty ways.

Jamie Cook (9)
Witton Middle School, Droitwich

There Once Was A Boy Called Fred

There was a boy called Fred
He always played in bed
He had a little car that went so far
And he read in bed

Fred goes to the shed
He gets a pencil lead
He goes back to bed
He plays with his little ted
And that is Fred

Then Fred went back to his shed
He got a ted called Ned
He went back to bed with
Little ted called Ned and that is Fred!

Lucy Solloway (9)
Witton Middle School, Droitwich

Magic Fingers

My dad has magic fingers
He wriggles them around all day
And he never ever has time to play
Oh my dad has magic fingers

My dad has magic fingers
He has very special powers
Because he can magic lots of flowers
Oh my dad has magic fingers

My dad has magic fingers
He points his fingers into space
When I am trying to tie up my shoelace
Oh my dad has magic fingers

My dad has magic fingers
Well he did long ago
Because now he is so slow
My dad used to have magic fingers.

Laura Roberts (9)
Witton Middle School, Droitwich

My Mixed Dream

In my mixed dream I saw a dancer
And Santa's reindeer called Prancer
While things were whirling round and round
I was glad my feet were on the ground!
Then I saw my very best mate
But she sprinted away as if she was late
As I was swept off my feet
'Hey, that's my math's sheet!'
Now I was drifting down and down
There's my mum without a frown
As I woke I was in my bed
I guess I'm glad there's nothing to dread.

Brittany Moss (10)
Witton Middle School, Droitwich

Food

Food is great, like cake
Cold ice creams and warm dates
Chocolate mousse and a fizzy Coke
Minty chocolate, After Eights

Chilli, curry, roast dinners too
Chicken, beef, lamb curry
Sweets too
Red berries

Milk, juice and flavoured water
Fish fingers, Crunchie, Mars
Have a hot dog too
Galaxy bars!

David McTague (9)
Witton Middle School, Droitwich

Are You An Alien?

Are you an alien? I commonly ask. With green tentacles wearing a mask?
If you aren't a human, are you a zog, a rog or a sprog?
If you come from out there do you need to breathe?
Are you an alien? I commonly ask, but yet none are wearing a mask!

Are you an alien? I commonly ask. With bright green hair and a purple nose?
If you're an alien and I'm human you'd better not eat me for an afternoon snack!
If you're an alien you have to be green with a blue spleen
If you're an alien you shouldn't have a normal nose
More like a nose like Michael Jackson's point!
So I close this poem by asking, 'Are you an alien?'

Mark Fell (9)
Witton Middle School, Droitwich

Do Not

Do not scream at nasty bears
Do not rock on three-leg chairs
Do not dance on sinking sand
Do not join a crazy band
Do not put ham in a pan
Do not take lessons from Ramichaban
Do not talk to a groovy bat
Do not shave the teacher's cat
And do not put it under a mat
Do not chuck a hard ball
Do not take over a golden hall
Actually it's better if you don't do anything!

Edward Burt (10)
Witton Middle School, Droitwich

Today That's Yesterday

Ants will grow thirty feet tall
And I will be squished by a big beach ball
Blue long grass will grow on the Earth
And big red petals will try to surf

Blue and white zebras will pounce on the moor
Whilst King Kong is choking on an apple core
The clouds in the sky will turn to mould
And penguins will feel the cold

The sea will instantly turn to ice
And I will have to eat big brown mice
The doors will be made out of lots of glue
And I'd see a caterpillar with just one shoe

And money will fall out of the sky.

Jacob McGarrity (9)
Witton Middle School, Droitwich

Can Dog's Squeak?

Can cats bark?
Can you stroke a shark?
Can you eat a snake?
Can mice drink a lake?

Can dogs squeak?

Can one camel eat cheese?
Can dogs ever say please?
Can a poodle ever pray?
Can an elephant lie in hay?

Can dogs squeak?

Can a dog have no hair?
Can you ever eat a prayer?
Can you a eat a pen?
Have you ever chased a hen?

Can dogs squeak?

Can you ever fly?
Would your dog say goodbye?
Can you ever be a bear?
Will you even see a hare?

Can dogs squeak?

Amber Cox (9)
Witton Middle School, Droitwich

And Pigs Will Fly

My teacher's face will turn orange
Nine-year-olds will go to college
There will be 33 days in May
Ducks will sleep on hay

Roses will smell of strawberry
One hundred girls will be called Cherry
Rats will go tweet, tweet
Bears will look so neat

Thirteen will be the time
There will be a new rhyme
My dad will have a lion's mane
Me, I will not be quite the same

Dogs will lay eggs
No one will have legs
Everyone will wear a tie
And pigs will fly.

Roxane Kirkham (9)
Witton Middle School, Droitwich

Pigs Will Fly

When oh when will pigs fly?
Will I ever say bye-bye?
Will I ever cry and cry?
Oh why oh why don't pigs fly?

Will oh will they ever come back?
Will they carry one very big sack?
Will oh will they be called Jack
Or will oh will they be called Mack?

Will they come back one day?
Oh will oh will they come in May?
Would they ever come and play
Or will they be called Jay?

Will oh will they come in care
Or even be hit by a bear?
Will they have loads of hair
Or will they sit on a chair?

Luke Girling (9)
Witton Middle School, Droitwich

Chocolate And More

Chocolate is like Heaven,
It's simply paradise,
You put it on your tongue,
And it melts like candyfloss.

Candyfloss reminds me of fairgrounds and fun,
Riding the merry-go-round in the sun,
You put it in your mouth,
And it tastes so sweet, like sugar.

Sugar is in lots of things,
Veggies, fruit and sweets,
But the thing I love most with sugar in is . . .
Chocolate!

Chocolate is like Heaven,
It's simply paradise,
You put it on your tongue,
And it melts like candyfloss.

Georgina Biggin (11)
Witton Middle School, Droitwich

And Horses Will Have Six Legs

Cats will grow on trees
And flowers will grow from peas
People will have green hair
And I will rule like Tony Blair

Cats and dogs will fall from the sky
And deer will start to fly
Deserts will turn to grass
And I will learn to play the double bass

The sky will turn purple
And I'll have a gerbil
A princess will marry an ugly man
And in the winter you will catch a brown tan

And horses will have six legs.

Jessica Bailey (9)
Witton Middle School, Droitwich

Wasted Sea

The awaiting deckchairs empty
The promenade unused
The band stand silent and
Brass instruments stand still

The excited deckchairs filled
The promenade heaving
The band stand roaring and
Brass instruments pulsate

The deckchairs rest exhausted
The promenade feels calm
The band stand whispers and
Brass instruments all sigh

The deckchairs now are empty
The promenade retires
The band stand peaceful and
Brass instruments retreat

And the legacy is the discarded waste
In the forgotten sea.

Jack Solloway (11)
Witton Middle School, Droitwich

And The Moon Is Made Of Cheese

Every ant will play ball
I will give the Queen a call
Britney Spears is a fool
Have a look at my chocolate pool

I will rule the world
I will have my hair curled
I will never ever pick my nose
I have seen the blackest rose

When a seal starts to cheer
My dad gets his car in gear
When I see a rabbit eat
I start messing with my feet

And the moon is made of cheese!

Rachel Hackett (9)
Witton Middle School, Droitwich

Paper Will Be Impossible To Scrunch

Paper will be impossible to scrunch
People will never eat lunch
Water will be able to float
Paper will make a super fast boat

Ants will grow sixty feet tall
Rugby players will only play football
The sand will turn green
My best friend will turn mean

A hen lays a golden egg
And all the footballers will break their legs
Dogs will be able to fly
Babies will never cry.

Kyle Barker (10)
Witton Middle School, Droitwich

And The School Will Fly

The first thing I say will mumble
The school starts when I tumble
The month is May
And it is Wednesday

Oh there's my cousin
But who are the other dozen?
My rubber will walk
And my pen will talk

The lions will be my friend
And the silliness will never end
I'll be there one day
But I'll be there first okay

And the school will fly!

Ashley Chan (9)
Witton Middle School, Droitwich

Have You Seen These Animals?

It's winter, turn the heating down
A bumblebee has flown into town
I know a cat committed a crime
I have dog who loves lager and lime

I know how to fly a flea
Can you catch a bumblebee?
I've got a rabbit who drinks tea
You've got a bird who holds a key

My uncle has a talking pet
Have you seen a hamster make a bet?
My dog can lay a golden egg
And my pet fish has just one leg

My word, have you seen these animals?

Kimberley Blueman (10)
Witton Middle School, Droitwich

Beetles Will Grow Huge

Ants will grow so very big
And I'll see a funny dancing pig
Bees will sing a tune
Eminem will come back soon

Rooney will be a ballet star
And I will drive a great big car
Aeroplanes will drive on the floor
Aliens will knock on your door

A frog in France will say hello
Now it's gone down below
Bugs will grow so tall
There will be a shiny hall.

Ben Lane (9)
Witton Middle School, Droitwich

I Will See A Dinosaur

I will see a dinosaur
And Greeks will find a Minotaur
Pigs will eat with knives and forks
And sheep will open bottle corks

Dinosaurs will rule the Earth
Ghosts will have another birth
Dogs will go to Tesco Express
And my hamster will buy my mum a dress

Fish can live outside the pond
And all the sea will turn blonde!

John Dipple (9)
Witton Middle School, Droitwich

Technology

T otal waste of time?
E lectronics, do we depend on them?
C an they pave the way for society
H ow will we cope if it all stops working?
N asty or nice?
O ur future?
L ife enhancing?
O ur friend or foe?
G reat achievements?
Y es to technology or no?
   What do you think?

Reece Reynolds (11)
Witton Middle School, Droitwich

My Cat

Slow and patient does she wait
A mouse by the door she does hate
Licking the milk from her bowl
Calm and svelte she does stroll
Fast asleep in the chair
Licking and touching her long hair
Straight and beautiful she does sit
A bee by the door she wants to hit
The wind is blowing, she is growing
Happy and hot
She sleeps a lot.

Parissa Bagheri (11)
Witton Middle School, Droitwich

The Car

Here stood the car of my dreams
Sleek, fast and my favourite colour - red
It shone beautifully under the bright lights
Gloriously positioned for all to admire
The tinted glass giving nothing away inside
The prying eyes desperately trying to see within
The wide tyres and alloy wheels
Screaming to be driven at top speed
If only I owned the key to this power machine
I would truly believe I'd died and gone to Heaven.

Harry Lake (11)
Witton Middle School, Droitwich

Countryside

The countryside is a wonderful place,
Birds twitter in the trees,
The colours of the rainbow brighten up the sky,
Rabbits hop through the meadows followed by their babies,
Flowers of all types, from daisies to poppies,
Crops and vegetables grow,
Nothing is always the same in the countryside.

Holly Newton (10)
Witton Middle School, Droitwich

The Monkey

T hey are really cool, swinging through the trees,
H anging around by just the means of their tail,
E ating fruit and vegetables.

M essing around making the trees bounce like a bouncy ball,
O ver the ground they jump and leap,
N ot forgetting who they loathe,
K icking and screaming when having to get cleaned up,
E volved into humans who are quite intelligent, .
Y ou have them as relatives, just like me!

Alexander Stallard (10)
Witton Middle School, Droitwich

The A To Z Of The Staffroom Fridge

A is for apple (from 1885),
B is for balloon (not sure why it's there though!),
C is for cheese (the first thing that's normal),
D is for doughnuts (to cheer the teachers up),
E is for emu (rather squashed, but hey),
F is for frog porridge (a must for every Monday morning),
G is for goat (it got out of the creative play area),
H is for ham (all curled at the edges),
I is for ice packs (for those little accidents),
J is for jam (for the early morning toast),
K is for KitKats (for that break time snack),
L is for lemonade (burp!),
M is for mould (for tomorrow's science experiment),
N is for no milk (when you need it most),
O is for octopus (what's he doing there?),
P is for party food (left over from Christmas),
Q is for quiche (with custard and veg),
R is for rhubarb (with the poisonous bits still on),
S is for sticky bun (tut, tut!),
T is for thallium (we're not that naughty!),
U is for use-by-date (they're never ever fresh),
V is for vegetables (with extra sprouts too!),
W is for water (it's a bit hard though!),
X is for xylophone (that one's a classic),
Y is for yeast (for food technology next week),
And finally Z, is for zebra (why is it in there?
Because it's the staffroom fridge!)

Laura Compton (10)
Witton Middle School, Droitwich

Teachers

T echnology, that has gone a bit too far,
E ccentric creatures with razor-quick eyes to spot trouble.
A cademic tutors and strict, strict, strict
C autious with every move, determined to coach the pupils.
H ermetic and humane.
E mphatic in ways and they are in endless endeavour.
R abid sometimes but other times very resourceful
S mart and to the point and also very sly!

Omar Qasim (11)
Witton Middle School, Droitwich

My Henry VIII (The King And I)

Serving the King, slaving all day,
Nothing he gives me, no money - no pay,
I ask of him nothing, too frightened to ask,
Who knows what hides behind that good, kind mask,
Moonlight can come, no time for fun,
There's always exhausting work to be done.
The King rules over me and I can't object,
I cook for him, do anything for him, but that doesn't affect.
The lifelong reign he has over me,
Which I joined when I was too blind too see,
The cruelness, the bloodthirstiness which is encased inside him,
On every part of his skin, showing in his eyes and lying in every limb.
The King is my master, there's no partnerships, no together,
I got myself into this mess, now I'm in it forever.

Natalie Rhodes (11)
Witton Middle School, Droitwich

A Kite

Mum bought me a kite,
I took it for a flight,
It soared up in the air,
It didn't have a care,
I ran to the sea,
The kite chasing after me,
The day turned to night,
The moon shining bright,
The kite was no longer in sight,
It had left with the night,
The day was at an end,
And I had lost a friend.

George Mills (11)
Witton Middle School, Droitwich

Peace

P eople not at war
E veryone joining together
A ll helping each other
C hildren safe and happy
E arth should be like this.

Ceri Jones (10)
Witton Middle School, Droitwich

The Big Game

Running out onto the pitch,
The fans were cheering,
I was marking a titch,
He was sneering.

The match was away,
The defender had a kip,
I must not say,
But he let rip.

Not long had gone,
We scored the first goal,
The ref tripped up,
And fell down a hole.

The away fans went mad,
Jumping up and down,
The home fans were sad,
Wearing a frown.

A foul in the box,
They won a pen,
The striker pulled up his socks,
A goal from Mark Hen.

Two minutes to go,
The ref put the whistle to his mouth,
The pitch was covered in snow,
It was coming from the south.

Steve Stone had a shot,
It hit the back of the net,
The ref lost the plot,
He had lost the bet.

Kieran McArdle (10)
Witton Middle School, Droitwich

Toddlers

Nose blower
Tantrum thrower
Mess maker
Toy breaker
Attention seeker
Nappy leaker
Ribbon wearer
Dolly carer
Clothes muddler
Teddy cuddler.

Jess Goodall (11)
Witton Middle School, Droitwich

Grown-Ups

Oh bossy, bossy grown-ups!

Do this, do that!
All grown-ups have once spat
'Comb your hair
And brush your teeth!'
Said grumpy old uncle Keith

Wash your face!
Sit in your place!
Tie your shoelace!
Put it in your case!
Work at a quicker pace!
Wash your face!

Do this, do that!
All grown-ups have once spat
'Get dressed into your PJs
and go to bed!'
Yelled uncle Ted

Wash your face!
Sit in your place!
Tie your shoelace!
Put it in your case!
Work at a quicker pace!
Wash your face!

Really I like grown-ups but oh . . .
Bossy, bossy grown-ups!

Lauren Dipple (10)
Witton Middle School, Droitwich

!Missing!

'No ,no, no!' the teacher said.
'Where is your brain and your thinking head?'
'I don't know Miss, can't you see
It's not here so where can it be?
I've checked in the toilets and in the classroom,
Oh Miss, oh Miss where can it be?
I need my head, I need it you see!'

Ella Houghton (10)
Witton Middle School, Droitwich

The Night Of The Living Cutlery

Everything was calm. Everything was still.
Just then - commotion on the window sill!
In the darkness something hidden rang,
Unseen objects sent out a clang.
Eating utensils slowly awakened,
Preparing for the night that had begun -
The Night of the Living Cutlery.

The knives clashed together with ear-splitting clanks;
The spoons thumped together with rhythmic bangs.
Suddenly *quiet!* The forks shushed them all
And told them of their plans to pillage the hall
On the Night of the Living Cutlery.

And thus the hall was subject to a great raid,
And not one shoe or coat came to its aid.
The sleeping cat was caught unawares
As the legion of steel clattered and clambered up the stairs
On the Night of the Living Cutlery.

Into the bathroom the knives led several lethal charges
And beat the Lego men from their barges.
The bath was crossed and out of the window they dived: all the knives,
                              the spoons and the forks,

As swift as foxes, as vicious as hawks
On the Night of the Living Cutlery.

Clobbered were the cowardly mice and rats,
Harassed were the hunting and swooping bats.
It was then that the cockerel crowed his horn
Signifying the arrival of dawn.

They fell to the ground dormant and once again kind,
Unaware of the damage they left behind
On the Night of the Living Cutlery.

Chris Rouse (11)
Witton Middle School, Droitwich

Tornado

T errifyingly treacherous all over the world,
O bliterating trees, houses and even cars,
R oaring over land, whirling over sea,
N otorious for destruction,
A ll is lost, when it hits,
D ecimation of everything in its path,
O blivion kneels in front of you.

James Swingler (11)
Witton Middle School, Droitwich

Who Cares?

Who cares about the colour of skin?
Who cares how we look?
Who cares if we're thin or fat?
No one should.

Who cares about the environment?
Who cares about the wildlife?
Who cares about the world we live in?
We all should.

Who cares about the little things in life?
I do.
Who cares about life around us?
I do.
Who cares about all of these things?
I do.
Who cares? Who cares?

Charlote Perry (11)
Witton Middle School, Droitwich

Hobbies

Can you tell me if you please whose hobby is chess?
Bess likes chess
How about Kate?
Kate likes to skate
How about Paul?
Paul likes ball
How about Mike?
Mike likes to hike
How about Trish?
Trish likes to fish
How about Kelly?
Kelly likes telly
How about Dennis?
Dennis likes tennis
Okay then, how about Catrinamahbahadapetelon?
She plays with her friends!

Elliot Pulver (10)
Witton Middle School, Droitwich

Winter Blues

Winter nights are long and dark
No more visits to the park
Winter days are slippy too
No more visits to the zoo
In my house I stand and stare
All the trees they seem so bare
There is nowhere left to go
How I wish that it would snow
Then we could have lots of fun
Playing in the winter sun
Instead all we get are coughs and sneezes
Viruses and cold diseases
Broken arms from slipping on ice
Now that really isn't nice
It must be time for spring to appear
Everyone let out a great big cheer
Say goodbye to coughs and flu
Say goodbye to winter blues.

Jack Hoban (10)
Witton Middle School, Droitwich

Hyper!

Hyper, hyper, hyper me
That's the way I love to be
Even though my mum would disagree
Hyper, hyper me, me, me

I love to jump around
And fall to the ground
I love to prance through the air
Which makes my mum pull her hair

The noise I make
The bangs that shake
The screams that wake
They could create an earthquake!

Hyper, hyper, hyper me
That's the way I love to be
Even though my mum would disagree
Hyper, hyper me, me, me.

Lauren Dyson (11)
Witton Middle School, Droitwich

Food!

Food can taste delicious
Celery sticks and peas
All of which are nutritious
Although my favourite food is cheese

Unhealthy food is tasty
Chocolate, crisps and sweets
It's fine to have a small amount
As long as it's just a treat

Party food is great
Ice cream, cakes and jelly
All can make you sick
And give you a big, fat belly

Juicy fruits are good for you
Oranges, apples and pears
But knowing most children
They'd rather eat éclairs

Food can taste delicious
Celery sticks and peas
All of which are nutritious
Although my favourite food is cheese!

Dominic Forte (11)
Witton Middle School, Droitwich

Dragons

Dragons are big, some are small
They have sharp teeth and they can be brutal

They have red skin with long and sharp claws
When they fly they make a gale

They have sharp bones coming out of their backs and wings
They breathe bright orange and red fire

The dragons are scared of the dragon slayers
The dragon slayers have spears, not many dragons have been killed

When a dragon sees a dragon slayer they fly like the wind.

Daniel Merriman (10)
Witton Middle School, Droitwich

Your Imagination

Whether the weather is fine or not
Fairies, princes, kings that rot
Help me save her, he's got her
The Big Bad Wolf has grabbed a pig
There are fairies everywhere
I believe in imagination

Your imagination takes you everywhere
It takes you to Wonderland
It takes you just about anywhere
Prince takes princess' hand so bare

Spanish dancers sweat like hell
Witches from Charmed like the Halliwells
Your imagination takes you here and there
And you know wherever you go, there will also be someone there
You can find your imagination everywhere

Imagination takes you wherever you want to go
If you are so bored let your imagination take you over
Like birds as clowns and clowns as birds
All you need is your *imagination!*

Tara Gregory (11)
Witton Middle School, Droitwich

Classrooms

Classrooms, classrooms, classrooms
They are full of pens and pencils
Classrooms, classrooms, classrooms
In a classroom children get taught
Classrooms are used to teach people
Maths, literacy, art, geography, history
Classrooms, classrooms, classrooms
Teachers teach in classrooms
Children learn in classrooms
Children use things like pens
Pencils, books, paper, scissors, games
Teachers teach children to learn
When pupils are older they
Can teach their teachers things
Classrooms, classrooms, classrooms
You can get taught and taught
It's either boring or interesting at school
Classrooms, classrooms, classrooms!

Catherine Kelleher (11)
Witton Middle School, Droitwich

What To Do . . .

What to do on this lovely day
Go outside and play?
What to do on this rainy day
Stay inside and watch TV?

What to do, what too do
So many choices, so little time

What to do on this windy day
Stay inside have some lunch or
Make a tent out of towels and blankets?

What to do, what to do
Ride a bike or take a hike?

What to do on this sunny day
Play doctors with my friends or
Go to the dentist and have a check-up

What to do, what to do
It puzzles me!

Charlotte Burridge (10)
Witton Middle School, Droitwich

And Poor Africa

We are poor, we live on rice
All we have is nasty old mice
Nowhere to go or sleep
Out of the window they cannot even peep

No food and water to drink or eat
The cave smells of smelly old feet
No blankets or bed sheets
No animals to have wool except a sheep

No family or friends
No hens or pens
Schools and halls nowhere to be seen
Just food that makes you strong like beans.

Bethany Haynes (9)
Witton Middle School, Droitwich

My Ponkey Poodle Dog

My Ponkey Poodle dog is such a funny one
Running through the grass really, really fast
Jumping in and out, chasing leaves and trees
My Ponkey Poodle dog has two best friends - Reggie and Blondie
He loves his walks and he plays boldly with them
My Ponkey Poodle dog answers to Jasper, he is black and cuddly
And he is ten months old, but never does as he his told!
We love him very much, he is one of us
My Ponkey Poodle dog is a funny one, when he is clipped he looks just fab
The most handsome dog around, he just looks so proud
That's my Ponkey Poodle dog!

Georgia Whitehouse (9)
Witton Middle School, Droitwich

My Poem About The War

W hat have we done to deserve this?
A ir raid sirens howling - please make it stop!
R ound and round the rattle swings, off into the shelter again!

Rachel Peacock (10)
Woodcote Primary School, Ashby de la Zouch

Scared

E vacuees are scared
V ictory is going to be ours
A s we defeat Hitler
C hildren will be safe
U p in the sky planes are flying
A s German ships are bombed
T he worst thing about the war is at the
E nd when the dead are counted.

Jake Insley (9)
Woodcote Primary School, Ashby de la Zouch

My War Poem

W orld is at war and we want Hitler to be defeated
A ll people are in danger of Hitler today
R unning for their lives, because bombs will come.

Jamie Hardy (10)
Woodcote Primary School, Ashby de la Zouch

War Is Here

W hat has happened to the city of London?
A nderson shelters are no longer there, nor the people inside
R unning into the air raid shelter, waiting for the bombing to pass.

Perry Clayton (10)
Woodcote Primary School, Ashby de la Zouch

War

W ar is beginning again
A ll the people are scared
R unning to the shelters from the bombs.

Mickey Manship (10)
Woodcote Primary School, Ashby de la Zouch

My War Poem

E arly in the morning
V ery sunny light
A t the station waiting
C urling up on the bench
U ntil the train comes
A nd saying goodbye
T aking a long time
I n the line I wait
O h I don't want to leave
N ot now, not ever!

Loren Bradshaw (11)
Woodcote Primary School, Ashby de la Zouch

Feelings

Noise and confusion everywhere
Mums crying and waving their children goodbye
The organ grinder and his monkey trying to make everyone laugh
The trains are leaving, taking the children away with tears running out of their eyes
Hoping for the war to end, so they can see their mums again.

Dale Needham (10)
Woodcote Primary School, Ashby de la Zouch

My War Poem

E very child at the station
V ictory will be ours
A way we go to a place unknown
C arrying our brown bags full of our needs
U nder the tunnels we go on the train
A way from London
T he train is steaming hot
E verybody knows that until we win the war no one can go home.

Paris Emmerson (9)
Woodcote Primary School, Ashby de la Zouch

War Is Starting

W ar is starting
A ll the children need to escape
R ailways crowded with children and adults.

Jade Vazquez (10)
Woodcote Primary School, Ashby de la Zouch

War Feelings

W ar has begun
A ir is full of bombs
R un for your lives.

Jade Harasymiw (9)
Woodcote Primary School, Ashby de la Zouch

War Is Coming

W ar is coming to Britain
A dolf Hitler is coming
R age is coming with guns.

Harry Sawyers (10)
Woodcote Primary School, Ashby de la Zouch

War

W orld is at war
A nd all the men go to fight and drop the bombs all around
R un, run to the shelters to protect yourself from the bombs.

Sahith Nama (10)
Woodcote Primary School, Ashby de la Zouch

Evacuate

E ight o'clock in the morning
V ery, very early
A t the station, at the rise of the sun
C urling into a ball on the bench
U ntil the train comes and screeches
A nd I'm saying goodbye to my mum
T hinking about her so much on the train
E ight o'clock at night I arrive at my destination.

Daniel Pink (11)
Woodcote Primary School, Ashby de la Zouch

World War II

E very child gathered at the station
V ictory is needed before the children return home
A ghast families are split apart
C rowded trains are ready to go
U nknown lives lie ahead
A way we go
T he bombing has begun
E veryone is grieving.

Alexandra Elliott (10)
Woodcote Primary School, Ashby de la Zouch

World War II

E veryone lining up
V elvet coat making me sweat
A ll children getting ready
C arrying our small brown bags
U nsettled children crying
A ir raids will go off everywhere
T errified! Horrified! What's going to happen next?
E verywhere chaos.

Danielle Slattery (10)
Woodcote Primary School, Ashby de la Zouch

YOUNG WRITERS INFORMATION

We hope you have enjoyed reading this book - and that you will continue to enjoy it in the coming years.

If you like reading and writing poetry drop us a line, or give us a call, and we'll send you a free information pack.

Alternatively, if you would like to order further copies of this book or any of our other titles, then please give us a call.

Young Writers,
Remus House,
Coltsfoot Drive,
Peterborough
PE2 9JX

Tel: 01733 890066

Email: youngwriters@forwardpress.co.uk

Website: www.youngwriters.co.uk